THE SECRET DEFECTOR

THE SECRET DEFECTOR

CLANCY SIGAL

Aaron Asher Books

HarperCollins*Publishers*

Grateful acknowledgment is made to reprint from copyright material: "THE POLITICIAN" (Bruce Jack, Peter Constantine Brown) ©1968 DRATLEAF LTD. All rights on behalf of DRATLEAF LTD. administered by UNICHAPELL MUSIC INC. All Rights Reserved. Used By Permission.

HarperCollins books may be purchased for educational, business, or sales promotional use. For information, please call or write: Special Markets Department, HarperCollins Publishers, Inc., 10 East 53rd Street, New York, NY 10022. Telephone: (212) 207-7528; Fax (212) 207-7222.

FIRST EDITION

Designed by Alma Hochhauser Orenstein

Library of Congress Cataloging-in-Publication Data

Sigal, Clancy.
  The secret defector/Clancy Sigal.—1st ed.
    p. cm.
  "Aaron Asher Books."
  ISBN 0-06-019011-6
  I. Title.
PS3569.I4116S43   1992
813'.54—dc20   91-50473

92 93 94 95 96 MAC/HC 10 9 8 7 6 5 4 3 2 1

Hello now, baby, get into my big black car
Hello now, baby, get into my big black car
I want to just tell you
What my politics are.

I'm a political man
And I practice what I preach
I'm a political man
And I practice what I preach
Don't deny me, baby
Not while you're in my seat.

I support the left
Though I'm leaning, leaning to the right
I support the left
Though I'm leaning, leaning to the right ...

—*"THE POLITICIAN," THE CREAM*

They say I look like Woody Allen. Personally, I think I'm more like Clint Eastwood or Paul Newman. But to be on the safe side I take off my horn-rim glasses when talking to a woman. A little vanity is overlooked in a serious man.

I am definitely serious. My mother laughed at everyone but me, my wife and I split up because she took me so seriously. My whole life is heavy with meaning—the search for justice, resistance to tyranny, and so on. My vital spark—Lenin called it *iskra*—glows brightest when fed certain cue lines. WORKERS OF THE WORLD UNITE. BAN THE BOMB. FREE THE ROSENBERGS. NO BLOOD FOR OIL.

My eyes mist over, my spine stiffens. As if on automatic pilot, my body tenses for the inevitable collision of torsos on the picket line. I've trained myself not to recoil when police or scabs make the first rupture in our locked-arm column. No celebrity, I'm usually in the second rank, ready for the shock and counterattack. Never more alive than when hurling myself against a real, physical enemy. A BAS LES FASCISTES!

But that was then.

BOOK 1

GOING
AWAY

S*cene:* The London maisonette of Rose O'Malley, an African-born white writer. Shabby two floors in Hammersmith not far from where the Thames snakes upriver. *Time:* Summer '58. My "two weeks in another town" has lasted more than a year and I haven't even seen the Tower of London yet. I'm dog-tired. My dad must have come in off the road like this: rumpled, unshaven, rain-drenched. I've been up in Yorkshire, not to visit the Brontës' house in Haworth but in a strike-bound coalfield. Now I'm back home, with Rose.

"H'lo, Maggie," I called, letting myself in. Though it was before dawn, I knew Rose would be standing at the top of the hall stairs, an invisible rolling pin tucked in her angrily folded arms.

"Top o' th' mornin' to ye. And wot's fer br-r-r-eakfast?" I asked in a stage-Irish accent I'd picked up from Eire-born building workers on a strike at the South Bank McAlpine site.

A mistake. Knew it immediately.

"I'm Rose. Your mistress, remember?" she said through nicotine-stained teeth. She had on a pale blue shantung silk blouse and Cyd Charisse–style wool skirt I'd bought for her. I'd also supervised a new, closely shaped hairdo that dramatized her high cheekbones and slightly unfocused eyes, emphasizing even more her resemblance to the film heroine of *Laura*, Gene Tierney. Rose had protested when I gathered up her dowdy old rags—tomboy jeans and checked lumberjack shirt—and chucked them in the fireplace, but she cheered up when I blew the last of my money taking her to Harrods for a whole new refit. Even persuaded her to turn in that cheap

Woolworth's lipstick for different eye shadow. But though I pum-
iced them myself, the small, even teeth remained stubbornly un-
glamorously yellow. She'd give up anything for me, Rose swore,
except cigarettes and writing.

Weakly, I explained the Irish joke. *Maggie 'n' Jiggs* was an old-
fashioned cartoon strip I grew up on. Maggie was always waiting up
for Jiggs with blood in her eye.

Rose wasn't laughing. "And who was he screwing to provoke
her?" she demanded.

Here we go again.

"Actually, nobody, you stupid woman," I replied. "He was out
playing poker with the boys."

"So that's your story, is it?"

She wouldn't have believed it anyway.

Climbing the stairs, I tried to push past her to the small room I
rented from her. A bargain at two pounds (ten dollars) a week, con-
sidering the extras.

"You and your lies." Rose blocked my way.

She was small, almost tiny. More Veronica Lake's size than Gene
Tierney's, though I couldn't see Rose as a peekaboo blonde. I could
lift her with my little finger. Something told me not to try it just now.

"You're just like my mother," I yawned. "She never bought it
from Dad either."

"Ha! Convicted out of your own mouth," Rose said with satisfaction. Oh no: I'd done it again.

She put both small hands on my shoulders. "Please, darling,"
she pleaded. "For both our sakes. See a doctor."

That same old song. I was too tired to argue. "I'm incurable,
baby. Either rustle up some food, fuck me—or shut up."

She hated being called "baby."

Rose was no quitter. "I love you," she said.

"Blondie loves Dagwood," I said.

She was distressed for me. "You can't keep behaving like someone in a cartoon strip—"

Also, I reminded her, a Columbia B-movie with Penny Singleton
and Arthur Lake. Sometimes Rose liked my cinema pedantry.

Rose laughed. "You're quite mad, you know."

Ah, the fight was over. I looked down at her faintly Asiatic, lively
round face, noting that as usual her blouse—which I'd got for her in
Burlington Arcade—was only half buttoned. I leaned down and

kissed her breast, brushing my stubbled face back and forth until I felt her unbrassiered nipples erect through the fabric.

"Oh," she said.

I sucked her nipple. "Mmm," both of us said.

"Oh God that's nice—you bastard," she said.

She arched her pelvis into mine, rubbing until I was stiff. I unlatched my silver cowboy belt with one hand while keeping the other clamped to her tight, writhing buttock.

"Have mercy on a poor sinner, Rose."

She did, unzipping my jeans with a practiced hand and taking my cock. We fell backwards onto the stairs, but she didn't let go. Before I knew it her legs were on my shoulders. I was inside her. For reasons mysterious to me, Rose and I never had sex problems outside bed.

A minute ago I could hardly walk. Now I was home.

Just on the verge of coming, I looked up—to God?—and saw a small boy in red flannel pajamas peering at us between the railings on the top floor. Calmly he studied us as we scratched, bit, and wrestled together until we shudderingly collapsed, gasping hard.

"There's blood on Gus's shoulder. Should I dial 999?" the boy asked. 999 was Emergency.

Rose and I looked at each other in mortification. Staring straight into my eyes, she yelled, "Go back to sleep, Alastair O'Malley!"

Aly merely settled himself in his front-row seat by the bannister.

Rose straightened her clothes, slipping out of me in the process, and sat up with a semblance of dignity. Her South Africa–accented voice again commanded Aly to go back to bed.

"How do you vote, Yank?" Aly called down. "Sleep is so boring when you two are at it."

I rolled over on my back, pulled up my jeans, and buckled them. Then I hauled myself up the stairs and stooped over Aly, who gave me his best innocent look. I reached down a hand, and the chubby ten-year-old scampered up it like a monkey until he was on my back: a familiar routine between us since I'd barged into his life. He began whipping me, shouting, "Giddap. Giddap, stupid horsie!"

I made hoofbeat clucks with my tongue while galloping up and down the top landing next to my room. Aly was almost beside himself with ecstatic rage. He began hitting me really hard.

"Ouch," I said.

"Horses don't talk," Aly reminded me sharply.

I told him jockeys aren't cruel to their mounts if they want to be taken to Lords today for the Test Match. The kid and I loved bribes. "Hooray for Len Hutton!" he shouted.

Aly astride me, I turned to look down at Rose, now fully self-possessed. She gazed inquiringly at us.

"Keep this out of your novel, Rose," I warned.

From somewhere she produced a cigarette and lit it from a matchbox in the pocket of her trimly flared skirt. She leaned against the downstairs wall, coolly examining us both.

I shrugged, then looked over my shoulder at Aly.

"Smile, kiddo," I said. "She's taking our picture."

Rose was a refugee too. The politics of apartheid had driven her from her native South Africa, where she'd grown up in the bush country and married a coffee planter. "I was the perfect memsahib, the baas's woman—until my local doctor sent me to a specialist in Johannesburg. I'd been having all these hot flashes and moodiness, see. None of the hysteria pills worked, and my husband, poor damned soul, suggested a few days shopping in the big city would cure me. I dropped in at the specialist's office as an afterthought. The bloody wonderful man, a Jew of course, converted me to Communism and nonpassive sex in the same afternoon. We had this terrific secret affair until the authorities arrested him for sedition. Meaning, he hated the color line. They also found this dynamite in his back garden he was safeguarding for some black radicals who were using him, don't you see. The idiot was lucky they didn't hang him. He's still on Robbins Island, I can't even get letters to him. Well, when I kept going down to Jo'burg for his trial and got my picture in the paper with all those nasty white liberals cheering him on, my husband did the right thing: threw me bag and baggage out of our house. In front of the kaffirs too!"

I loved lying in Rose's large, rumpled bed listening to her past. We never had enough time to tell each other about our lives. I had been born into the international movement she had freely joined. In Rose's case, she had chosen to be an anti-apartheid South African, an outcast white, and now a British Communist ... well, ex-. Like many of her intellectual friends, she had angrily quit the Party over the bloody Soviet suppression of the 1956 Hungarian uprising. But nothing much had changed about her politics, it seemed, except for turning in her Party card. The big thing was, we spoke the same language—of love and politics if not sex.

Why didn't Rose understand about sex? She was always talking about love instead. "You're such a child." She'd shake her head, and the debate was on. She didn't get it. Sex without love was good, and love was a killer of good fucking.

"But why does it *have* to be bad if you love someone?" she pleaded, reaching out for my hand as if to console me.

"Don't know, just is," I mumbled.

"That's no answer," she protested. "You have to be conscious, be aware, to be a complete man."

How did she know what it took to be a man?

"Because a man is a person, and I know about people, don't you see?" Then she fell back, exhausted. "It's all that Hemingway you American writers are so keen on."

When she called me a writer my heart warmed to Rose again, and I stood up and grabbed her, and she came like a drunken woman on the heaving deck of a ship lost at sea, saying as always, "Oh ..."

God, I thought, I sure don't want to fall in love with this woman. That would ruin everything.

I was an ex- too. Most Communists are. It was like getting stung by the same bee nine thousand miles apart. The delicious venom of Marxism still circulated in our bloodstream, heightening sensation, adding tang to dull duties. Rose and I, like most trained Reds, simply took for granted that only a special sort of person became a "leading edge" Communist, a cadre of the vanguard. It appealed both to Rose's inbred social snobbery and to my macho military fantasy. As a World War II GI, I'd volunteered for several high-risk elites like Airborne and OSS but was always turned down for "security reasons." It probably saved my life, but it left me with an unsatisfied longing to be in the front line, anyone's front line.

The odds were against my living this long. Look what happened to my corner gang, ROCKETS ATHLETIC CLUB OF GREATER WEST SIDE CHICAGO (LAWNDALE) *stitched in red thread on our blue fake-satin team jackets. Four of the seven of us didn't make it. Otto, a B-17 waist gunner, went down over Schweinfurt, Jackie was blown up on an ammo ship in Leyte Gulf, Marv was crushed by a tank in a training accident at Fort Campbell, and Vic, a born hero, got his posthumous Silver Star for storming a Siegfried Line pillbox. The percentages were all wrong.*

Nobody drafted so late in the war got hit that bad. Except us. Four out of seven. We never had a baseball season so good. Of us three survivors, Bobby has sunk without trace, and even worse, Joe was chairman of the Skokie Campaign to Elect George Bush.

So I, the last of the Rockets, am left with the honor—or crushing burden—of representing them in the world. But how do you carry the flag for six other guys who never asked you to?

Rose never grasped how seriously I took the Rockets. To her, they were simply my pre-Communist party; to me, the Party was my post-Rockets gang. You can't build an ideology on a streetcorner experience, she told me, that's what the Nazis did. But we were all Jewish, I said. That's no excuse for thinking with what's between your legs, she argued. I laughed: Oh yes it is. She'd shake her head yet again: My darling, you're proud of all the wrong things. You know your trouble, baby? I'd say. You became a Communist without ever being a socialist. Ha! She'd rare back, teeth bared. You have a nerve lecturing me from your morally lofty position....

In matters of love if not ideology, my Rose was a hard-liner. Sometimes the only thing we agreed on was that our histories were also our future.

Take mine: The Great Depression wasn't bad for a kid who hated change, because there was no money to repair the neighborhood or for couples like Polly and Jake to divorce. Poverty = stability. Then Joe Louis began to speed things up by losing in his first bout with Max Schmeling, a hint that my universe was changing. Pearl Harbor made things better, if you saw it that way. Mom got her first regular job in a long time sewing army uniforms in a Loop sweatshop. We moved out of other people's houses, where we always rented a room together, to a tiny apartment of our own on Fifteenth Street. Jake took off for good now we could support ourselves. And I got drafted. Even then it held. I can't specify where, exactly, it all began to shift and roll under my feet. I came back from German occupation duty ... became an organizer like Dad ... planned a career, my life, in the labor movement. Conventional stuff.

Then, wham, it hit. Truthfully, I loved the Red hunt called McCarthyism, actually Trumanism, but why quibble? Bang! goes my union job along with every other Red's in labor; zok! goes any other work I try to find in factories or even as counter help in a department store; whump! my college career shortcircuits when UCLA's dean of students tells me to get lost, I'll have to attend the University of Cuzco if I want a degree because he'll hunt me down anywhere else.

Get the picture? The whole enchilada: Smith Act trials, McCarran-Walter, the Hubert Humphrey Senate amendment to "detain" Reds in Arizona camps in a national emergency, loyalty oaths, purges, blacklists. Even that buffoon the L.A. county sheriff got into the act on local radio by urging patriots to report anyone who got their mail in plain brown wrappers, God forbid it might be the *Nation* or the *Daily Worker*. One phone call from your neighbor to any of fifteen police agencies and it was like winning the Devil's lottery, with FBI, sheriff's deputies, LAPD Red squad, and very likely the Sea Scouts camping on the front steps. Hey, guys, I'd shout through the screen door, form a line.

An enemy in my own country, an ex-Communist "friendly drop," I kept ahead of my FBI tails via thumb or U-Rent-It car, hitting almost every one of the forty-eight states like a crazy pinball. Mutt and Jeff, the Federal agents assigned to my case, brilliantly deduced that only a Soviet agent could be devious enough to stay one jump ahead of them. (This was before computers.) I had to be a spy, an agent, a mole: the harder I was to find, the worse my subversion grew in their Mormon eyes. The truth was, my worn-out tires were chewing up state lines as a substitute for sex and the talent I didn't have yet but was pursuing the way Mutt and Jeff chased me. Fellas, I'd say when they'd catch up with me, I'm only trying to be a writer. Today, my FBI file (courtesy Freedom of Information Act) reads, "Subject explains persistent abscondings by stating he is writing a novel about the Bureau and needs more raw material."

The truth was, I was a traveling salesman of resistance, Willy Loman with leaflets in my battered suitcase instead of nylon stockings. Crisscrossing the U.S.A. in other people's Studebakers and Kaiser-Frazers, I was peddling the notion of a Committee of Correspondence, dreamed up either by Leo Huberman of the Marxist *Monthly Review* or I. F. Stone, can't recall which, whereby independent leftists kept in touch as we imagined Paul Revere and Sam Adams did in 1776. A scribbled address, a vague contact, or merely a hunch and I'd parachute into the least likely places: Walla Walla, North Platte, Mobile, Knoxville, Conneaut, Troy—anywhere readers of *I. F. Stone's Weekly*, *Dissent*, or *Monthly Review* were prepared to give me a cot for the night. Avoiding the big cities for places like

Toonerville, South Dakota, or anywhere I liked the sound of, I was unconsciously reliving a childhood when Polly and Jake used to stash me in strange small towns while they were either in jail or on organizing drives or both. At least, that's how Rose saw it.

But always, at trip's end, Mutt and Jeff waited for me on the porch of my little garage apartment within sight of Sunset Boulevard. "Now, Gus?" barked Mutt, the taller one, hitching back his seersucker suit to expose a .38 service automatic. "No, fellas," I'd say, as if they were vacuum cleaner salesmen, "try me next week." "Come on," half-pint Jeff would rasp, "don't be a pain. Help us clear up your file." "Yeah," agreed Mutt, who didn't know my dad used to carry a piece seven calibers bigger than his. Just confirm a few names for us. You don't have to say a word. Just nod your head." I'll bet.

Mutt and Jeff were sure I'd come in. "Sooner or later, you all do," boasted Mutt, but when I offered to take odds they lost their cool. Jeff, an edge to his little-tough-guy voice, called me "Schwartz," my mother's maiden name, instead of "Black," to which she'd changed after the Palmer Raids, when so many immigrant-born radicals, like Marrano Jews during the Inquisition, nationalized their names. Anti-Semitic FBI bastards. And Mutt—what an actor!—would draw his .38 quietly and let it hang from his hand, still civil, no threat, just letting me see it. FBI—why did most of them look like Steve Martin?—were smoothly steely-polite at first, but you knew they knew you knew the score: they'd run a friend of mine off the road in Colorado, driven another to suicide by chasing him from job to job. On the other hand, Mutt and Jeff were the only Americans who took my Marxism seriously enough to want to put me in jail. In the denatured fifties, that was the only real confirmation I had of myself as a man.

I sure didn't get it from my friends, mostly liberals, scared to death of fallout from the Great Purge. In a way, their fear was the worst. They were guilty of nothing.

For most victims, being blacklisted was, as John Henry Faulk said, like being blindfolded in a dark closet and getting beat up by six guys and never knowing where the next blow was coming from. But for me, it's hard to explain, still less justify, the witch-hunt was also a gas, a high, if—a big if—you were single and had no family or (thanks to repeated blacklistings) no steady job. Janis Joplin says freedom is nothin' left to lose, and I was a bird in flight, with nothing to do except make trouble for J. Edgar Hoover and Senator Joe

McCarthy, who were making trouble for me and others who were more tied down and couldn't or wouldn't fight back.

We Few—the scattered Committees of Correspondence—were the least fanatic people I'd ever known on the left. Stress, the strain of all those subpoenas and anxious looks over your shoulder, perversely relaxed us. We made jokes about it. A New Opposition, a dissent movement of sorts, came into being. My dream of a non-Communist independent left, thinking and acting for itself, making history rather than history making us, was coming true.

It was great to be alive in that springtime for an American Hitler who never came.

I was high on battle. Adrenaline pumped through me, chains of paranoia snapped. Sex of an intensity I'd never known; friendships I've kept for forty years; a supernatural clarity about who I was. Nothing could touch me, no bullet, no corruption. I even stopped looking for work where it was easiest to find, on the docks or in the warehouses, both organized by the longshoremen's union, the ILWU, which didn't care if you'd been blackballed. Pirating around, light as a feather, a taxi-driving job here, a sheet-welding job there, drumming my fingers half the night on a borrowed Underwood thinking talent came from hard, repetitive work (it does), I was as open as I'd ever been. A girl I knew put in a good word with her supervisor on Sunset Strip; I was hired. Shortly after the 1953 East Berlin workers' rising and the execution by electric chair of a New York Communist couple, Julius and Ethel Rosenberg, for alleged atomic espionage, I became a Hollywood agent, a flesh peddler—and loved every minute of it.

"But how could you?" Rose asked, turning over in bed and looking down at me with a kind of puzzled delight. She was used to serious lovers, not Hollywood bandits. Her previous guy had been a neurologist, and the one before him a Foreign Office diplomat, all info courtesy Aly, who added, "But you're more fun because you take us to the flicks, which they never did." Both Rose and her kid adored my sprawling in the back row of the Hammersmith Odeon, hanging my legs over the seat in front like a teddy boy, and spinning tales, some true, of my encounters with the stars up there on the screen. Rose and Aly were awed almost into silence because I'd "represented" the writer and director on *Gunfight at the OK Corral*, currently their favorite film. "Where *did* Burt Lancaster get that gorgeous shirt?" Rose kept whispering until I promised we'd go shopping tomorrow for a female version of it.

My little family, as I thought of it, one arm around Rose, the other around Aly, in the Odeon's flickering darkness, at peace, content. A soldier on furlough. When did a temporary pass become AWOL or desertion?

That last year in America—1956—I'd gone into overdrive. Sold talent like crazy, won the biggest Christmas bonus in the Benedict Agency office, recruited one of my secretaries to the clandestine Correspondence group that met in my apartment every Friday night, collaborated with blacklisted writers (Jarrico, Trumbo, Maltz) to sell their scripts under the table to producers who paid knockoff prices because they could get away with it, became a complicitous part of the blacklist machinery when my boss, Bess Maree, asked me to help "clear" a client of unspecified charges (you could buy clearance for five thousand dollars to a Beverly Hills lawyer, Martin Gang, plus a "tip" for the HUAC snoops and a pious promise that your client would henceforth attend, religiously, so to speak, services at a church or synagogue it didn't matter which so long as he was seen there), and loyally joined the six p.m. ritual of the Benedict secretaries bringing us martinis to get us through a final flurry of phone calls. It was nuts. I who'd been hunted was now a hunter.

That I'd been blacklisted from Columbia Pictures was an open secret, but Bess had made an arrangement with Columbia's Harry Cohn to let me alone in exchange for a couple of deals he wanted on Aldo Ray and Judy Holliday, both Benedict clients. "You're getting that valuable to us, kid, so don't blow it," Bess said over Bloody Marys at Perino's, where we usually met our Paramount clients. Suddenly the comfortable certainty that my political past would exclude me from becoming an American success—all those suburbs!—was gone. Now I truly got worried.

As usual, Bess Maree, Hollywood's most stylish agent, delivered the punch with kid gloves. One night after work, when everybody but the cleaning ladies had cleared out, she invited me into her Art Deco office, with the signed photos of FDR and Bogie staring at each other on her inlaid ebony desk. The agency's partners, she cheerfully commanded, were getting tired of my posing as an artist, i.e., refusing to wear a two-piece suit and parking my prewar Pontiac in the agency lot alongside their Lincolns. "Maybe it's time for you to grow up," Bess said, "and start showing at our

Sunday brunch pool parties"—indispensable for agents to prey on and sign up talent. "We have a fair idea of what you do with your own time, Gus. Your secretary—I'll dock your bonus if you're sleeping with her—is blabbing all around the office that you like to play weekend revolutionary. It's Marx or Minnelli, kid. We can't afford another scandal." The Benedict Agency, which once had legions of lefties on its artist roster, had been hit hard in the pocket by the Hollywood purge.

I owed Bess a lot. She'd protected me, taught me, pushed me. "You've got a future in the business, Gus. Make up your mind."

Next day, over lunch at Scandia, I made my last deal with Bess, who frowned, adjusted her Hattie Carnegie hat, and finished her fifth Bloody Mary. "What makes you think you can write?" She shook her head. "No, don't tell me. Okay—here are my final terms. Go to Paris, six months maximum, starve in a garret, and get it out of your system. Then come back, forget politics, they haven't done you much good by all appearances, and help make us money from this goddamn new television thing it's not nearly as much fun as pictures but the clients are demanding it, okay, kid?"

"Okay," I said, meaning it.

Two years later I was still in London, doing what I seldom did in L.A.: swinging a hammer, using a saw, and whitewashing walls.

Time: Early 1959. Britain finds Eldorado in North Sea oil, Castro throws Batista out of Cuba, and Buddy Holly dies. *Scene:* The partly finished interior of the Maquis coffee bar in Fitzrovia, London's traditional bohemia off Tottenham Court Road. The Maquis, housed in a dilapidated Georgian-era building off a twisting alley not far from Dickens' home in Doughty Street, is purpose-designed as Britain's first political coffeehouse since the days of Addison and Steele. Even in its present unfinished state, it's the hub of a new but increasingly influential group of young New Leftist radicals who trace their lineage back to John Wilkes and beyond him to Wat Tyler and John Ball's peasant guerrillas. They call themselves—in an odd mixture of Cardinal Newman's "New Christianity" plus the latest buzz word—New Commitment, or New-Com.

On no money and fabulous idealism, the New-Comers—a mixture of former young Communists, Young Labour, and Young Liberals all fed up with their respective rigid bureaucracies—are trying to revive a legacy of London coffeehouses as a breeding ground for dissent. The present Conservative government's collusion with France and Israel to invade Egypt in '56 because Colonel Nasser wanted to run his own Suez Canal, plus the British Communist Party's hard-line support of Soviet tanks in Budapest at the same time, has fueled something entirely new in British politics: a revolt of the young. Largely due to the New-Comers, morality and culture are now on the agenda along with economics and defense. New-Com is also the brain trust of another, even more widespread movement gaining members daily, the Campaign for Nuclear Disarmament.

The Maquis' front door faces a brothel Hogarth might have sketched (card above bell: MADAME SUZETTE, FRENCH LESSONS & RUBBER GOODS). Inside the embryonic coffeehouse there's a chaos of scaffolding, ladders, open paint pots, a smell of sawdust and sound of sawing. Side by side, two figures in paint-smeared overalls swing hammers at nails in the floor while one, Gus Black, belts out a Leadbelly tune, "Goodnight Irene," to keep them going.

Arnold Robins (né Rubinsky), my best London friend aside from Rose, looked over at me admiringly. "I do like it when you do those American folk songs. So authentic."

I collapsed next to Arnold, a darkly aesthetic twenty-two-year-old Cambridge graduate with lank hair hanging over one brow like an eye patch. "Arnie," I reminded him, "I'm a city boy who learned them same way as you—off a record."

"Maybe it's your accent." Nearsighted Arnold almost whopped off his thumb with the hammer. "We English never seem to get it right."

I glanced at Arnie, the hyperenergetic Music Man of the discordant band we called the British New Left. Inside the smooth olive skin of this scholarly young Marxist lurked the ghosts of W. C. Fields and Groucho's Dr. Quackenbush; in another life he would have been Dickens' master thief Bill Sykes. But in Prime Minister Harold Macmillan's Britain he was the sly, soft-spoken dynamo whose sparks got this whole enterprise going. His specialty was conning cash out of conscience-heavy businessmen and titled ladies who, fearing Arnie might burst into tears in front of them (an ultimate threat to the English), gladly donated to a coffeehouse committed to the eventual destruction of their class. The Maquis was his baby; none of the other New-Comers had his shameless practicality. I had stopped counting how many of his checks bounced to keep the thing alive.

Something was on Arnie's mind. I could always tell when he brushed his hair out of his eye more than ten times a minute. "Of course," he added cautiously, "there are a few things you don't always get right either." He saw my look. "Don't misunderstand me, Comrade Gus. You already seem like one of us. And you've only just practically arrived." Two years and I'm still a new arrival?

I rolled over on my back. "Okay, killer," I said, "spit it out." He liked my James Cagney imitation.

"Talk—or I'll put ya to sleep in a concrete slab." I did George Raft. Arnie shivered with mild delight.

"Is it that obvious?" he apologized. "I'd do anything not to offend you." Arnie's apologies were masterworks of sincerity with barely a visible trace of malice: a trademark of Oxford-and-Cambridge, I'd found.

"That bad, huh?" I asked.

Arnie looked as if he'd swallowed a frog. "We've had an emergency meeting about you. When I was still in the Party we'd have called it a plenum. Took up the entire evening."

I groaned. Up on charges again. *Plus ça change.* I reached out with my hammer and heedlessly whacked a nail next to Arnie, who jumped.

"I explained to our editorial board that it was just a conflict in national styles," Arnie said hastily, edging away from me. "You're so ... so, well—public. We're not used to it. We're a bit like the Japanese that way. Even the left. Especially the left. We keep things in."

I squirmed for a better look at Arnie. He sat tensely on his haunches. My oh my, I thought, they stick it to you and make you feel as if you're doing it to them.

"You want me to keep my voice down to a dull roar at meetings?" I asked.

Arnie did a strange number with his head, as if bobbing for apples. "It's not only that you lecture us about our own political dilemmas—going back, may I remind you, at least ten centuries," Arnie said. "And it isn't even your jokes that come too painfully near the mark, especially for some of us who have the misfortune of being recent Stalinists." Arnie was a red diaper baby whose parents had been founders of the British CP. "Or that you come drunk to meetings—"

I interrupted. "Arnie, I've told you. A shot or two keeps me from falling down in panic."

But Arnie, like most other English comrades who'd been to public (private) school, was embarrassed by any reference to my gut-griping anxiety. "Yes, I know." He nodded sympathetically. "Our beer takes getting used to."

Worse and worse, I thought.

Arnie now was shaking his head from side to side, gulping air, almost seeming to beat his head on the unpainted floor: picture of Marxshireman getting ready to speak bluntly.

"You having a heart attack, comrade?"

He stopped. "That's the sort of thing we mean."

"No, it isn't, killer."

He took another deep breath. "All right." He plunged in. "You handle our women. Roughly. Improper advances. Oh, God, this is difficult."

I smiled. "Who complained?"

"Juliet, Sally, Penelope—"

"Holy Mary!"

Arnie said, "She's the only one not heard from yet."

"But I haven't slept with any of them," I protested.

Arnie replied, "Not a word has been breathed to Rose."

"Ah, Rose."

Accusingly: "*Your* Rose."

"So I'm an adulterer as well as a criminal rapist."

"About sums it up." For the first time he positively beamed.

I dove at Arnie and we fell over into the dust. Then, sitting on him, I pretended to pummel him with my fists the way I used to do as a Rocket, being careful to miss. Arnie just stared up at me through his tortoiseshell glasses without struggling. He said calmly, "I never was any good at school fights. Sorry."

"Good," I crowed. "I don't like hitting a man who fights back. Or making passes at girls who say no."

"Juliet Macpherson is my girl!"

Aha. Now he tells me.

"But you're not fucking her," I blurted.

Arnie's eyes grew moist with hatred. "It's all true what they say about you."

I rolled off him, and we lay side by side staring up at the unpainted ceiling.

"Arnie, how do you expect to keep a woman if you don't make love to her?"

Now it was his turn to laugh.

"On the English left, old boy," he said, "sine qua non. Sine qua non."

If you're an American radical, it's sometimes hard to find a confirming image out there. Most of the time you think you're slightly crazy for wanting to change a system that works even when it shouldn't. You need a faith outside yourself. So, from my earliest Tom Mix and Buck Jones flickers, hardly a day passed when I didn't pretend to be a movie hero. Hopalong Cassidy on a picket line, Rhett Butler preaching surplus value, Scarface cranking out leaflets. The Party used to haul me up for crimes like infantile leftism, bourgeois opportunism, and right deviationism. If only they'd accused me of Cinemascopism, I'd have pleaded fair cop, guv.

What timing: I had arrived in England on the very day the British exploded their first H-bomb. The United Kingdom, always held in low regard by "real" leftists as a backwater of revolution, had unpredictably erupted with semireligious rage at the Suez adventure, the Russian crushing of Budapest, the Bomb. To the angry, conscious young, the old ruling class—five percent of Britons owned eighty percent of the wealth—seemed part of a worldwide gerontocracy that included Stalin's satraps. It was, we felt, the same fight everywhere. Indeed, for a moment, it even seemed as if our opposite numbers in Eastern Europe—Imre Nagy, Gomulka, Wolfgang Harich—were showing us in the West how to be both free and socialist. Then the night closed in: Nagy was hanged, Poland's Gomulka removed, Harich jailed in East Germany. The British New Left, inspired by their martyrdom, threatened to put the heart back into the idea of socialism itself. I was like a kid with a sweet tooth let loose in a candy store.

For the first time in my life, I was placed within a solid national framework of an agreed-upon, democratically arrived socialism. In the late gray fifties, the Tories might still run the government and own the property, but somehow they were irrelevant, even to themselves. The energy was on the left—and the right knew it. It almost seemed as if the Conservatives were deliberately prodding the Labour Party and radicals further to the left like us New-Comers to come up with fresh ideas to keep the rickety old barge of British capitalism afloat.

My curiosity about all this drove Rose mad. Ignorant of everything but the need to bring it all back, this or next week or month, to the jail that America had become for me and my friends, I kept asking, Who are they? How does it work? What's their history? Tell me again I didn't get it the first time....

Rose, exhausted by ceaseless interrogations sandwiched between interminable descriptions of what I was seeing and thinking, finally snapped, "You're worse than Alastair. At least he gets tired now and then so I can get some work done. Can't you see, Gus—I'm a writer!"

As if I didn't know.

Living with Rose O'Malley was like signing up for the Creative Writing course I'd avoided at UCLA. She kept telling me I had all a writer's equipment except self-confidence "and that's bound to come, my darling, if only you sit still for a moment and let it happen." But sitting still in the middle of a democratic revolution seemed awfully tame and irrelevant; I didn't then know what a talent it was. "How do you expect to write your first book?" Rose demanded. Her assumption that I was incubating more than one book angered me. I wasn't going to live that long.

Then she'd come over and tousle my hair, sit on my lap, and unzip my fly. "Oh, Gus," she murmured, "how long will you insist on functioning as if the Gestapo was on your heels night and day? Checking up on your every move, eavesdropping, opening your mail?"

"When you stop doing all those things," I said, nailing her.

Except for the FBI, nobody had ever been so interested in me as Rose. It was terrific being the center of someone's attention again.

It worked this way. After one of our quarrels, usually over "other women," I'd flee upstairs to the tiny but cozy room Rose had rented me, and for relief scribble in my ledger-sized journal my version of the fight, including plenty of gory details about my bouts of puking, vomiting, and fainting, which I somehow wanted Rose to feel sorry for and cure. Then, meticulously, I'd deposit the diary in the middle drawer of my bureau, carefully tying a nearly invisible black thread between the knobs of the bottom and top drawers. Anyone breaking in would have to snap the thread—a trick I learned from de Rochemont's *The House on 92nd Street* and other spy movies. (Back in L.A. it was also how I knew the FBI had come poking around.) Then, with a loud banging of doors, I'd slam out of Rose's pad ...

whereupon Rose would sneak upstairs, read my journal, and rush back down to her old Royal typewriter to use my self-exonerating arguments in her own manuscript ... parts of which, as time went on, she'd oh, sort of accidentally on purpose, drop around the house, in glaringly obvious places like the kitchen table or even on our bed ... for me to read and, like Pavlov's dog, dash upstairs to respond in my diary, which she'd break into, read, and then run back to her typewriter, which she left untended for me to scan its pages so I'd hotfoot it back up to my room to ...

At least it got me writing, if only in a notebook.

After a while I got a perverse kick out of helping Rose write her new novel, which she'd titled *Loose Leaves from a Random Life*. Ah yes, I'd think, picking through the prose she'd left atop her typewriter for me to see, so that's how you introduce a new character, make an exit, establish a transition. Hmmm. I could see her struggle with the American figure named Teddy Blue. Teddy? I was no toy bear. Neatly I crossed out the first name and inserted "Jim." More manly. Next day she crossed that out and wrote "Jonas." We compromised on "Paul." All without exchanging a single word about this strange silent collaboration.

At first I didn't mind the Paul Blue she sketched as a Communist truck driver from Pennsylvania. It was so wrong, so far from the real me, that it didn't hurt. Then one day, stuck in her machine, I found part of a chapter in the form of a note to herself.

THE CASE OF G.B. Ex American Red comes to London. Finds woman on her own who takes him in. Thinks he's escaping FBI but in reality running from unresolved attachment to mother. Disguises his Oedipal terror as randiness. Born exploiter of vulnerable women who can't help nursing this crippled cat disguised as romantic hero. Hates women he fucks because they give him temporary refuge. Everywhere he turns, especially in bed, comes face to face with mother he's terrified of. Wants to die for "cause" because he can't see way out of infantile dilemma....

It sucker-punched me in the stomach. The woman was zeroing in.

Stumbling upstairs, I sprawled gasping on my bed, so panicked I couldn't even get out my journal to respond to Rose's brisk, precise, wounding analysis. My breath came harder, my terror inflated unimaginably. I didn't know if Rose was right or wrong about me, but it didn't matter. Suddenly I wanted to get off her *Candid Camera*.

* * *

"How dare you go through my private papers?" Rose surprised me over one of her usual magnificent breakfasts—bacon, sausage, beans, scrambled eggs the way I liked them (twice over), fried potatoes, fresh-squeezed orange juice even in January, a mountain of toast made from her home-baked sourdough rye bread, gobs of strawberry and cherry jam from her cupboard of homemade preserves, and that special Nicaraguan coffee from beans she trekked all the way across town to buy in a little shop in Whitechapel because she knew I hated what passed for English brew. What a chef!

"Well?" she rasped like my FBI Mormon Mutt. "Don't lie to me again. You've been reading my novel!"

I blinked. "What gives, baby?" (She loathed my calling her that.) "You know I've been soaking up all those pages you leave around the house. Isn't that the point? Why stop now, just when you and Paul Blue are getting into the hot stuff—?"

In a rage Rose stalked from the kitchen into the front parlor that doubled as our bedroom. Pale and trembling, she sat in the wicker chair by her typewriter and lit a Woodbine, assuming The Pose: knees crossed, shoulders hunched, one hand on hip, the other holding cigarette at port arms. Exactly like her book jacket photograph. (Rose had published several novels and a short story collection.)

Suddenly cold and harsh, she said, "Well, my friend, what shall we do about it?"

I wanted to finish breakfast. "Come on, Rose, you know I hate cold eggs."

She peered up at me with those lovely, wise, unfocused eyes. "You'll never take me seriously, will you?"

What did that mean? "Look, baby, what's upsetting you?"

"DON'T CALL ME THAT!"

"Okay, Rose O'Malley. What's the beef? I know you know I know you know. So what? I can live with it if you can."

"'What's the beef?'" she mocked. "Why don't you speak proper English? Do you think Chicago gangster language will make you a better writer?"

Actually, that was exactly what I thought. Upstairs I was experimenting with trying to copy Nelson Algren, but it kept coming out all wrong, like Norman Mailer with a hernia. But "gangster" was definitely a step up from "guttersnipe," which was what she usually called me.

Rose's voice softened, she stubbed out the cigarette. She opened up the blanket around her shoulders, and I knelt in its comforting canopy, nuzzling her leg. She played with my hair. But instead of bending down to kiss me, she said, "You must see, we can't go on hurting each other this way."

Uh-oh, she must be near finishing her novel. My stomach crawled; the middle of an English winter was no time to get slung out of Rose's warm embrace.

"Well," she purred, "how are you going to untangle this little knot you've tied us into?"

I yawned. "I dunno, ba—Rose. Pack my bag. Set fire to your manuscript. Maybe beat the shit out of you. Look, I'm hungry. Any sausage left?"

She smiled bleakly down at me. "Doesn't your self-respect and dignity mean anything to you?"

"Sure," I said. "But can we eat first?"

Pure swagger. My insides were on fire. It was ridiculous for me to try to be a writer like Rose's literary friends. They had been born into a thousand-year-old tradition. What was mine?

Meanwhile, Rose pleaded with me to *talk* to her, closely, warmly, intimately. How else could she help me? But if I spilled my guts to her they'd just end up on the pages of her book. I had to keep something for myself. "That's what's killing you, darling, don't you see? Both as a man and as a writer. Let go. You have to just surrender and let it take over."

It was a real dilemma. If I talked too much to Rose, she complained I was interfering with her work; if too little, I was withholding myself. I'd hoped that my-diary-into-her-novel and back again might be a solution, but it looked as if this strategy, like all good things, was coming to an end. Anyhow, Rose rather liked me being what she most mocked, some dumb American from an RKO dark-of-the-night thriller, walking into her life like Robert Mitchum or Dana Andrews. Where were these guys when I most needed them?

□ □ □

Thurcroft, a South Yorkshire pit village. Cold gray pebblestone National Coal Board–owned houses with small scruffy gardens or allotments. Windswept streets all seem to lead to the key that winds up this grimy toytown: a constantly revolving wheel at pithead. Lovely frost-crusted moors and heather surround Thurcroft, a No.

19 bus ride away from Sheffield, a bowl-shaped steel city in England's industrial middle. A few miles away there is an early Saxon church where decent shopkeepers worship and bury their dead. But Thurcroft isn't for God-fearers or shopkeepers. It's hard, tough, fatalistic. Miners in the late 1950s are like their fathers and grandfathers, they don't expect to live too long, if a rockfall doesn't get you, the black lung (pneumoconiosis) will. You can always tell a British miner of this era by his cough, his stoop from working in a two-foot-high heading (this is before widespread mechanization), the blue scars that run like veins over the visible parts of his body. Many if not most colliers have the odd missing finger, ear, or even eye. Coal getting is a wounding business, like war but without the glory.

I'd found Thurcroft by accident; or it found me. When domestic storms buffeted my frail flying machine, I had a habit of pulling the ejector handle, blowing me into Britain beyond the Wash. It could have been any pit village, but Thurcroft was the one I wandered into after a particularly galling fight with Rose down in London. By now, 1958, two years after Suez and Budapest, I had names and contacts all over the north. In Thurcroft it was Len Doherty. We hit it off, and I've been coming back here practically every weekend because it's the one place in England I have a guaranteed, no-questions-asked welcome. "Aye, the bluidy Yank's here again," was the colliers' refrain. "Musn' be his woman threw him out o' bed again." And the pit props themselves seemed to shake with the dry, knowing laughter of tired, near-naked men.

As usual I bypass the pit manager's office for the miners' washroom, where I kit myself in the coal hewer's uniform—flashlit helmet, battery belt, boots, and jockstrap—and lift a spare metal tag from the safety shed wall. The winding operator at pithead nods familiarly and drops me twenty-five hundred feet like a stone.

Thurcroft Main No. 1.

Crab-fashion, I squeeze along a conveyor tunnel past wall openings called headings. Pitch-black, dust-swollen, sounds of shovels and picks. No pneumatic self-advancing metal props here, just men inching forward and supporting half a mile of earth above them with a few delicately placed timbers. I feel my way along a lifeline of rock-chipping click-click-clicks and pass a dark crypt where a miner rests for his "snap," cold tea and raw bacon sandwich.

"Oh aye, lad," the black statue called, "didn't tha recognize me in mah tuxedo?"

I turned my headlamp on Len Doherty, who wore only boots and a kind of dirty diaper. Sharply he reminded me of the first lesson he'd taught me below: "Get that damn light out of mah eyes!" Turning my head away, I crawled into Len's heading, where he gave me half his sandwich and shared his thermos of supersweet tea. His partner was sick that day, so he was alone at the face.

We sat and ate in silence. Then, "How's it goin' for tha down in Lunnon? Rose at tha again?"

"It's not Rose. I can handle her," I said unconvincingly. "It's her friends. Big mouths, sharp teeth." I admired Rose's circle of writers and artists, virtually a salon, but felt inferior to them because they were doing the real thing. They had begun chewing me up.

"Oh aye," Len confirmed. "I've felt their bite and all."

I hadn't known that he and Rose—

Len shook his head. "Was nothing really. But enough to start their tongues wagglin'. Lunnon's worse than Thurcroft that way. Up here tha can sort it out man to man. Down south I get so frustrated. Rose used to tell me not to waste my energy hitting people to stop their talk. She doesn't understand, does she?"

I told him I'd slugged Basil Bullock, the Marxist literary critic, because he gossiped that I was Rose's fancy man.

Len laughed. "Are tha?"

Well, Rose fed me, fucked me, and didn't always insist on the rent. But—

"Laddie," Len sighed, "tha'rt in miners' heaven. What's thy complaint?"

"Rose says I should have more self-respect. More dignity."

"Oh, that," Len said softly. "Don't even try makin' it oop to women, Gus. Tha have what they'll never have, and that's the start and finish of it. Don't tha know th' score yet, tha mad Yank?"

"You can't boil everything down to penis envy," I insisted.

"Now tha tell me," he mocked. Then, more seriously, "Tha may know Ah'm the world's shit, and Ah may know tha art. But we cannot allow *them*—" he gave the coal face a whack with his pick for emphasis—"to say it to our faces. If they do tha've no choice but to hit out."

To Len I could blub, moan, complain, share secrets I wouldn't tell God. Thurcroft's rules, I told him, didn't work for me in London. I was getting a bad reputation because, stricken by unnameable terrors, I fell from speakers' platforms, stepped on small men's toes, and couldn't disguise my contempt for some of the male bitches who surrounded Rose, even if they did write books and paint pictures. All my envy and resentment poured out: "And they can't even shake hands like a man!"

Len laughed. "A hangin' offense for sure."

We sat in dark silence broken only by the faraway rumble of a conveyor belt. Then he nodded. "Has she called thee an uncivilized brute yet?"

"Worse. A Chicago guttersnipe."

He clapped me on the shoulder. "And so tha art, so tha art. Guttersnipes of the world, unite!"

Snap time over, we heard the pit deputies coming to check on the job. I got up to go, sharply banging my helmeted head on an overhang, and dropped with ringing ears back to ground. Unconcerned, Len started slowly, rhythmically swinging his pick against the massive black wall, wrenching the stuff out with a practiced hand to be shoveled onto the conveyor later.

"How do I get out of this godforsaken hole?" I asked.

Attacking the coal, Len said over his shoulder, "With dignity, lad. With dignity and self-respect."

I owed my sanity to Len Doherty, a Communist miner. Thinly handsome, but with the artificially broad shoulders of a coal-face worker, he was known in literary London as a "proletarian novelist" because he'd written two books on a miner's life. But in Thurcroft his writing was either ignored or lightly jeered because it detracted from his prowess as coal getter; the village son of whom they were most proud they had the most contempt for. Miners were a complex tribe. Guilt-saddled because he wrote, because he was starting to dream of horizons beyond the village, Len bowed to Thurcroft's verdict and, on publication of each book, scrambled that much harder down below. This double life was killing him physically; he'd do a full night shift (for the overtime), then stay up all day writing. And I wasn't a help hanging around eating up his spare time.

Rose was of two minds about my making Thurcroft a second home. Wasn't I overdoing it? After all, coal mining wasn't my culture. "Rose," I said, "I'm drinking with them, not sleeping with them." Rose pressed her lips together firmly. "You just watch out they don't break your heart too"—then clammed up. Ah, so she and Len really had been lovers. Why, then, did she go on at me about what I did outside the house?

"You'll never understand, will you? A woman on her own is a free woman despite herself. It's undefinable in our bourgeois society so far. We never say 'free man.' A woman alone is more vulnerable, less protected, than a man alone. Each man she meets isn't a scalp on her belt, as a woman is for a man, but an exploration of her contingent freedom." Her what? But Rose was in full flood, excited by this new possibility of helping me understand the sexual frontier she bestrode. It wasn't like her to philosophize abstractly about sex.

"Rose," I asked, "what the hell are you talking about?"

She fixed me with an almost loving glare. "Noreen," she spat in her tight, controlled, jealous voice. Ah, Noreen.

Telepathic Rose—or had she good spies?—somehow managed to keep tabs on me in the darkest corners of England. Just like my mom always knew, even before I got home, that I'd been in a fight on Fifteenth Street. Polly Black too had been a woman alone. Does it give them X-ray eyes?

"You can't," Rose harangued as she dashed from fridge to fry pan to cupboard to fix me a sumptuous lunch (endive salad, roast brisket with gravy, garden peas, more fried potatoes, gooseberry fool), "understand the English working class by screwing all their women!" She practically threw a side dish of buttered asparagus, lightly sprinkled with Romano cheese, in my face, still marred by caked nose blood and a blue eye I'd brought back from a Thurcroft pub brawl Len had got me into. "When," Rose shouted, ladling out the gravy as if she wished it were molten lead, "will you stop using your penis for a reporter's pencil?"

Rose was stubbornly, grimly convinced my trips north were a thin excuse for sexual misconduct. Dead wrong, at first. But what Rose, and my New Left comrades like Arnie Robins, never understood was that lovemaking was the only really permissible contact between strangers like me and the daughters and even wives of the miners, furnacemen, and loom weavers with whom I stayed in these often claustrophobic "face-to-face primary communities," as academic sociologists called places like Thurcroft, Dinnington, Glossop, Maltby, Worksop, and Ashton under Lyne. It would have cost my life to be seen merely talking to a woman in such male-defined industrial barracks. But fucking her was a lesser sin.

Rose slammed the quivering green gooseberry dessert in front of me. "Noreen—ha!" she repeated.

How, I asked, had she found out about Noreen? Rose's eyes blazed. "When will you stop treating me like a Chicago 'broad'? I *always* know!"

It wasn't the moment to tell Rose that Chicago broads always knew too.

The whole village knew about us, Len told me on my next trip up, including Noreen's collier fiancé, Don. Yet far from getting up the villagers' noses, the affair almost made me a celebrity. Men I hardly knew came up to shake my hand in Miners Hall, and Noreen's guy smiled slyly at me. Even the wives, that mysterious, rollicking subculture fiercely suspicious of anyone (including Len and his books) who threatened the regular rhythm of the village, called out bawdily, "Hey, Yank, how's thy love life?"

"What's going on?" I asked Len.

Exhausted from night shift and the strain of my visit, Len said, "Funny place, Thurcroft. The men respect thee for goin' after what tha' want and getting it. And the women are payin' back the men for it." He grinned weakly. "And we all admire thee for thy tricks, tha crafty Jew."

Jake, my pop, a general organizer (troubleshooter) for the between-wars American Federation of Labor, in which he was widely known as "the little Jew," used to knock anti-Semites down for less. I told myself that the Yorkshire miners' prejudice was, like the beer, mild and bitter, more antiforeign than Jew-hating. Still, it stung.

"Smile when you say that," I said in the Miners Hall bar. Len, sweating and red-faced, almost dropping from the lingering effects of Thurcroft Main Seam's hellhole heat, but still strong enough to reach out and grab my collar, suddenly roared, "Tha've no soul because tha've no roots, Jew. Noreen told me. So's Rose. Ah know thee, Jew, but tha'll never know me!" Thunk, and we dragged each other out to the scratch garden back of the pub and slugged away until the stone ground came up to bash us both. Then I took Len home like a sick soldier to his wife sitting up next to the fire in the grate, her eyes flashing malice. "It's a good job tha'rt goin' soon, aren't tha, Gus?" she said as she lifted Len off me with a practiced air and headed him upstairs to their freezing cold bedroom. "Another naght with thee and he'd be more fit for infirmary than pit. Can't tha see? He's helped thee all he can. Now he's all showoff. For all our sakes—go."

I waited till morning to talk to Len, but he only confirmed my departure. "There's too much talk about th' lass and thee, lad. It's comin' back against me because Ah brought thee here. Ah've enough problems. So either finish it or take her away with thee."

When Don went on shift, I took this slim, lovely girl in a plain print frock on a last stroll overlooking the village. She had the high forehead, straight nose, and lush lips of a movie type that would soon become fashionable—Julie Christie. But also the slightly round shoulders and incipient droop of her race of Yorkshire industrial wives. I didn't care: I wanted her.

At first, very formal, Noreen said she was sorry to see me going so soon. "Come south with me," I said.

Neither coy nor flirtatious, she drew us down to the moorland ground. In the distance we could see the smokestacks of Barnsley, where she was a chocolate wrapper in a candy factory. "And who'll pay my wages? And what'll thy Rose think of me movin' in with thee?"

I didn't mind her taking for granted that I was crazy about her.

"Sex. Pure sex," she said.

"And what's wrong with that?" I tried to kiss her, but she gently pushed me off.

"Tha'd soon grow tired of me, of it. Or ashamed. Ah don't fit into thy world."

Suddenly I felt even more eager to take her with me. "This is your chance, Noreen. You're nineteen and you've never been south of Sheffield—"

"Nor have most girls Ah know. Those that do disappear lahk they've been swallowed up," she said primly.

I told her that was the point of London. You *could* disappear. "Nobody cares, nobody condemns. It's totally anonymous."

She drew back. "And tha like that? Lahk Len says, tha must be daft—or American."

I assured her that the metropolis was full of northerners chancing their luck. She'd adjust.

A Londoner was the last thing she wanted to be, Noreen said. "Ah'm a Thurcroft lass. It's my world."

I told her she'd be old at thirty if she stayed.

She nodded her head. "Like me mam, Ah suppose. Ah don't care about leaving Don, he'd be relieved in a way. Ah do get at him Ah'm so bored here sumtahms. But Ah couldn't leave me mam and da." Her father was a third- or fourth-generation miner, imprisoned at home with a broken back on a microsopic pension.

She turned to look at me. "Tha'rt truly ignorant, Gus. Ah've no education. Like everyone else round here Ah left school at fourteen.

Ah've nothing but these hands to wrap fruit-and-nut bars. Tell me Ah'm lying. Ah dare thee."

I was fighting a whole history of class defeat.

Slyly she added, "Of course, tha c'd always come live here. Among us."

And do what? Go down pit like her father and brothers? I'd last a week, if that.

"Try it," she dared. "Lahk the way tha want me to try London."

"I'm American. We don't work in English coal mines."

"So it's good enough for Hungarians, Poles, we've even got a Jamaican down pit."

Damn her, I was a writer, not a coal miner.

"And Ah'm a Yorkshire woman, not thy whore."

She put her arms around me in a friendly way. "Ah cannot go with thee, luv. Tha must see that."

Relieved and disappointed, I lifted her work-hardened hand and kissed it. Gently she drew it away and looked at me a little quizzically.

"Now try to go without getting killed by any of Don's mates. And without making it worse for me. Tha don't really know this place. The villagers are already taking sides against me. It's like what Ah heard happened to girls in your American South who went walkin' out with black GIs in the war. Missa ... missa ..."

"Miscegenation?" I offered.

"That's right," she grinned. "Thurcroft is like Alabama that way. So if tha don't mind, Ah don't want to be the first Yorkshire woman ever to be lynched."

A street in Hammersmith, west London.

Just in time I saw the police waiting for me back at Rose's place and scarpered down the street to a phone box. Press button B, "Rose, what's up?"

"The usual," Rose whispered into the phone. "Don't come home till Aly fetches you. They're scarfing up all the raspberry tart I made for you, but not to worry, I promise to make more." Good Rose was marvelous with the bobbies every time they showed up on the doorstep. "The trick is," she'd told me, "these are just nice working-class boys who joined the force for security. They practically doff their helmets once they hear a middle-class voice like mine. Thank Christ for the British class system!"

And for a Bonnie who shielded her Clyde by not dropping her aitches.

I was an illegal immigrant, on the run, from almost the moment I'd landed in England. My U.S. passport, on which depended my U.K. visitor's visa, was not renewable unless I signed an oath that I was not, had never been, a member of any of the U.S. Attorney General's two hundred and fifty "subversive" organizations. It would be a perjury rap to deny I'd belonged to about half of them. (In L.A., Mutt and Jeff used to joke that the only people more active than me were paid FBI plants.) No laughing matter. I was trapped in a foreign country with a woman nine years my senior and her son who sometimes seemed older than both of us. This was not what I had in mind when I came to England to follow in the footsteps of those other literary "London Yankees," Henry James, Mark Twain, and T. S. Eliot.

"That's why you American writers are so horribly screwed up," pronounced Rose once she'd got rid of the Special Branch men, as my eyes searched for traces of the raspberry tart expropriated by the brutal agents of the capitalist state. Before Rose started in analyzing my predicament (again), I wondered if she had any more of her meatloaf left. But no, she wouldn't be put off by my lesser hungers. "When will you learn it's only writing, not an orgasm, Gus."

Rose was right (again), of course. She'd introduced me to many of her writer friends—Shelagh Delaney, Robert Bolt, Colin MacInnes, Angus Wilson, Olivia Manning, Kenneth Tynan, and the "five Johns," Wain, Braine, Mortimer, Osborne, and Berger—and none of them even remotely like Hemingway and Mailer, who'd tracked the Big Cat to its lair. Rose's circle, with their pale handshakes and mumbly hangdoggedness (i.e., depression), looked more like Dickensian clerks, an impression fortified by their shop talk, which was about as exciting as eavesdropping on chartered accountants: to them, it was a job, almost like adding up figures, not a mission. Fah, I had something more muscular and virile to say.

"But darling," Rose pointed out, "the fact is, you're not saying it."

What was I doing in literary London anyway?

I'd stopped off in Paris, which lived up to all my expectations but one: I hadn't had even had the guts to approach my hero Richard Wright, the Chicago black writer, who held court in a small cafe off St.-Germain. He might have solved my problem of how a dedicated street boy turns himself into a writer fit for the best literary company.

Couldn't write. Couldn't even speak about it, except to Rose.

Literary London was a disappointment. Sadly I realized that London's past, not its current reality, had pulled me across the Atlantic. Like so many Americans before me, I'd been conned by English history.

I cannot pretend to be a completely average Chicago wise guy (though I was), because somehow, through the city's public libraries and later the training academies of the Midwest left, I had stumbled on British writers to whom I strangely connected. God alone knows what I made of Auden and Isherwood, whom I read while still devouring Dick Tracy *and* Boy's Life. *Even before I was done with* The Three Musketeers, *I found Auden's "September 1, 1939" in a library magazine.*

> I sit in one of the dives
> On Fifty-Second Street
> Uncertain and afraid
> As the clever hopes expire
> Of a low dishonest decade ...

This was the first "serious" poem I had ever read outside school, where "Horatius at the Bridge" and "Hiawatha" were the norm. At fifteen, I thought Auden was a tough New York drunk, my preferred style. Terrified of, implicated in, the "fascist menace," I snooped around till I found Caudwell's Studies in a Dying Culture, *which led me to old copies of Cyril Connolly's* Horizon *magazine, Negley Farson's* Way of a Transgressor, *Sir Bruce Lockhart's memoirs of his spy years, Graham Greene's* Ministry of Fear, *and Patrick Hamilton's* Hangover Square *(I'd seen the picture). At the same time that my favorite music was Harry James's "Sleepy Lagoon," with Freddy Martin's "Tonight We Love" runner-up, my promiscuous reading led me to E. M. Forster, whose film* Letter to Timothy *gave me an appetite for English-style documentaries like* Fires Were Started *and Auden's* Night Mail, *which sometimes got shown, to sparse and uncomprehending audiences, at the New Gold theater, rumored to be run by a local Roosevelt Road anarchist.*

Slowly, images of England, much assisted by Fox Movietone newsreels, formed in my sex- and politics-addled head: grainy pictures of blitzed, faintly sinister London; a Devon countryside full of East End evacuees (gas-masked kids, only slightly younger than me); coal mines worked by black-smeared men smiling with terribly white teeth; and packed, steamy public houses. Elegant England simply was not on my imaginative agenda. I had re-created a nation out of random jabs at unknown writers who spoke a language of fearful despair but also dim hope that I seemed to grasp, or more accurately, to need. Above all, there was a place, London, a sort of Gaylord's Hotel of smart, defeated, hard-drinking, combat-weary, hugely articulate non-fascists whose "message," as I heard it, was "Hang on, lights are going out all over Europe, but you the would-be writer carry an incandescent flame that triumphs even over death." No, I didn't understand this in so many words. But like many people who come unawares upon Jane Austen or the Brontës or Dickens, I selected images that told me a necessary story about a national landscape I busily constructed in my own brain in collaboration with unknown, often dead writers of an England we never quite lose in our heads.

Postwar London was my place too.

Yet the more I tried to do the actual writing, the angrier I got. Wild with self-disgust and boredom, I used my elbows, knees, and fists in the demos that Rose said were my way of evading writing—and proved her dead wrong about political violence. It *was* a substitute for life.

Rose nagged me to see a shrink. "You need more help with your breakdown than I can give you, Gus. You'd be such a fine writer if a tenth of that energy you put into infidelity and street brawls went into your work. It's all locked up there"—she'd reach across to tap my head and chest—"not there." Ah, there. Her small, skilled hand there, her dark eyes that narrowed in heat, those two top buttons of her blouse undone. I grabbed her. "Oh, Gus, you can't keep denying all that infantile repression forever," she moaned on her way down to the floor with me. "And—"

"Rose," I gasped, "just shut the fuck up, okay?"

She did, for now.

Rose's team was the latest I wanted to join but it would take more than the sidearm slider that made me starting pitcher for the Rockets A.C. "Our lot," as she referred to her literary set, "have more in common than just talent, Gus. Anyone can be blessed, or cursed, with that. It's insight—insight, man!—that makes the difference. Self-awareness. Struggle." Struggle for what? I asked. "Pain," she said simply.

Pain was central to Rose's worldview. If you were prepared to confront and accept the supreme agony of self-knowledge, you had a chance, slim but real, of becoming a writer. Otherwise, you became what Rose most loathed, "a perfectly decent nonentity." Only the toughest, most self-committed souls could take the blistering heat of digging into the fiery depths of their troubled, shit-strewn psyches to come up with the pearl of knowledge that might, or might not, be the key to unlocking their talent. There were no guarantees.

Sometimes, when Rose laid down the laws by which I might—not would—become a writer, it sounded like African tribal rituals she had witnessed as a child: the bloody circumcision or mutilation of flesh that proved you were worthy. Pain made you a warrior of knowingness.

Pain, pain, and yet again more pain: the West Point of the artist's spirit. In this sense, pain made Rose happy. Increasingly, if I read her books accurately, she generalized from her own woman's pain to the world's.

I looked around at Rose's crowd. Of course she was right. How else could they do their plays and novels? I almost felt like going up to Shelagh and Arnold and the Five Johns and asking them where they got their pain so I could get some too.

"Child, child," Rose clucked, "it's here, in me, in what you do to me every time you philander or lie or brutalize me with your neurotic evasions. Your pain won't go away if you treat me better. But it will be a first step, don't you see?"

The pain team was choosing up sides, and I didn't want to be left out.

My panics intensified, chatter poured out of me instead of written words. At first generous with her time and maternal about my troubles, Rose began to wilt under the sheer weight of my complaints. Her temper shortened as her diagnoses lengthened, and for relief I turned to Aly.

The kid knew all about the fights Rose and I were having, including the ones about him. If Aly was home from his boarding school, for example, I insisted that Rose put a chair up against the door of her writing room/our bedroom because he sleepwalked. Rose hated it, and Alastair O'Malley scoffed. "I know all about that stuff," he boasted. "We get S.H."—sexual hygiene—"instead of R.I."—religious instruction—"at William Morris Hall," his A. S. Neill–type school in the wilds of Hampshire. "All that fuss you grownups make about doing horizontal what we teenagers, well, I will be next year, do vertical." And he'd roar with sad adolescent laughter as if the joke was on me and Rose.

To say I identified with Aly is an understatement: he was getting to be my kid as much as Rose's. We had much in common, including being raised by single, smart women. Except to the riskiest places, I took him everywhere with me, cricket and "footie" and skiffle clubs, long meandering bus rides, Routes 73 and 30, 28 and 9, to nowhere except the depot and our mutual favorite, East India docks, where we lazed away whole days of his "hols" just mooching about watching the barges go up and down the Thames.

And we shared the problem of Rose.

"Ma means well," the boy told me as we dangled our legs over a pier facing Greenwich across the river. "She's a writer, you know," Aly said matter-of-factly. "Not like other mums. She's creative." He was apologizing for her. "And men haven't been specially good to her." He echoed her complaints to me about her previous lovers. "Pavel and Gunter wouldn't even sleep over nights. They had their wives, you see. You're the best so far."

I was faintly shocked at Aly's casual mention of Rose's other guys. My own mom, Polly Black, would have cut her tongue out rather than let on when I was Aly's age that, when Jake was gone for a year at a time, she had "gentlemen callers." But the pseudosophisticated little toerag wasn't letting me off the hook either. "You should let up on Ma, Gus. You're such a child—she isn't at her best with children." I looked over at him, but he wasn't putting me on.

Aly's voice was just starting to break from angelic to a deep, juvenile bass; he'd be shaving next. Normally his sweetness of temper calmed me down, but this new, supernaturally cool "maturity" spooked me. "Not you too, Aly," I moaned. "I can't take any more wise adults in my life."

"Oh, I'm not," Aly protested. "It's just my pose, Ma says." Blessed Rose was on to all our stratagems, including Aly's artificial composure, which was settling into a sort of detached scrutiny of the world, making him into an inside-out version of herself.

"Hey, kid," I said, "you're not ready for the old folks home yet."

He looked at me and said, "Older people, hmph—those kids!"

He meant it.

It really was getting hard to tell if I was Aly's dad or he mine. If Rose, as she insisted, was my mother and I was her son, who was also Aly's surrogate father who treated his son as a brother who had to father his mother who ... oh, to hell with it.

Aly looked up from the pocket draughts game we were playing on the pier. "I know that look of yours, Gus. It's time for you to go away again, isn't it?"

"Hey," I said, "I don't need you to remind me of how to live."

"Oh yes you do," he said, taking all my kings at one move.

All aboard!

My freedom road pointed north on a pair of smoked-up, cinder-strewn steel tracks—away from Rose's painfully shrewd lectures, away from the Maquis coffeehouse's New-Comers, who gave me a second political youth but shrank from the Ugly American they'd revitalized, away from London's horrendously talented artists who made me feel like an ape on Parnassus, my hairy knuckles scraping them the wrong way, across Britain's central divide, the one between men and women. "Where to, please?" the railway clerks asked at Euston, St. Pancras, Kings Cross, and Liverpool Street stations, all serving the north and west of England. "Here's all the money I have—you pick," I'd say, emptying out my wallet. They'd take a quick look at the departures board, shrug, and punch me a ticket to glory.

Escape.

Up, up into Black Country, iron bridges and factory canals and village war memorials (Accrington Pals wiped out July 1, 1916, on the Somme) and fields of yellow rape to get lost, and on warm days to sleep, in with my U.S. Army halfpack for a pillow before striding into the next town to call on the newspaper editor or Labour agent or police superintendent or union steward. "Hi. Name's Gus Black. From the U.S. of A. Nice little place you've got here. Where do I find a cup of tea? Say, that's mighty kind of you ..." Seldom failed, because they too had seen old Gary Cooper and James Stewart movies. All I asked was a bed for the night—and a yarn, any story they felt like spinning.

What I got was an "oral history" of Britain from the Flanders trenches and the 1926 General Strike to El Alamein and rockin' round the clock ("That bloody Bill Haley and his jungle-bunny music"), Elvis the Great Emancipator, the revolutionary abolition of third-class travel, Princess Margaret's affair with the first of her commoners, all those longhair lunatics traipsing on Easter weekend to Aldermaston summat lahk tha' whyever? *Sputnik* and *Enosis* and those nignogs rioting in Notting Hill and and and. The blunt, stubborn traditionalism of even the most Bolshie class-ridden root-and-branch Mechanics Institute Marxist militant never failed to amaze me. "Stay for the night, Yank. And when you go back to New York or Oklahoma you tell them you've not found Jerusalem but a decent English workingman's house in Bolton where money isn't king and that damned Jewess in Buckingham Palace—she's German, you know—isn't queen of this house ..." Sad, tired, strong men and women who'd been through one if not both wars, three counting the Long Depression, had few illusions but kept a faith—call it a collective common sense—that their spokesmen and "leaders" ritually invoked but had lost all touch with. Always reticent at first, even suspicious and tight-lipped, not open and confessional U.S.-style, but once you primed their memory pump with curiosity or beer, the spoken autobiographies came steady, coherent, exact. Recalling a lived history, a consciousness of the past to be shaped, even when despised, like clay of which they were a natural part. By sharing different pasts, we claimed our own.

"Yank, are you? Had those Eighth Air Force lads billeted in this village. Brave chappies. We'd count the Flyin' Forts coming in after every raid. Plenty of hearts stopped for a moment, I can tell you, when the sums didn't add up. 'Attrition rate,' they called it, but they were men we'd come to know. A couple of our local gels became those GI brides. Neither worked out in the end. But then. Come in. You don't look the type to steal our lasses, will you?"

And in every city, town, village, as in America, the odd Communist working-class brain, natural anarchist, Spanish Civil War vet (lots of these especially in the mining valleys), active socialist, hungry reader, once-sailor-returned—the men who knew about Big Bill Haywood, Gene Debs, Clarence Darrow, Mothers Jones and Bloor, Tom Mooney, John Reed, and John L. Lewis of the United Mine Workers of America or any other gone-away homeboy who'd made good on his own terms. Once on Glasgow's Clydeside I met a tool and die maker who'd actually known Swede Hammeros, long-range IWW commando, who taught me how to organize, of all things, the Nabisco cookie factory on Chicago's Division Street. And when all else failed to connect us, there was the movies: Hampshiremen wide-eyed at *Mrs. Miniver*, East Suffolk horse breeders agawk at *National Velvet*, Rhondda miners who marveled at *How Green Was My Valley*. I'd sat next to men sobbing their hearts out at John Ford's film while they observed, "Fuckin' unbelievable bullshit, isn't it? If they're so ridiculous about us, how can we believe them about their own Texas or California, tell me that, will you?" But we believed what we saw up on the screen, not what we knew.

You don't really make friends with the British in their homes but in the public places. So, anonymous and free, exactly as I'd once done on Highways 30 and 66, I deliberately lost my way to infiltrate the station grills, pubs and clubs, B-and-Bs from Crewe to Carlisle. My cock an antenna, my frazzled nerves a weathervane, I redrew Britain's map to fit an imagination fed on American preoc-cupations. Though England was only the size of Oregon or Okla-homa, in my head it became a larger U.S.A. in which to work out the visions and schemes I'd misplaced four thousand miles away on a blue highway between Canton, Ohio, and Wilkes-Barre, Pa. No more, no less, I was doing what those other émigrés Charlie Marx and Fred Engels (as one weaver called them) had done in the British Museum reading room a century ago, creating a dream empire where the just ruled, the powerful were marginal, and for once the cold chasm between worker and thinker was traversable by the good in heart.

I'd found exactly what I was looking for: a solid working class with a socialist political arm in a country that did not deny legiti-macy to its left, trade unions taken for granted if only because they were less alarming than unorganized eruptions by the anarchic poor, and a national consensus among all classes that the bad old past had no place in Welfare Britain. In other words, an America I'd known, or imagined, in childhood.

But no illusion, this time, that it was home.

A local newspaper editor in Blackburn told me, "I came to Lan-cashire from Clwyd, only a few miles away, forty-six years ago. You know what my closest friends still call me? 'Taffy the Welshman.' They never accept you, you know, not really." And the London Marxmen kept saying, "Oh? You still with us?" And the U.K. Home Office kept sending its pairs of policemen around to Rose's flat to arrest and deport me. Rose said she'd marry me to make me legal. I said why spoil a good thing, look at the fun Bogart or was it Paul

Henreid had suckering the Gestapo in *Casablanca*. She said sadly, "Fool. You'll never find another woman like me." I said, "Is that a promise, Rose?"

No city stands still. London changes, regenerates, evolves. But London was strangely static, like Chicago in the Depression, when I first saw it twelve years after V-E Day. Bomb craters still pitted much of the landscape. War wreckage had been cleared away, leaving huge holes where houses, shops, and churches once stood. Weeds and flowers, sometimes even small trees, sprouted from the bomb sites, giving them a semipermanent look. I walked everywhere, as on a carousel jumping on and off the massive red double-deck Routemaster buses not caring where they went, always knowing that an inspector or off-duty driver at the depot would give me a cup of tea and some chat. I dated clippies, conductresses, until I knew London's maze of bus routes by heart. Even today, I dream of No. 13 Finchley Road, 25 Bow, 12 Elephant and Castle, ever useful 73 Chelsea to Kings X. Rumbling along the narrow roads, I had a Panavision view of London from No. 31's top deck; riding buses gave me plenty of time to think about what London had gone through in the war. The Blitz had been folded into its history as cunningly and carefully as the Great Fire and Queen Victoria's Jubilee. It had all happened, London had endured. To be part of it was to take out an insurance policy on life itself, I felt.

Rose warned me against getting too sentimental about London in the Blitz. "People were appalling to each other then. The women especially had it bad. There's an untold story there, you know." I knew, but every time I tried to find out from the ladies of London, Rose balked. How else, I wondered, can you get to know a great city unless you love its people?

Passportless and illegal, I hid in Britain's crevices, skulking in odd corners Special Branch detectives seldom penetrated: Notting Hill's black ghetto, dockland, Soho alleys, Thames barges whose lightermen sometimes let me ride free from Tilbury to Greenwich, back streets of boroughs not even some Londoners had heard of. And I ran with Britain's young fascists not because they were "colorful" but because that's who was actually there on those streets.

For the first time, Rose was scared for me. "Don't be fooled just because they don't carry shotguns like your KKK," she warned. "They're mean and ugly, and I've known them to kick a man to death with their steel-tipped boots."

What did I have to lose?

I began hanging around a teenage club down Hammersmith Broadway a few streets away. Normal sixteen- to eighteen-year-old working-class school dropouts, the bottom of the bottom. No-hopers, on probation, full of sex, energy, and extremist politics. "We're shat on from a great height by all the capitalists and Jews on top," Peter, a Gas Board apprentice, confided between Lonnie Donegan records on the scratchy player in the corner of the all-purpose dance hall. "When we get to power we'll do what 'itler did to the toffs who copped 'im— Stauffenberg and that mob. Strangle 'em on meat 'ooks." His eyes gleamed with pure pleasure at the prospect. Stauffenberg, I pointed out, wasn't a Jew but a General Staff officer. "Then 'e deserved double 'angin'," Peter decided.

Peter and a core of his friends, all of whom had left school at the statutory age of fourteen, were disciples of Sir Oswald Mosley's Nazi-aping Union Movement. Mosley, interned in the war as a Hitler agent, was making a comeback by exploiting white working-class resentment of greatly increased immigration from the Caribbean, black men and women lured to Britain to take transport and hospital jobs Peter and his pals weren't too keen on. My Hammersmith lads were the only teenagers I knew interested in (a version of) European history. "Them Jews in Versailles," Peter declared, "put 'itler in prison for agitatin' against Masons. My dad's a Mason, 'e's worse'n a Jew."

"But Peter," I said, "I'm a Jew."

He and his mates, slouched along the youth club wall waiting for girls to come ask them to dance, stared at me. "Nah," Peter said, "you ain't."

"I am."

"Nah," said his pal Derek, "you're an American. So it doesn't really count, does it?"

If I insisted, they said, I could be an Israeli, because Israel was fighting the Arabs, whom they identified with the immigrant "nignogs" foisted on them by the same officialdom that had begun the Suez adventure, then caved in to American pressure, "that fucking Jew Dulles" who had advised President Eisenhower to withdraw U.S. support for the pound sterling unless there was a Mideast cease-fire. In a nutty sort of way, it was half true, and I couldn't help but admire the Mosleyites' poisonous long-term perspective, involving patience and persistence in spreading the word in pubs, workplaces, and clubs like Hammersmith, where my New Left was too educated or afraid to go. Angry and hemmed in, Peter and Derek and the boys got their kicks, and their solidarity, from unleashing a ferocious, envious hatred on incoming "blackies floodin' th' fuckin' country from John o' Groat's to Land's End, stealin' our women, takin' our jobs, livin' off the dole while drivin' Rolls-Royces—they deserve a good 'idin,' they do, wanna come with us to bash the nignogs up Notting Hill?"

It didn't take a genius to figure out that the menacing Hammersmith boys were crudely "acting out" racial attitudes that trickled down from the politest levels of British society—the office-holding classes forced by a postwar labor shortage to fill vacancies with blacks they despised for coming. It also didn't take a big brain to refuse to go with Peter and Derek on their lynching expeditions. (Peter said, "Your pal Marlon Brando woulda—why not you?") Anyway, what did this have to do with becoming a writer?

As far as I knew, the only other person even vaguely interested in British fascists, who to this day remain extremely effective if hardly noticed by the media, was one of Rose's pals, an English-Australian author and BBC broadcaster named Colin MacInnes. We kept bumping into each other in my hideouts, especially Notting Hill, where we'd trade an unspoken salute based on nothing more than our glaring whiteness in a predominantly black district and a few nods in passing. We were the only writers—I kept stubbornly trying to think of myself as one—who sensed that the free-flowing energies of London teenagers signaled something entirely new in British society. It made me feel terrific that with an easy wink or tip of the finger in my direction in an All Saints Road early-morning caff, MacInnes seemed to be acknowledging my right to be there as a reporter-in-making.

In September 1958 white-black tensions erupted into Britain's worst race riot, in Notting Hill. My Hammersmith lads had been among the worst offenders, with MacInnes's black friends—raw material for his novel *City of Spades*—the victims. After the riots, a High Court judge, Mr. Justice Salmon, sentenced the white hooligans, including Peter, to stiff jail terms. "That bloody Yid" Judge Salmon's decision had shocked my Nazi pals into inaction. Wha'? Four years porridge jus' fer kickin' a blackie—wass'is country comin' to, mate?

One night after the riots, I wandered into a shebeen, a Ladbroke Grove after-hours club full of smoke, smokers, and a smoky Caribbean band. This was not my normal turf; race baiters were my venue. Across the room Colin MacInnes gestured me over. I hesitated, knowing he spent most of his time with London blacks while I ran with their sworn white enemies; also, I wasn't in the mood for one of Rose's literary lions. But he came by—"Don't be such a bloody snob—they only eat white people in daylight"—and dragged me over to his table.

He'd been drinking hard with a stunning black youth. I looked at MacInnes, dressed in a "mod" style that later became sixties street gear: corduroy cap, suede zipper jacket, tight drain trousers, semi-winklepicker brass-buckle shoes. On any other gray-haired forty-year-old it would have been absurd, but MacInnes simply looked gorgeous.

I scanned the room, crowded with Caribbean islanders and Africans he knew so well and I didn't. MacInnes awed me. I'd read his elegant essays in *Encounter*, and he had been a real soldier in a real war.

He bought me a drink and congratulated me for mixing with some of the thugs who beat up his friends. It was, he said, a clever way of gathering material.

"That's what Rose says," I muttered. We'd just had another fight after she accused me of being in love with street violence for its own sake.

"Ah, Rose," he said.

"Screw Rose."

"I leave the hard work to you," he said.

I told him it was okay for me to bitch Rose but not him. Please God, not another fight, not here.

"You tell 'im, mon," his young friend said. Skin like ebony, eyes like Rita Hayworth's. Colin sure could pick them.

MacInnes sat back. "You don't think much of our sceptered isle, do you? Or its literati. Can't say I blame you. Too many big fish in a tiny bowl. That's what you and I are about, isn't it? Breaking the fishbowl. Messy business." Here he placed a hand impishly on his hip, mimicking the sort of homosexual he was not. "But isn't it *fun*?" He was a combat veteran of Montgomery's Eighth desert army.

Moodily I began giving him my usual complaints about the piranhas who swam around Rose—their nerveless handshakes, pale voices, "and love affairs, from the look of it, that are all talk and no orgasm—"

Moise, his friend, nodded at MacInnes. "With Colin it's all come and no talk."

Quickly MacInnes cut in. "Tell the American gentleman you're only joking." He tightened his arm around the nineteen- or twenty-year-old black beauty.

Uneasy, I started to rise. Colin laid his other hand on my shoulder. "You're embarrassed. How charming."

I joked that we should stop meeting this way. Last time it was in a Bermondsey jazz club where hardly anyone else was over sixteen.

"Yes," he said, "we're both into it."

"It?"

"Beginners. Absolute beginners." I'd never heard the term before.

"Well, whatever it is," I said, "it gets me out of the house."

He replied, "I've never heard a more cogent justification for—what is it they say we do? 'Documentary reportage'?" In one of his essays I'd read, MacInnes scorned this phrase as just another put-down of realistic writers by critics who would never dream of hustling streets to talk to "ordinary" people.

I protested I hadn't even published a single article yet.

"Then," MacInnes said, "why don't you go home, dear child, and plant that beautiful arse of yours on a chair and start typing. Or do you use a quill pen?"

"But where do I start?" I wailed.

He sighed at my stupidity. "What did you do today?"

Shrugging, I told him. "The usual." Stopped by the teenage club on Hammersmith Broadway, and the kids had a motor so we tooled over to Shoreditch and met up with those Mosley types who—

Moise, who obviously knew writers, put his lovely black face in mine. "Don't talk—write it."

I looked to MacInnes for advice, but he just grinned wickedly. Then he sent up Moise's Nigerian accent. "Mon, go home. Fuck your woman. But first—get it down."

And he and Moise burst out laughing at me.

They were all laughing at me, I felt. Rose, her circle of writers, her African friends, my New Left comrades, even the local shopkeepers who knew I ran errands for Rose, fetching her cigarettes and newspapers in the morning. How had I, a future Hero of Socialist Writing, a once and future Jack London or John Reed, become a kept man?

"You know the type, curious but never listens. Pig ignorant. Won't learn. Loud, forever complaining about our cold, our food, our women. Thought we'd seen the last of 'em when the Eighth Air Force went home. This one's a Red, says Rose. Possibly FBI, I've heard. All that anti-Stalinism just a cover, if you ask me. Why else ask all those questions? Stumps me what Rose sees in the fella. Sex, pure sex. What can you expect? She's not English, y'know. Not really. Colonial, like him. It's what comes of spending too much time in the bush with the gollies. She'll get rid of him once she's pinned his wings to her typewriter."

—*PART OF CONVERSATION OVERHEARD IN OFFICE OF* New Statesman and Nation, *BRITAIN'S LEADING LIBERAL JOURNAL*

But she didn't. Get rid of me, that is.

Somehow our little Hammersmith family—Rose, me, Aly, the cat, and Miss Cocks, the char—prospered all through my second winter as an undesirable alien. I sulked a lot, waiting for writer-lightning to strike, but otherwise stretched and yawned in front of the fire exactly like the cat. Our days settled into a lazy, lovely routine interrupted only when I'd have to scramble upstairs if the police came knocking on Rose's door. Aly and I'd worked out an escape route through my window and over the roofs of Cromwell Gardens down some fire escapes to Brook Green. For a shilling a week the kid kept my window sashes soaped for easier access. Then, if the coast was clear, I'd sneak back home for my meals.

Aly enjoyed our little cat-and-mouse game with Special Branch. Pavel and Alberto or whoever hadn't been nearly as much fun, he said. And I loved being the man of the house, playing draughts with Aly and protecting Rose from the coveys of men, real and imagined, who fluttered around her. Her horrific tales—about all those aging rad-lib public school boys with their whips and chains and demands that Rose urinate on them while wearing a Grenadier's or policeman's uniform—made me glad I had appointed myself her chief bodyguard. I would do for Rose O'Malley what Dana Andrews' Detective Mark McPherson gallantly had done for Gene Tierney's Laura Hunt and what Gus Black had never been able to do as a child for his mother, Polly: rescue her.

With a single dismissive glance McPherson could pass judgment on a whole roomful of Laura's New York dilettante friends. I was pretty good at this too. Especially with her own personal Waldo Lydecker.

There were times when Basil Bullock, England's leading Marxist literary critic, was exactly like Waldo, a fussily overprotective would-be lover. Craggy as Olivier, silky as Gielgud, Basil was my comrade enemy. Together we sat on the editorial board of *Chartism Today*, a Marxist journal with connections to East European dissidents—Kuron, Djilas, Harich, etc.—who were trying, often from Stalinist jails, to reconcile socialism with freedom, prosperity with planning. *Chartism Today* perfectly complemented my other base, Arnie Robins' *New Commitment* magazine, which focused on "cultural politics" and youth rebellion. Between them, these two collectively edited periodicals, each with its own coherence and credibility (and, miracle on the left, readability), were the "wives" I ferried between like Alec Guinness as the bigamous sailor in *The Captain's Paradise*.

It took me a while to figure out the sexual politics of my new comrades. Being from Chicago (which excuses nothing, Rose railed), I like to know who claims whom. In all kinds of coded ways, Basil treated Rose as "his" woman while apparently never bothering to make a proper pass at her. "It puts me in this impossible situation, don't you see," confided Rose. "Basil uses his marriage as a shield against women who try to get too serious with him, but he also pretends, or maybe it's true, that he's miserable with Henrietta because she's even higher-minded than he is, if that's possible. God preserve me from the children of clergymen. Well, whatever, poor Basil—his constant mooncalfing drives me spare. Give me a sweaty hand up my dress any day. But that's not his way, he's furtive is our Basil, his thing is to talk you into talking him into bed. It's all so silly."

I wanted to be Basil's friend, but he practically trembled with dislike of me. When he stuttered and stammered around Rose—such a change from his bold, almost heroic platform manner—I'd say things like, "Spit it out, Baz—lust is nothing to be ashamed of," and he'd crumple. By far the best way of giving him the elbow was simply to ask him about his World War II battles; most public-school-bred men at arms deemed it frightfully bad form to boast (whereas Thurcroft miners delighted in regaling me with their goriest combat stories). The last time Basil skulked out of Rose's house, Rose warned, "Basil is a perfect gentleman, Gus. Henceforth be careful never to turn your back on him."

How right she was.

Episodes of International Socialism (1): Basil, ex-major in Special Operations Executive, and Gus, ex-Pfc infantry replacement, are early for a meeting of the editorial board of *Chartism Today* in the Camden Town home of the journalist-novelist Leo Rossiter. While Leo and his wife are upstairs making tea and sandwiches, Basil and Gus are left uncomfortably together in the basement-level parlor. Naturally everyone's late, so the handsome, elegant Englishman and the American in a fisherman's cable-knit have been sampling some of Leo's Dewar's Special Blend, drinking harder and faster in a foolish race to see who can put who down first.

We sat opposite, belting drinks rather than each other. Suddenly Basil smiled.

"Pretty little Brooklyn boy."

Here it comes. "Brooklyn" is English mandarin code for "Jew."

"Baz, I'm from Chicago." Bullock hated being called Baz.

"Ah yes," he mused, slugging another, "city of big shoulders. Al Capone. Chicago gangster. American thug with pretensions."

"Watch it, Rupert."

"How did you know my middle name?"

"Just guessing."

"Now let me guess. How old are you, Gus?"

My weak spot. "Baz, I never jumped out of planes and fought with Tito's partisans like you."

"The Yanks were spared the real war, weren't they?"

"Tell that to Patton's Third Army."

Basil shifted his long cricketer's legs up on the couch till he was lounging like a Roman senator.

"What's your story, Gus? What are you doing here among us? How much longer can you dine out on this 'victim of McCarthyism' tomfoolery?"

"I said watch it."

He chortled. "Or you'll do what, Big Shoulders, punch me in the nose? I hear you're quite handy with your fists—especially with women."

"I don't hit women—but I'll make an exception in your case."

"By God"—he slapped his knee heartily—"I'm in favor of Thigmoo, This Great Movement of Ours, taking in all kinds. But the line should be drawn somewhere."

A fast drunk. Baz's head lolled on his shoulders. But his brain would fire on all cylinders once there was an agenda and resolutions.

"Look, Baz, I don't want a fight—"

"That why you signed up in the forces a bit late?"

I tried delicacy. "What an obnoxious creep you are. Harrow, the

Guards, a private income, an estate in Berkshire—I may be Al Capone, but you're pure Tory vermin."

Basil grew philosophic. "What a pair we are, Comrade Black. Both of us bloodsucking leeches on the healthy body of the English working classes. They're better off without us."

I laughed. "Schmuck, they *are* without us."

This hurt him. Basil, whatever his snobberies, was committed to workers' education. "My WEA studentsh," he slurred, "thish term are going through the whole of Wordshworth. Bloody intereshting poet, bloody intereshting man." He looked up at me as if suddenly surprised I was there. "You write poetry? He too lived off women." He got up unsteadily from the couch and stood over me. Tall. "Know what you are? The lasht of the Yank Air Force crushed-hat glamor boys. Overpaid, oversexed, and over here. Go home, Yank." And he swung on me from a great height.

From my seat on the couch I let his fist graze my forehead and stuck mine into his stomach. S.o.b. had a belly like granite, but he tumbled sprawling over a chair. This seemed to sober him slightly. He shook his head, refocused his eyes, got up, straightened his jacket and tie, and fell down on the couch again.

"Bloody silly, this." He was breathing hard. "'Pologize. Stupid of me."

I raised my glass to Basil Bullock, DSO MM. "Just the internal contradictions of the international working class," I toasted.

Basil looked around for his glass and raised it back.

"God help the British workers," he said, "if they depend on the likes of you and me. But we're all the poor buggers have."

He laughed softly and opened his arms in a sort of despairing embrace. I knew better but went over and gave the bastard a comradely hug.

Just before Leo and the rest of the *Chartism Today* crowd trooped in, Basil's whispered parting shot in my ear was, "Don't think too badly of us, Gus. We're the wounded trying to heal the healthy." Then, as if repelled by the intimacy, he pushed me violently away. He was still, or pretending to be, drunk.

"Pretty little Brooklyn Jew boy."

Ah, things were back to normal.

You won't find Marxshire on any U.K. map, yet it has its own language, customs, and special culture. It is where most of the action of this story occurs. A strange province, a little like the science-fiction landscapes of Asimov and Bradbury. For us Marxshiremen time is an Alice in Wonderland thing: the future lies in the past, past looks like the future, our present is spread equally between myth and utopia. Although physically we resemble Earthlanders, our tongue is from another planet. It is called Marxism (or its derivatives), the speech of class struggle. It's a bit like Aramaic or ancient Assyrian, a subject for scholars endlessly scratching at the Rosetta Stone of the sacred texts to discover their "real" meaning. The hardest thing for Earthlanders to understand about Marxshire is this language, which is impenetrable except to the convert or Old Comrade or Ph.D. candidate. In its English form, it is virtually unreadable except to normals with a talent for breaking the Old Germanic code in which it was originally set down by the Tribal Patriarchs, Marx and Engels, as revised by their Aftercomers, Lenin, Stalin, and Mao. An Outcast named Trotsky, reviled and martyrized for his Great Betrayal, also spoke the language of his murderers.

Come. Come with me into Marxshire, where the jokes are Polish, the policies Irish, and the plots as easy to grasp as the movies made by the brothers of the same name.

Rose was sure "the comrades" were using me to get at her. "You don't know this little village we call England the way I do. Gossip kills, it really murders—as it's meant to. So many of our friends hate my writing, my independence. Bloody socialist puritans. Can't you hear the way they patronize me?"

To be honest, I couldn't, but I took Rose's word for it because she was my guide to Marxshire's rules. Love your comrades but watch your back. Don't expect them to live up to their high-minded principles and don't fall on your sword if you can't either. And, most surprising, "The left hates artists. It exalts them but despises them at the same time. You'll find out."

I hoped so.

Meantime, I pursued my praetorian duties with zeal. Any guy showed up around Rose I'd swell like a gamecock and push him off with a flutter of my wings. Amazing how easy it was to get Basil and the other "perfect gentlemen" to stay pushed. If you are educated at Oxford or Cambridge and hold dear such values as decency, common sense, and a humanely low-key attitude to personal relationships—Walter Pidgeon in *Mrs. Miniver*, Trevor Howard in *Brief*

Encounter—you'd rather die than suffer an undignified scene. Ergo, an ugly American makes a fuss and off you scatter like a flushed partridge.

The Africans were harder to push.

They included the exiled black nationalist leaders of most of what are now known as "frontline states" in the struggle against South African apartheid. Later, they'd become famous as the presidents and prime ministers of their newly independent countries, but I mainly knew them as inhumanly patient competitors who could outsit, outtalk, and outwait me without flinching. What sexual athletes, without even moving from their chairs! I envied the common bond of Africanness they shared with Rose, a haunting memory of savannahs and veldt and bush—but was slightly taken aback by her unsentimental view of them. "Bloody male chauvinists, the lot. They think a woman living on her own is fair game to a royal tribal prince, which most of these kaffir Lenins are. Please, darling, make yourself obvious when they're here, all right?" Making myself obvious was one talent I had.

No English gemmun these. "Who is this silly white chap our comrade Rose taking up with so scandalous?" they wondered aloud, in my presence, around Rose's kitchen table. So I stooped to naked racism, with jokes like "Say, Ken, did you hear the one about the cannibal and the missionary?" Of course they complained to Rose, who publicly apologized to them but in private was intensely grateful. "They may be black heroes of the national liberation struggle, but my God, they compete to sleep with a white woman. That I know some of their wives doesn't deter them even for a moment. You wait and see," Rose prophesied, "when they come to power they'll be males more than they'll be socialists."

Rose was pure African. At times, bronzed by a rare two- or three-day stretch of London sun, she even looked like a pale Zulu with her slightly ovaloid eyes and easy comfort with her own body. She didn't so much "identify" with black Africa as feel a real part of it. "If just once," she enthused, "you'd seen giraffes in full flight or a veldt sunset or a black woman with a baby on her back hoeing in a mealie field while humming softly to herself, you'd know the secret soul of the real Africa. They're my people as much as they're Nkrumah's." Her voice always strongly inflected near-Afrikaans in these bemused moments.

An anti-apartheid militant who'd been expelled from South Africa for her activities, Rose didn't try to deny her own contradictions. "Yes, I'm a white settler—that's who I am, don't you see? I'm as racialist as any African black or white, no less, no more. I know what you're suggesting, Gus—that because I've never slept with a black man I'm irredeemably racist ..." Rose, I protested—then stopped. Well, what about it?

"You're impossible, and insolent to boot." She stormed out of the kitchen, leaving me to fill up on what remained, after the African politicians had been at it, of her delicious lamb stew cooked in fennel and lightly braised with ginger.

Gutter rat, even gangster, okay. But insolent? Damn it, I was her lover, not her footman.

□　□　□

I was having a nervous breakdown, Rose assured me, though sometimes she diagnosed my puking, dizziness, and cotton-wool detachment as a "literary pregnancy," a breakdown of the sort I had to suffer through in order to get a grip on my nascent talent. Nice to know all this, but how was I going to stay on my shaky feet?

"Insight, my darling," Rose said. "There is no substitute for self-awareness." Balls. Militance was the answer. The clenched fist might be squeezing me to death, but at least it was a firm embrace. Can't write, no status, no passport or money except what I win in midnight crap games in Soho alleys, Thurcroft won't have me anymore, even the Hammersmith boy Nazis nix me because I was seen standing guard with some New Leftists over a besieged black-owned house. Have to keep going, keep doing what Rose says is killing me, keep up at any cost. It had saved me on Route 66 and would save me again in Kensington High Street ... yes?

The core issue was antinuclear.

> "Men and women, stand together
> Do not heed, the men of war ..."

... we sang in the pouring icy rain on the First Aldermaston March to the dread bomb-making nuclear station outside Reading, Herts. Only a few dozen of us began the trek, in fair weather, but then, like a judgment, hail came splattering down, so I dashed home to get dry. Rose, suspicious of my growing involvement with younger people (i.e., including women), had refused to join us New-Comers; she was surprised I'd been so taken in by my comrades' near-religious

enthusiasm. Nothing would drag her out, she insisted. But her attitude changed with the onset of bad weather. "You just don't understand the left in Britain, darling," she muttered, grimly pulling on
her Wellington boots. "Puritan Roundheads every man jack of us.
We positively thrive on adversity," as she led raincoated Aly and me
out the door to join the suddenly swollen throngs heading west
along Hammersmith Broadway. This was a new Rose, vibrant with
solidarity, ironic but involved. Naturally, as a published writer, she
gravitated to the front rank occupied by the movement's "stars"—
photo-opportunistic priests, politicians, and union bosses, name
writers and movie actors.

Back in the ranks, Aly and I trudged under the same poncho,
arms around each other, having a perversely good time, like kids
stomping in a wet gutter. This was the life; only on rainy marches or
in street fights did I feel anything like inner peace.

Like Votes for Women—a few surviving pioneer suffragettes
marched with us under their tattered blue-and-white flags—Campaign for Nuclear Disarmament was a middle-class movement, but
with echoes of the 1930s Hunger Marches and even of Dunkirk
troops slouching back to their defenseless homeland in the rain.
Moral tension, a fever of almost imperial gladness, permeated CND
from the moment the great historian A. J. P. Taylor brought us to
our feet at that first crowded meeting in Central Hall, Westminster.
After briskly listing the effects of an H-bomb explosion, Taylor
began pacing the platform until the audience fell silent. Then his
squeaky voice asked, "Is there anyone here who would want to do
this to another human being?" Even the hecklers fell silent. "THEN
WHY," he suddenly demanded, "ARE WE MAKING THE DAMNED
THING?" We poured out into Downing Street alight with indignation and the joy of joining battle without shame.

The shadow of the Somme, when Field Marshal "Butcher" Haig
sent two hundred and fifty thousand men to their deaths in a single
day on the Western Front, lay heavily on almost everyone who sat
down, blockaded, marched, or tore through barbed wire. Hardly a
person in that duffel-coated crowd had not lost a grandparent or
uncle or even father in the Great War abbatoir. In their view, the
same military establishment that made the Somme was now
preparing a nuclear apocalypse. Robotlike staff minds that in 1917
couldn't see the difference between a German cavalryman and a
Krupp machine gun didn't grasp the enormous blasting power of
the smallest nuclear bomb compared to even the most murderous

of World War II conventional weapons. The police who rained down upon us that first night could not know we were settling a long overdue account. That "we." If you are of the left, you have obligations to a history other than your own. At its worst dilettantism, at its best warm personal solidarity with foreigners in trouble or need, the we-ness of the international left is both its sentimental weakness and its truest strength.

Most politicians, including Labour, thought CND absurd. Our cry, "Positive Neutralism," was hardly Churchillian; it was bland, dull, overbrainy, you had to think it through, figure it out. Workers in Slough and other industrial suburbs gave us puzzled frowns because only dafties would tromp about on a wet Easter Sunday, while respectable Conservatives glared from behind lace curtains but grudgingly conceded that yes, all right, we did pick up our litter.

Even while laughing at us, almost everyone in Britain regardless of politics agreed that CND was the first breath of genuinely fresh air in they couldn't remember when. And right up there under the lead banner were Rose and her friends.

"Commitment"—making a personal declaration on issues outside oneself—was in the air. Today, many of Rose's circle smile wanly at their youthful enthusiasms. Rose, of course, is totally at odds with her once-upon-a-time leftism. But then we all seemed to be Marxists, skiffling along in the same drenching rain in the same good new causes, sitting up till dawn apparently sharing the same seditious language. The late fifties in Britain was a crossroads where vastly mismatched people temporarily fell into step for a short stretch of a long road. Having just joined the flying column, I mistakenly assumed (a) we were all old soldiers of the Red regiment, and (b) this euphoria was permanent. It didn't immediately register that the writers and artists were loyal mainly to their own personal work. Since I didn't have a "work," my passion was still political, as I thought theirs was. Only later did I see that their commitment lay elsewhere, but by then my allegiances— the ones they were leaving behind—were firmly installed, like cement.

In Marxshire terms, Rose and her friends represented a "new class" of up-and-comers bent on breaking into, while threatening destruction of, the establishment. They were artistic outsiders ("Brigands down from the hills", Rose said) crashing a party whose hosts, England's cultural elite, nodded them in almost graciously. In fact, the fox-hunting, House of Lords seat-warming, landowning ruling network was lethally bored after a gray, static decade of ration-book austerity and Cold War, while the "new thrusters," an economic class hazily forming out of the exhausted remnants of the old imperialists, needed an art that reflected their own brashness, not the disappearing ink of an increasingly defunct gentlemen's agreement on which only the gentlemen, but certainly not the players, agreed. Our class enemies were starved of the vitality only we could give them.

"We" were South African exiles and Midlands proles and East End barrow boys and Caribbean poets and the occasional defecting Guards officer and Jews, Brummies, and Scouses—Alan Sillitoe, Alun Owen, Brendan Behan, Sam Selvon, Bernie Kops, Shelagh Delaney, John Osborne, Karel Reisz, Christopher Logue, George Melly, Andrew Sinclair, Joan Littlewood, Colin MacInnes, Kenneth Tynan, Lindsay Anderson, John Dexter, John Bratby—thieves bursting with talent nursed by the 1944 Education Act, swooping in from the colonies, provinces, or palest suburbs. And the young actors! Finney, O'Toole, Williamson, Bates: fierce, furious, commandingly, even sensuously angry, as if their stage voices alone could blow down at a single blast the Jericho wall of strangling snobbism that seemed to threaten the nation as Hitler had in 1940. A cry from below was being uttered—and heard.

Between quarrels, Rose explained it to me. "You can't know how new, how revolutionary, all this is. You see us as ineffectual aesthetes. But the great 'they' who control our lives feel threatened by us, and it's a most confirming experience. There's a joy here I haven't seen since I came in 1946 just after the war. We're actually having a good time tossing bricks through their gilded windows, metaphorically in some cases, not so in others, as you've demonstrated on occasion.

"You're American and take for granted that some imaginative starveling from nowhere can take your metropolis by storm. Isn't that what Thomas Wolfe and Tennessee Williams and oh I don't know how many others did? But this is Engah-land, my friend. Terence Rattigan, Somerset Maugham, Evelyn Waugh, Christopher Fry, even T. S. Eliot—stuffed corpses all. We're the masters now on the wilder shores of art. It's wonderful and magnificent and important oh my darling I'm so glad you've come into my life just now. What impeccable timing."

But not, as Rose often pointed out, such impeccable manners.

She liked my tough guy act when it protected her from the genteel harassment of well-bred pinkos. ("You put your hands on Rose like that again and I'll break them" usually did the trick.) But not in bed. She said I had terrible sexual etiquette because I was always telling her how to move to please me. "I don't mind you treating me like a whore, or that you handle my body as an object detached from my brain. It's obviously what you're used to." She wrapped herself in the coverlet and sat up in bed, shaking with cool fury and lighting one Woodbine after another. "But you make me feel so … so alone."

"But Rose," I said, "I'm always thinking of ways to please you too. And I'm not the one who gets out of bed in the middle of the night to transcribe on my typewriter what my lover has just gasped on the pillow." (I waited till next morning and wrote in longhand.)

Her narrow eyes smoldered. "If only you could relate to me personally instead of just me the womb, you'd feel infinitely more—"

I lay back, exhausted by her intelligence and my blunders. "Rose," I moaned, "can't we ever just fuck?"

She let the coverlet slip from her bare half-brown shoulders, stubbed out the cigarette, and snuggled up next to my body.

"Of course, darling," she breathed. "But this time let's give it some meaning."

I was impotent for the first time.

A far cry from: tight blue jeans, black turtleneck sweater, combat boots, and an attitude. James Dean, in *Rebel Without a Cause*, leans lazily against the kitchen door in Hammersmith, his thumbs stuck defiantly in his braided cowboy belt with the watch-this-space silver buckle, his spread fingers pointing unmistakably at his crotch. That's Rose's poster picture of me in *Loose Leaves from a Random Life*. My God This Man Made Me Suffer. Actually, the film was *Giant*.

Rose defended herself. "So I got the flick wrong. But you *are* James Dean and Marlon Brando and I don't know how many other Hollywood pretty boys all rolled up into one big mother problem."

To be absolutely accurate, I corrected again, Dean had a father fixation in *Rebel*, to which as an agent, need I remind Rose, I had supplied the writer and collected half a fee on the director.

"Don't you see," she persisted, "how neurotic you are, never knowing if you're Vladimir Ilyich Lenin or Erroll Flynn?"

Hold on. I knew who I was. Vladimir Flynn.

Who I didn't want to be, what I was in danger of becoming, was that most terrifying caricature, a political adventurer. I could always spot them in omoo—our movement. Living on air, terribly magnetized by seriousness in others while compulsively inconstant themselves, historically they'd been as organic a part of "the struggle" as our banners and barricades. High-minded mayhem causers, like Marx's son-in-law Paul Lafargue, they destroyed good women with a child's instinct to knock over delicate china: for no reason except it was simply in them to do so. Would nobody constrain me?

Not Rose, who thought I was incorrigible. Not Basil Bullock, Arnie Robins, or any of the other New Left crowd, which increasingly treated me as if I was Zachary Scott in *Mildred Pierce*, a pencil-mustached lothario with my sweaty hands in her pocketbook. Certainly not any of Rose's writer friends, who, except for Colin MacInnes, were insultingly uninterested in what I was seeing and doing on London's streets. In strict logic, I should have had most in common with working-class-bred writers like Bernard Kops and Arnold Wesker, but they were English Jews, a vastly different animal from American ones, and their non-pub-going preoccupation with their families made them alien to me. Only Len Doherty gave me *cojones*, but he was a basket case at the moment. Who, then?

On a hunch, I wrote to E. M. Forster at Cambridge. The author of *A Passage to India* invited me to tea. When I told him, in his rooms, that his novel was the best non-Marxist analysis of imperialism I'd ever read, he smiled. "Yes. All my Communist friends—Cambridge is an absolute hotbed of dialectical materialism, I fear, or should I say I'm glad to report—think so. But long ago I learned that what I write and what they read are not always the same thing. Don't you agree, Mr. Black?"

A slightly stooped, even deferential figure fussing over me as if I was a Punjabi prince, he smiled tolerantly as I poured out my troubles to him.

"Get to know us a little better," he advised, brushing shortcake crumbs off his vest. "You'll discover a violence and aggression that may surprise you. Don't be put off by our disguise of weary reticence. You can't know what it was to go through the Great War— the first one, that is. We lost everything, and everybody. Remember that if whole villages of farm lads and apprentice boys were wiped out in the trenches, the officer class—except for the generals, of course—was also decimated. Minds, minds. You don't recover swiftly from a catastrophe like two such wars in crippling succession. We've survived at the expense of selling our foreign assets and holding out a begging bowl to North America. But there's still a pride. Perverse, melodramatically understated, afraid to be defiant except in xenophobia.

"Part of what may be bothering you about your unpleasant friends in London is what I'm told you Americans call 'the problem of violence.' You sense the fever under the smooth skin but daren't name it because it goes so contrary to your, to put it kindly, idealization of us. We're quite a ferocious, warlike race, you know. No people as sexually repressed as the Anglo-Saxons can ever be anything but deadly messengers of a way of life we ourselves no longer can bear. Now that our Empire is collapsing, you and your countrymen may discover a few of these sad delights of power without pity.

"Trust your instincts, Mr. Black. After all, what choice do you have?"

My instincts were to practice the only art I had, any West Side boy's talent, hanging out. Learned to take the longest piss, drink the slowest cup of tea, just to let strangers get comfortable with me. "Oy, whatcha starin' at, mate?" You have to take the high moral ground quickly when challenged at two a.m. in a North Circular caff or a Seven Sisters Road dance hall. "I'm looking at you, buster." I'd put on my Yank growl and pretend to be a film producer talent hunting. It was such an outrageous lie, and anyway I had plausible Hollywood tales to back it up, that nobody seriously questioned my credentials. You want to know about Rock Hudson, Kirk Douglas, or Jane Russell—let me tell you, mate.

By listening carefully to the English, by telling them about myself—by sharing lives rather than interrogating them—I began to hear something important to me.

But I still couldn't write it. All Rose and her friends had to do was glance at a piece of paper and hey, presto, publishable words sprang onto its blank surface, or so it seemed. How *could* such limp-wristed wets be writers? Frustrated, I lashed out in rage and envy, and even took a punch at the playwright John Osborne backstage at the Royal Court Theatre—George Bernard Shaw's idea laboratory— where Rose was rehearsing a play. Lazily ducking, Osborne yawned in my face. "My mistress hits harder than that, chum."

Bloody hell.

"Poor lost child," Rose gently mocked. "Looking for Paris in the 1920s, Dos Passos and Pernod and lovely aristocratic nymphomaniacs in glamorous cafes. And what happens? You end up with us old ladies, male and female, chattering over teacups. What a comedown for you."

I fucked better than them (so Rose said). Why couldn't I write better?

Rose's wisdom, pouring down like gravel, only made it worse. "Don't you see, darling? They don't give a monkey's about your he-man pose. Well, perhaps one or two of my homosexual friends get turned on by your implied threat to beat them up. It's what you *do* that counts. The words, the words."

The words refused to come.

The gap between what I experienced and my inability to express it gave me an illness that only Rose's "hospital," our little Hammersmith family, could cure. I wallowed in the seedy, shabby, dusty, dirty chaos of Rose's ménage and its healing routine: all the morning papers (count 'em: *Express, News Chronicle, Daily Worker, Times, Guardian, Mirror, Mail*), followed by breakfast—those breakfasts!—midmorning sex, occasionally on the floor because the sight of her face glistening with sweat over a fry pan and those two top buttons always undone made me crazy for her, or any other way I had of delaying her rendezvous with her rifle-typewriter. All that exercise helped work up an appetite for Rose's spectacular lunches—roasts, chops, Eiffelesque salads, blastingly sweet puddings, munches, bites, nibbles. If it weren't for her work and Aly's presence in hols, I would have been perfectly content to commute forever between Rose's kitchen table and her Cocksed-up floor.

Miss Cocks, the char who came twice a week mainly to insult Rose, was rail-thin, whiskered, and mad. Yet Cocksie oddly cheered Rose; the same Rose who was so quick to resent even a whisper from the corner news agent or a New Commitment gossip seemed almost validated by the insane mutterings of her cleaning lady as she violently slammed her broom against the stairs in hardly disguised rapier thrusts. "O'Malley bitch. Whore. Cunt. Prostitute. On the game, is she? Taking in randy Yanks fucking their fucking johnnies up her fucking cunt. Opens her legs for the dustman, they say. Bitch, whore, slag." "Why don't you get rid of the old bag?" I asked Rose, who wouldn't hear of sacking the foam-mouthed, gap-toothed crone. Instead, she hovered around Miss Cocks so as not to lose a jot of the old woman's spleen. "You're crazy," I decided. Rose just gave me one of her you-wait-till-I've-had-my-say half-lidded smiles. Bonkers, the both of them.

But night was my time, lying in Rose's sex-mussed, sweat-soaked bed, when we relaxed by gazing at the dancing shadows on the ceiling from the Valor paraffin heater in the corner next to the wicker table on which sat her writing machine in which she now shamelessly left pages from her novel we didn't even bother to fight about anymore. Now I could shine, assisted by Rose's ancient wireless and Denis Conover's *Voice of Jazz* U.S. Armed Forces two a.m. radio spot. For once, the lectures came from me, soaring pedantry about Sidney Bechet, Bessie and Bix and Bunny and Benny. Rose, an apt student, had a good ear for my sort of music. Bessie Smith put her into a kind of trance. ("She knows, oh how she knows".) Outside, in the dark, cold fog, an occasional Morris Minor rumbled along Hammersmith Grove; soon electric milk floats would trundle past, tinkling bottles discreetly. And I, dreading morning, wet with the night's anxiety, would wait for first light to send me into action, any action.

But first, talk. How we talked!

At the start, talk was a release almost like sex. Our first afternoon together, when I'd knocked on her door looking for a cheap room, sent by distant friends of friends on the American "Red pipeline," we were two Communist hearts beating to the same fluttering pulse of the revolution betrayed. Exes are like vintage wine, it depends on whether it was a good or bad year. She was 1956 Budapest, I 1948 Czech coup. Each little Party flipflop—the 1939 Nazi-Soviet Pact, the Tito fiasco, the Khrushchev "revelations" at the Twentieth Congress—had shifted our lives off-center. Though Rose had been recruited in Johannesburg and I in Chicago, the same Lenin-clone cell chairman had put us to sleep with the old chestnut "Do White-Collar Workers Produce Surplus Value Comrade?" In no time Rose and I mutually recognized the dissident but loyal Party member in each other. We were old friends inside an hour, giggling uncontrollably on the threadbare couch I was to know so well.

It seemed as natural as breathing to lean over and kiss her, and for her to respond by lying back with a sigh against the couch arm, and for me to reach into her blouse, and for her to unzip my jeans and put her small, almost dainty, nicotine-stained fingers on my cock and take it from there. I picked her up—what a tiny weight—

and threw her on the bed the way I imagined Mitchum would. And though she was out of her clothes quicker than me, she looked up at me with a strange calmness. "You should know," she warned, "I've been hurt. By men. Please—be kind."

And so, driving into her for the first time, I vowed: I'd make it up to Rose. Somehow.

Getting married had always been in the cards. Half meaning it, I'd told Rose I wouldn't go with her to Aly's boarding school on Parents Day until she clarified her intentions toward me. But once she got steaming on her new novel, we both knew it wasn't on. Bam bam bam went the battered old Royal portable on the blue wicker table next to our bed. Pages flew from it like bullets from a Browning automatic. Phfft phfft, I tried to duck her sniper fire. What drove me especially wild was that Rose, even at her most productive, insisted she had a "block" like mine, that her high-velocity typing was just "finger exercises" to keep from cramping up. Yet occasionally, late at night, she couldn't resist jumping out of bed to read me parts. "Where are the jokes?" I asked once. "You and me get off some real corkers." "This is *not*," she insisted, "about you and me. It's an imaginative extension of—" "Forget it, baby." "DON'T CALL ME THAT!"

I was Rose's subject. But what was mine?

Arthur Koestler once said the next great war would be between the Communists and the ex-Communists. How did he know about Rose and me?

"You're so competitive," said Rose, who entered just about every literary contest around. "It's so ... so *capitalist*."

It didn't matter, she insisted, that I was a socialist, because the virus of commercial advantage was implanted in my Yankee genes. ("It was no accident, Gus, that you became a Hollywood agent.") The proof was how often I said things like "big deal," "no big deal." But when I protested that my speech patterns had been formed more by the Rockets A.C. than the Benedict Agency, she pounced: "Condemned out of your own mouth—don't you see how far back it goes?"

Translation: to Mom.

My mother, Polly Black, hadn't scared me half as much as the way Rose spoke about her. Ceaselessly psychoanalyzing my "behavior," Rose kept prying under the Oedipal rock to show me my darkest secrets, the worms and maggots of my unearthed past, which were the last thing I wanted to confront. No, I shouted, I would *not* go to a shrink, I would *not* submit my troubles to a stranger, I would *not* castrate myself for someone who might turn me over to the police, as had happened to some California comrades. No, I did *not* want to know the difference between the Kleinian "good breast" and "bad breast." And no, I could not recall, try as I might, in the sort of detail I envied in Rose, much of my childhood beyond dim, useless memories of hotel lobbies in small dusty towns and countless meetings in union halls where I was the only person under thirty, so what? "But don't you see," Rose asserted.

Nope.

What bothered me most was her implication that the real difference between me, and Rose and her artist friends, was that they had successfully climbed over a mountain of personal shit to arrive at hard-won insights that freed them to write or paint, while I cravenly avoided the Painful Ascent. Yet surely this particular form of self-exploration, with its harsh ironies and ambiguities, would kill me before it made me a writer. "Oh, darling, we all go through that in therapy. You have no choice, don't you see? Until you get help, you'll continue to smash us up, destroy yourself—even kill your talent." Reporters, I snapped back, find out about themselves on the streets, not the couch. I wished I could be like her friends, but my models were American journalists with few literary pretensions: Ernie Pyle, Homer Bigart, John Gunther, even crime-beat men like Ben Hecht. Reporters, not writers. "Categories, categories," Rose smiled, but in the end she accepted with some grace that I'd have to find my own way. Besides, I triumphantly quoted Matthew Arnold, "Journalism is literature in a hurry." "If hurry is your criterion, Gus," she said, "you're the most literary person I know."

Then my mother died.

It was a snowy night in the Berkshire hills, in Basil Bullock's large Edwardian house overlooking a valley and fields his family had once owned but gradually had to sell off for death duties. I was no longer surprised by the occasional property-owning socialist, just mortified that in common with the rest of their class, they chose to freeze most of the year in noncentrally nonheated country houses. Basil was one of the many who made fun of me for bringing a paraffin heater with me when I came for visits; the miners, at least, had enough sense to keep their front parlors blazing hot with NCB coal.

Basil and I'd made up our fight over Rose by pretending it really had been about politics. Who knows? Maybe it had been. Tonight he and the local Labour candidate and Leo Rossiter, of whom I was growing increasingly fond, were sitting around the minuscule fire in Basil's big, drafty drawing room while Henrietta, Basil's doctor wife, restored us with tea and Madeira cake after a long day's canvassing. It felt good to be tired among comrades.

The phone rang. Long distance, from California. I had to take it where we were all sitting. It was my Los Angeles friend Ruth Silverman, from the Committee of Correspondence. "Polly died this morning. A heart attack, on her way back from Las Vegas." My first reaction: "What was Mom doing in Vegas?" Ruth said, "Didn't you know anything about her? She went almost every weekend, gambling in the nickel-and-dime casinos, and dancing her head off. Maybe now is the time to get a shrink and find out who your mother really was."

Stunned, I put the phone down. Without thinking, I said numbly, "My mom's gone." Leo, Basil, Henrietta, and the Labour candidate looked at me with expressions ranging from acute discomfort to mild displeasure. Henrietta excused herself to the kitchen. "Bad luck," Leo muttered. "Ah yes," said Basil as if I had just contributed to his tutorial on Coleridge. The Labour candidate, who hadn't bargained for this either, stared fixedly at the ceiling. Then, as if nothing whatsoever had happened, the conversation picked up where we'd left it, at Labour's chances in the upcoming '59 general election.

I looked at them all, and felt it too: shame. I was ashamed Polly had died in their front room. For I don't know how long I sat there, then without anyone stopping me went up to my room. Nobody said anything.

Back in London, I told Rose. I wasn't sad up there, I explained, I was embarrassed by their embarrassment.

"Ah, darling." Rose wrapped me in a warm blanket while feeding me Scotch in a mug of tea with platefuls of hot buttered scones and strawberry jam. "God help you, you're becoming English—despite yourself."

No, not English. Marxshire.

□ □ □

I was content to remain indefinitely in my double womb—Rose's pad and the English New Left—but was rescued, against my will, by "the logic of events." The left did not simply disintegrate, it collapsed like a supernova from the center.

Our think tank, *New Commitment*, became an early sixties casualty when, hard on the heels of a Tory poll triumph ("YOU'VE NEVER HAD IT SO GOOD—DON'T LET LABOUR RUIN IT!"), it sold out to its class enemies. *New-Com*'s editors called it a "comradely merger" of the magazine with Basil Bullock's *Chartism Today*, a slight readjustment of priorities, but it was little short of a brazen capitalist takeover by the Rich New Left, which had even less time for roadhogging, unilingual Yankees like me.

Nothing corrupt or underhanded; the merged magazine's new owners, a gaggle of lean-hipped, slurry-voiced, Eton-educated sons of moneybags with a politely rebellious streak and a hatred for their fathers (for some reason—is this racist?—they all seemed to have the uptilted nose of *The New Yorker*'s Eustace Tilley staring at life through his lorgnette), simply marched in and bought out the joint by waving a Coutts & Co. chequebook. Unlike us Not So Rich New Left, who at times were seriously guilty of romanticizing the English working class, the rich boys, representing an Even Newer Left, despised ordinary people, about whom they knew nothing and wanted to know even less, preferring more glamorous Third World revolutionaries in Algeria or Cuba; in place of our English gods, Leavis and Hoggart, they worshiped violent French philosophers like Althusser (who strangled his wife) and Lacan. The rich rebels, whose families holidayed in Tuscany and the Dordogne, saw the world differently, perhaps more broadly, than did we little Englanders, who were fiercely focused on Britain and its perils. But at what a price!

Briefly and angrily, spurred by nothing more honorable than an animal suspicion of *New Commitment*'s incoming landlords, I campaigned against the merger-takeover, but the fix was in, Chicago-style. After only three years, the New-Comers were tired or had lost their nerve. Following an exhausting Night of the Knives, when the fait was accompli by exchanging money and little deeds upstairs at the Maquis, Arnie Robins led me down for a consolation espresso in the now completed coffeehouse. "Sorry, comrade," he said. "Maybe now you and I can finally get on with our own lives and work." We looked at each other: neither of us really wanted to do that.

We'd had a good inning. The New Left's search for a new ethical foundation for socialism, which had been fatally compromised by Stalin's gulags and (at an infinitely lower level of misery) the exhaustion of the social democratic welfare state, had been worth it. We'd tried mixing the unmixable: Gandhian nonviolence with Christian syndicalism with "early" Marx with C. Wright Mills, Camus, Fromm, Paul Goodman, and A. J. Muste. What a stew. But before Fanon and Marcuse, before Castro's "new man" and R. D. Laing and Timothy Leary reinjected the left with revolutionary authoritarianism, we who worked in the marching laboratories felt absolutely free to combine, dismiss, try, always try, new ways of living and thinking.

The demographics were against us. We were never more than a tiny fraction even of the intelligentsia, let alone the workers, who were massively immune to our ideas. "An intellectual," I was told in working-class pubs from Bolton to Bridport, "is someone who sleeps with another bloke's wife." Bloody hypocrites, so did they, I'd thump my glass on the old wooden tables. "Watch it, lad," they'd warn, "you need us more than we need you."

So we hadn't broken through. But it had been a hell of a lot of fun trying.

I hated being an adult.

So, with all my earthly goods—the Maquis and *New Commitment* magazine—firmly in the hands of Eustace Tilley, I had even less excuse for not writing. And that, surprisingly, is what happened.

Without warning, my engine—fed by Rose's cooking, E. M. Forster's kindness, Colin MacInnes's example, above all Len Doherty's generosity in giving me Thurcroft—sparked. The small, nearly unused Corona portable, which I'd lugged all the way across the Atlantic but which usually sat mute in a dusty corner of my room, began erupting and spitting words almost without my willing it. Out of nowhere, steam rose from the typewriter keys like mist from the Yorkshire moors on a cold, sunny day. Looking into the swirl, I saw a tipple, a revolving wheel, a coal mining village. Enveloped in the mist, I began to write about it.

I was on my way.

And in vogue. That is, *Vogue.*

BOOK 2

THE VIEW FROM HANOVER SQUARE

Long spindly legs, invisible waists, storklike stride, breasts smaller than the nipples: who were these women?

"Slaves to the solitude of fashion, heterae in the service of style, what Mary Wollstonecraft and Aphra Behn would be doing if they were alive today—and a trifle less ugly, of course," cracked my editor at Britain's premier clotheshorse magazine, *Vogue*. With that, Benjamin Gadsden Tyler passed me some glossy ten-by-ten photos of stunning English girls riding camels in Tunisia, posing on top of sand dunes, and trying to look sultry behind swirls of veillike synthetics. "Give me some literate captions for these, will you, Black? Nothing too poetic—remember, our basic reader is under a hairdryer out in Tooting Bec. Where in God's name is that?"

I was perhaps the only writer on British *Vogue* who actually knew where Tooting Bec was. It's probably why they hired me.

"Don't flatter yourself," said BenGy Tyler (as he signed his articles), the magazine's American-born number two and my direct boss. "I asked for you after I read that article of yours about the Yorkshire miners—your book's out soon, right? Anybody who could make those dreary lives accessible to shallow minds like mine has the sort of talent it takes to help me get this dinosaur of a publication into the 'swinging sixties'—I'll dock your pay if I see you using that detestable phrase." BenGy, who had been thrown out of more prep schools than I had bars, apparently had decided that his calling, aside from a deep talent for dissipation, was to worship at the altar of words put together by writers other than, and in his own eyes superior to, himself if he felt they were worth it. God's grace existed for BenGy only in literary craft.

"I am going to do for High Episcopalianism what Graham Greene does for the Catholics—attack it the way I do women, from the rear. Something I believe we learned from the ancient Hebrews, if my reading of Edmund Wilson is correct," he mused over vermouth cassis at La Terrazza, the ultrafashionable restaurant he liked dragging me to on Greek Street. He smiled wickedly. "Do Jews have souls, or just guilt?"

Then he rose to greet our dates, two tall debutantes who doubled as *Vogue* models. "Tell me about it later, Black. Much later."

Amanda and Caroline rushed breathlessly over to our table, where BenGy graciously handed one of them to me. "Caroline," he said deadpan, "is the Foreign Secretary's daughter. Perhaps you can enlighten her on aspects of international socialism she may have missed at Bedales." "Oh yes, please," chirped Caroline in a skimpy sheath dress Twiggy was about to make famous, "I've never met a real socialist."

BenGy signaled the waiter to bring a menu. "Neither," he said deliberately, "have I."

Just outside Thurcroft's coal pit was a small, serene, grass-knolled reservoir used by the village boys for skinny-dipping. Len Doherty and I sat on a sludge bank chewing dry summer grass while watching a blood-red sun go down behind the tipple. Snap pail at his side, Len was due on night shift soon. He looked like hell. Between us lay a typewritten manuscript I'd brought with me.

"Well," I said, "what do you think of it?"

In his gruffest Yorkshire, "Tha've got soom a th' wage rates wrong."

I picked up the manuscript and penciled in his corrections. "Anything else?"

He thought, then shook his head. "Nay. Th' back rippin' is nearly raght. But th' bit about th' pit props maght need soom lookin' at by not much."

I prodded him for a real opinion.

He didn't speak for a few moments. Then he looked over at me. "Lad," he smiled, "it'll make thy reputation for sure."

Which it did.

I felt odd trying to be famous by writing about people who never would be. How did a real writer like Len deal with this?

Before putting me on the 19 Wigmore bus back to Sheffield, via Rotherham, Len said, "Ah've got enough guilt for both of us, Gus. Tha deserve soomthing good. This book of yours will help tha get up in th' world. If tha'rt lahk me, tha won't enjoy it a lot. Just see it doesn't kill thee."

As my bus pulled away I watched his figure grow smaller and smaller in Victoria Road. Some men going on shift joined him, and en masse, a company of industrial soldiers, they turned up the narrow path leading to the mine. Len didn't look back.

Nor, after a while, did I.

There was a delay in publishing my miners' book because the printers went on strike. I could have strangled the bastards, why couldn't they wait, they made more money than me, or at least give me a comradely exemption? "I should have warned you," Rose teased. "There's no such thing as working-class solidarity when you're nervous about your first book coming out. But you won't let a little thing like the quest for immortality make you middle-class, surely?"

She should talk. If I was making it on Len's back, what was Rose doing?

Scene: A Lyons Corner teahouse near Sloane Square, Chelsea. *Time:* 1961. Alastair O'Malley and I have just been to the premiere of Rose's new play at the Royal Court theatre. Called *Sol and Me and the Rest of Us*, it's about a London lady writer, her absurdly macho American lover, and her young son. It stars a New York Method actor as me, a RADA cherub for Aly. On complimentary tickets Aly and I sit in the Grand Circle pretending to enjoy it but duck out on the backstage celebration to have one of our own. As if this is our last meal, we gorge on sweet buns. Finally Aly wipes his mouth and we just sit there looking at each other.

"You first." I broke the silence.

Aly shrugged. "It wasn't bad, Ma's play. Y'know, she's having this affair with the actor bloke who's you. So now she's got three of you in her life—the real you, what she wrote about you, and this guy pretending to be you." He sighed melodramatically. "Frankly, I don't know how she keeps track."

The kid was keeping his cool. I was boiling.

He chattered on. "That child actor who's me. Fairy for sure. Is that how she sees us?"

I launched into a windy spiel about fact versus fantasy in the artistic imagination, but he cut me off. "You sound just like Ma when some family cousin in Jo'burg sends her a letter complaining how she writes about them in one of her stories. As soon as Ma says 'imagination,' you know she's lying."

Was I as crazy in real life as the actor who played me?

"Sometimes."

A little shamed, I wondered if that was also true of Pavel, her, um—

"Her last lover," he cut in dryly. "You don't have to treat me like a kid. I *am* almost fifteen, you know."

"Sorry, pal."

Aly mused. "No. Pav was different from you. He wore smart suits to visit Ma. And he was gone in the morning."

"Respectable. Not like me."

"Married. No, not like you."

"Be nice, Aly. I'm still in shock."

Aly looked at me like Rose sometimes did. "You really hate what she's done to you?"

I couldn't be dishonest with him. "A kick in the stomach would hurt less," I admitted. I looked carefully at him. "You don't mind?"

"Nah. I've been been through it before, you see." He ticked off his fingers. "I'm in three of Ma's short stories, two novels, and now this. I reckon I'm owed danger money, don't you?"

I was impressed. "She's really blitzed us."

Aly shrugged. "You get used to it. Ma says it puts food on the table. Can't complain, can I?"

"Sure you can. Magna Carta. Habeas corpus. Rights of Man."

"You're like Ma," he observed, grabbing his fifth, I counted them, cream bun. "She tells me to be honest, then makes me feel a right turd when I am."

"We're both turds tonight," I said.

He smiled sadly, brightly. "Speak for yourself, Captain Turd."

I did just that.

When Rose came home that night from her theater party, I stood at the top of the stairs just as she had in the recent past. Arms folded, grim face, the works. As soon as she opened the downstairs door, I shouted the first words that came into my head.

"And the sonofabitch is a lousy actor too!"

She stared, blinking, then walked cautiously up. She looked splendid in a new, softly tailored gray wool suit I'd made her buy.

"Don't be silly." She brushed past me.

I stalked her into the kitchen, where she was already wrapped in swirls of blue Woodbine smoke.

"You're fucking this fag from New York. Who else is there?" I demanded.

"If you must know"—she returned my gaze evenly—"Phillip and John and—"

I whacked her. She scattered in all directions on the kitchen floor, then stared up at me with absolutely no emotion.

"Phillip?!" I roared. "You let me make love to you after you'd been with that crummy hack poet who hasn't written an original line in his life? When he dies there'll be a special court in purgatory for Brecht and Neruda to swear out plagiarism writs on him. Does he even ever take a bath?" Then, despite her protests, I helped her up, sat her in a chair and—for the first time since we'd been togeth-er—boiled her a cup of coffee. I poured the coffee, sliced some of her home-baked rye bread, slabbed butter on it with a couple of slices of Polish salami, and pushed it at her. "Eat," I said.

She did. After a second cup, she said, "Look here, I wouldn't have let them make love to me if you—"

"EAT!" I commanded.

She smiled, once again composed. "You are"—she drew a firm breath—"such a child."

I went to the bathroom and brought back a sticking plaster for the small cut on her chin. She sat still while I licked away a trace of blood. "This won't get you anywhere, you know," she said as I applied the Band-Aid. "You insisted I become what I've always despised, a 'modern woman.' Now you can't stand it. It's so incon-sistent, don't you see that, darling?"

My God, the bloody woman was still lecturing me.

After that, Rose never mentioned my slugging her and I didn't raise the subject of her play. Gradually, while still sleeping together, we censored out the painful parts, which grew in number as our separate careers prospered. What had happened to the two Com-munist hearts beating as one?

Political animals prowl differently from most cats. While others sleep, we take to a night of dreams and visions that propel us into a world sometimes only loosely connected to the normal jungle. We define our-selves not solely according to our daily bread but to future power, or "singing tomorrows." Left or right, we feast upon offal that repels our

*brother beasts—faction fights, all-night meetings, incessant maneu-
verings for position, and a tiring struggle to reconcile our ideals with
our lusts. All this Rose and I took pride in because engagement, real
commitment, bestowed an illusion, and often the reality, of wholeness.*

*Perhaps we did not reckon as strongly as we might on the injuries
to self, on the shearing away from our moorings, that can occur in
trying to translate essentially nineteenth-century premises and values
to a world whose modernity we were products of. We'd signed up for a
more conventional struggle without seeing the invisible ink on the
contract that said, This far ... and much, much further.*

"We're eloping!" Rose was in the habit of saying when I got too
much for her or even for Aly to handle. At such moments, in my
small room, the two of them would gather over me like Jonas Salk
and Florence Nightingale having a medical consultation about a
particularly fractious patient. A collusive look passed between
them, and Rose would say, "We're eloping!" and they'd tiptoe out
like lovers. Later, Aly would return. "We didn't really elope," he'd
reassure me. "It's just Ma's joke. Tell you what, why don't you two
get hitched and save all this bother?"

But it was too late for that.

Rose began to hate me. It happened—quick as a wink!—after her
play opened, which coincided with publication of *Loose Leaves from
a Random Life.* Almost overnight her attitude changed, as if my very
core repelled her, much as she said I rejected her soul-center in the
act of love. She started prowling around the house looking either
frightened or angry, I couldn't tell which, except that her lips stayed
permanently pressed together in a thin white line I was so used to
from our quarrels. She also took to scrutinizing Aly and me as if we
were strangers. When I confronted her about this, she loftily asserted that it was "inappropriate" for me, a grown man, to laze about
all day and half the night with an adolescent, because it stopped
him from making friends his own age and, by the way, made me
even more immature. (Quite the opposite, I thought, but still.) Of
course she had a theory. "He's you at his age, clearly. And I'm your
mother. You're trying to repaternalize your infantile psyche by
appointing him your surrogate self and me your—" "Rose, lay off,"

I'd beg, "the kid's only thirty-four, I mean I'm only fifteen, oh ... what the hell." And, triumphantly, she'd put one hand on her hip, run the fingers of the other through her hair, mussing the new Jean Seberg–style hairdo I'd suggested, and look fixedly at me with a nearly sweet smile, as if waiting, but for what?

I had almost forgotten that I was illegal. Hiding had become a reflex. As my star rose higher, I sometimes spoke every night from a different platform, and my name got into print, and that's when I saw that what really made sense to English police were coded signals. Cops, whether MI5 or Special Branch or just local bobbies, had class antennae, and they understood, in time, that I was under the protection of somebody important. In fact, they smelled it even before I did, and backed off smartly. Extraordinarily, this important personage was Rose, plus her friends, plus the New Commitment crowd, who the police grasped were not to be trifled with. Yes, freely bashed in demos—fair's fair, guv—but not on a matter where Questions might be asked in the House of Commons, in which we had our friendly, or tame, Members. It was a Mexican standoff, English-style.

Thus, I almost regretted getting a telegram from the American Embassy in Grosvenor Square telling me that courtesy of a Supreme Court decision in the Paul Robeson case, no U.S. citizen could be denied a passport merely for his or her beliefs, therefore a valid new passport would be issued me. *Voilà*, no more hiding in bushes, no more writing under a false name or dodging policemen or paying Aly to soap my window sashes. I was free.

When I got back from the embassy and showed the new green-as-gold document to Rose, she hardly glanced at it. We both knew what it meant.

Suddenly no more dramas. No reason for hate, or help. It felt lousy. Rose said it was because my psychology had been formed around a stone of high risk and that—

"Rose," I cut in, "do you always have to have an opinion about everything?"

"Well, yes," she said tightly, "that's who I *am*. Don't you know who I *am* by now?"

We looked at each other more directly than we had in months. It was settled.

And no last straw, or final bitter rift. Or need to talk, explain, defend, assert. We were like two boxers who'd gone the full fifteen rounds and were too exhausted to slug it out anymore. The fight was over.

In bed, I looked down at Rose's face, now in repose after months of strain. She'd never been so relaxed. Her small green eyes, usually keenly alert, were half closed, her nostrils unflared for a change. She looked as open and beautiful as the first day we'd met four years ago. I pulled the coverlet down and studied her sturdy body, which had never quite lost its African tan. She examined it too and smiled wanly. "I know what you're thinking." She put her arms on my shoulders the way she sometimes did when she wanted to express both friendship and distance. "It's a battlefield, this scarred old carcass of mine, isn't it? Where you and I have dispatched our squadrons and flying cavalry every day like one-eyed generals in some forgotten war. Maneuver and counter-maneuver, tactics and strategy, retreat and attack ... and all so pointless, my darling." She shook me in the friendliest possible way, then gave that eloquent sigh that was her signature for dismissing a subject too baffling for us foolish mortals—or one she'd made up her mind to write about.

"Oh well ..."

A chill went up my spine, which she was detachedly massaging. "Oh well." Aly, too, was getting into the habit of saying "Oh well" exactly like Rose when things got too painful. He shouldn't get too wise, not at fifteen going on seventy-something.

But Aly wasn't any of my business anymore either.

He came into my room while I was packing. He looked at my few things—a U.S. Army duffel bag, my typewriter in its case now bulging with molten words, a few clothes spread out on the single bed I'd hardly used—and he said, "It's funny, but I always thought you'd go out the window, not the front door."

"We'll still see each other," I promised.

"Uh-huh," he said flatly.

When I went over to wrap my arms around him he punched me, hard. "You're dumb," he said.

"Let's wrestle," I said.

"Grow up," Aly said.

I shouldered the duffel bag, and he took my typewriter down for me. In the kitchen Rose was smoking. "Got everything, then?" These two amazed me. I kissed Rose, who said, "See you."

Outside, on the Broadway, I looked for a taxi in a slight drizzle. For the first time Aly and I had nothing to say to each other. I asked him if he was going to be in *Toad of Toad Hall* again this year. "Ha," he said, "that's for juveniles. I'm rehearsing *Uncle Vanya*." Up ahead a black Austin cab made a tight turning circle in response to my two-finger whistle.

Aly put down my typewriter, his eyes dry as dust. "You'll be going back to America, right? I mean, that's why you're leaving us?" Sure, I lied, why else? I got in the taxi and pushed the side window down.

"Give us a kiss, then," I said.

"You must be joking," he said firmly. "Kissing is for children."

The taxi went off. I wished the little sod had let me kiss him.

It was all coming together for me, finally. Work, by-lines, recognition, a job—and even a passport.

Rose made clear that just because we were parting we didn't have to separate "that way" too. Lots of ex-lovers, Rose claimed, still slept with each other without strings or even much passion, out of friendship and a shared past. She knew I was always pursuing a Big Romance—Americans were like that. But I might find our new arrangement "rather a relief, what do you say, Gus?"

"Will you still cook for me?" I asked.

"You bastard." But she said it with a smile.

A serious person like me does not take seriously a trivial publication like *Vogue*. It is printed on glossy paper, and the articles are hard to find in the foliage of fashion plates and ads. Then there is the matter of tone, which for BenGy was identical with substance. "Tone," insisted this elegantly foppish company man, "is what makes our organization truly great. Before us there was no style, only fashion. But how a woman looks is her statement in the world, wouldn't you agree? We want a woman to want to look her best—her desire, and how she arrives at it, is our business. We're not fools, *Vogue* knows real women in the real world don't actually look like the Shrimp or Twigs. Any ordinary woman who tried it would die of malnutrition in a week. And we also know that most of our readers, not the 'fashion leaders' but the under-the-hairdryer readers on whom our advertising manager depends, cannot begin to afford the gear. That's not the point. Tone is all. We take life a lot more seriously than all your old New Commitment gasbags. Women create life and read *Vogue*. We create *Vogue* by reading women. Beautiful symmetry, don't you think?"

Even though there was a tight, cold, mean spring inside BenGy Tyler that coiled and uncoiled like a mechanical snake according to the shifts and eddies in fashion and who was paying him to chart its circuitous route, I loved working for the King of Snobs. He was such a life-giving change from the comrades, whose ideals and personal lives they, we, had so much trouble welding into coherence but who passed judgment like a daily kidney stone. BenGy was a solid piece of human sculpture; you got what you paid for. Or rather, what he paid you for.

Off the job, in his social hours, BenGy could be bitchy, gossipy, hurtful, mean, a Fleet Street Iago. But at his small wooden desk on *Vogue*'s fifth floor, behind the thin partition that separated us from the models' changing room, he was a sort of word priest paying devout attention to copy deadlines and "good writing." Periodical journalism, which my Rose and most of her friends looked upon as torture if not humiliation, was BenGy's element, his glory. He was a magazine writer at a time when that particular form was coming into its own. "New Journalism," of which BenGy was a master and I a fast-learning apprentice, was turning into a cliché before my eyes, but not before I'd learned some of the tricks, like dropping conventional punctuation and holding the same high note for a page or two of fact told as fiction. "Think of it," BenGy lazily explained, "as pouring a magnum of the finest champagne into Styrofoam cups and having it keep its nerve—against all the laws of literature and good taste." BenGy's main human weakness was collecting first editions of modern American writers, which he would beg the authors, by letter or in person, to sign. "A compensatory affectation, but harmless, wouldn't you say?" The day he asked me to sign a copy of my miners' book I felt as if he'd given me a raise. Then I went in and asked for one. "Crass, Black, very crass,"—but he raised me an extra twenty guineas a week at a time when a pound and a shilling still meant something.

The Yorkshire collier Len Doherty I'd always thought of as my other half; now I found I had more than one and he was not a nice man. "Nice kills," BenGy said.

BenGy was a socialist's nightmare, bilious, not "sensitive," mocking instead of humane. Virginia gentry by breeding and a Manhattan street hustler by preference, he dismissed my political concerns, if he bothered, with amiable scorn. When in doubt he always cited writers we both felt to be irreducibly honest. "What would Orwell, Edmund Wilson, Mark Twain, or Jonathan Swift make of Rose O'Malley's bunch, hah? All you Commie pseuds ever did was make the fifties into an even shabbier version of the thirties—except where was your Auden or Morgan Forster? If you want the truth, which I don't suppose you do, it was 'angries' like you and Osborne and O'Malley who softened up the world for people like me. Political intellectuals have had their day, thank Christ for small favors. The pity is that the libraries are disintegrating along with your socialist virility. The only thing I know about your sainted miners is that they valued books and treated libraries like religious shrines. I can excuse them any idiocy for that. But five years from now I'll bet my socks there will not be a miners' library anywhere between Merthyr Motherfuck and Black Hole, Cumbria. The word is giving way to the image, son. And when your beloved working class loses the Word, it loses the game for power. I'm a hell of a lot better Marxist than you any day because I'm not afraid to see the world as it is."

Previously, BenGy had anointed me the magazine's chief correspondent and all-around arts reporter. Now, cynically, he added TV columnist to my duties. "That way," he noted, "you won't lose complete touch with the Great British Worker."

Billie Stoutheart saw to that, too.

Tall and skinny, with saucer-shape eyes that stared into David Bailey's Hasselblad lens with a gaze of stark terror: Billy had the perfect *Vogue* Look.

She was also black.

Well, not quite. But enough. Pale olive skin that she darkened to almost pure ebony with generous layers of foundation before a shoot. Billie, our official Black Is Beautiful girl, was in fact a Newcastle Geordie, the offspring of a Sierra Leonese sailor and a local South Shields woman. Her personal manager's name was—what else?—Chester le Prudhoe, an in-joke. "Ah, zo you 'ave tweeged to my leetle Tweegy," he acknowledged in his fake Hercule Poirot accent, then switched to pure local dialect, "but if you drop it in company, lad, an' lose us a day's wage packet, Ah'll smash in yer face, geddit?" His nom-de-*Vogue* he had concocted from Chester le Street and Prudhoe, two mining towns near Newcastle.

Most of Britain's port cities, including Newcastle, have populations, now into their fourth and fifth generations, of "half-castes" like Billie. Chester le Prudhoe was actually her brother Terry, a petty hood who used to make a living as a Tyneside slumlord's leg-breaker. Now Billie and Terry were the toast of London high society, along with the real Twiggy and Justin de Villeneuve, and Shrimpton and her David Bailey.

As in Thurcroft, nobody approved of our liaison. BenGy said the boss—our horse-riding, Royals-doting editor—frowned on *Vogue* staff diminishing the semimystical aura of her top models, and Billie's brother was determined to marry her off to an earl or a duke. Billie's main job was to keep her mouth shut to conceal (a) her bad teeth, and (b) a northeast prole accent you could cut with a knife. (Geordie, even more than Scouse or Cockney, is a regional dialect, more Scandinavian than English, impenetrable even to many northerners.)

Billie was fairly typical of high-fashion models then. Storklike and small-faced, of indeterminate class and without an immediately identifiable accent, they were glamorous working women who symbolized more than just a new visual trend: they were part of a fashion and gender revolution that was fueled, at bottom, by a sort of cool indifference, rather than anger or disgust, at the cruelties of the class system. Billie wasn't just another Eliza Doolittle, a freak escapee from her class. She and her stilt-legged regiment, the new models, were England's first baby boomers, born at the end of the war and remembering only peacetime's grim austerity and ration books and fair shares of dull, dull, dull grayness for all. Billie, who'd left school at thirteen, didn't know about any of that. "I'd go wi' th' Devil himself if he got me out of Byker," a scummy suburb of Newcastle.

With flair and natural drama, Billie had taught herself the new "London Look": straight black hair with bangs, deemphasize mouth, heavy into eyes with eyeliner that curled up at the ends and lashes blackened the color of chimney soot (had they seen Elizabeth Taylor as Cleopatra?), tons of Yardley cosmetics with faint lip gloss, mod miniskirts and Hullabaloo white boots. *Voilà*, swinging London, slick and straight and not at all suitable for the easels of Reynolds and Van Dyck, try Snowdon and Avedon.

And Billie was smart, smart enough to "blacken up" her already dark complexion in order to stand out from the other models, adapting easily to *Vogue*'s special, occasionally arduous needs, mainly sweaty shoots in far-off places orchestrated by the moody temperaments of different star photographers. What was hard for her was London itself. "I'm a Tyneside lass," she insisted, just like my Yorkshire Noreen, "and all these strangers put me off, don't they you?"

Unlike Noreen, she'd made the jump, out of the northeast and her native class, to London's swirl, but at a price. She was nervous all the time, a tight high tension that, under a lens, rendered her "a splendid animal" (according to BenGy), with "a look that can kill and caress at the same time" (Chester's PR). Given time, she'd toughen up, make money, marry well. For now, she was a shaky, half-submissive half-rebel nineteen-year-old with an awkward, anorexic body not yet quite tuned in to the swing of the sixties.

Scene: My new garden flat on a spacious Bayswater square near Notting Hill. Austerely but expensively furnished. Bachelor pad of which Rose has observed, "You'll go crazy here, it's so unlike you, or is that the point?" *Time:* After Bay of Pigs, before John Kennedy assassination. Billie, her thin frame encased in one of my bathrobes, sits on my handcrafted L-shaped mahogany couch obediently sipping a cup of tea like a little girl. She stares at all the books on my shelves.

"You must spend all your time reading," she said wonderingly.

"They help me sleep when I'm alone," I said.

"Oh, you." She smiled timidly. Was this the same "gorgeous, ferocious animal" *Vogue, Harpers,* and *Queen* plastered all over their pages?

"You're just a skinny kid." I smiled back.

"Who me? I'm 'Lady B, the Sensation of Mayfair'—or haven't you heard?" And she put on her mean, pouty expression.

Sure I'd heard. I'd captioned her that myself.

"Well," she said, looking around, "I'm doin' all right for meself. Sendin' money home and all. Or ... I think Chester, I mean Terry is."

"Some people," I said, "think you and Terry are man and wife." She looked so troubled I changed the subject.

"Is there inny future in it?" she asked anxiously.

I cinched up my own robe, an Old Bond Street silk job, and thought about it. By BenGy's calculation Billie had another three, four years as a top model. "No," I told her.

She sighed. "That isn't what Terry says. He says there's always the flicks. Justin got Twigs a movie part. I could do that."

"You're also black," I reminded her.

She pressed her lips together to concentrate. "That's a thought," she admitted, then brightened. "I could lighten meself up, like how Ah do it t'other way now."

"No, you can't," I said. "You're selling black." White Billie would be like any other *Vogue* girl.

She relaxed. "I'll wait for Terry to tell me the next move. He says there's a lot out there for us right now. Sky's the limit."

"What would *you* like to do next?" I asked.

"Oh, me," Billie shrugged, "I left her behind in Byker."

We'd all left ourselves behind in Byker. That was the point.

□ □ □

Vogue's splendid glass-and-steel office at Hanover Square sure beat working for a living. For BenGy, *Vogue* was a real job; for me, a reprise of the Benedict Agency on Sunset Boulevard, a holiday from morals. BenGy made it easy for me. "Sellout," he lectured me, "does not consist in working for the class enemy. Me, in this case. I let you learn your trade. You only sell out by excusing yourself."

The possibility of "sellout" had never really occurred to me before. It was what talented people did, or right-wing socialists who became millionaires, or Bronx novelists gone to Hollywood. After all, wasn't I still just a punk in a fake-satin team jacket hanging around Fifteenth and Kedzie with a toothpick in his mouth? BenGy would have none of it. "Take responsibility for what you do, Black. Politics is inescapable for the likes of you. I can just see you now, brooding about how to turn Hanover Square into your Finland station. Forget it. You're a revolution addict, and for once you've hired aboard one that's successful."

Britain's "revolt into style" was the fashion parallel to what Rose and her pals had done a few years earlier: a great cultural turnover led by outsiders swiftly absorbed into the mainstream because the children of the powerful were hungry for more than the gruel their war- and Depression-haunted Mummies and Daddies had eaten and pronounced fit for heroes.

Suddenly, in the early sixties, the raunchy classes (teds, mods, rockers) began to look fascinating to large numbers of nice people tired of quiet dignity and a tradition of polite reticence increasingly seen as repressive and boring. The new style started, as usual, with the working class, whose dropped aitches and slightly wonderful threads looked, well, y'know, a bit risky like. A Jewish tailor, Cecil Gee, who catered to the outrageous young, was now "in." The very rich started talking like Cockneys to show how hip they were. Yesterday's narrow, sanctified, understated style, personified by the bemused, grouse-hunting prime minister, Harold Macmillan, was discredited. Christine Keeler, the Notting Hill trollop who brought down the government, was the uncrowned queen of England. And my boss, BenGy Tyler, was her Disraeli.

Clotheswise, I became BenGy's Rose O'Malley, a dress-up doll to play with and "improve." "The point of 'making it' as a writer is not"—his gimlet eye ran over my black pea jacket, jeans, combat boots, and crew-neck sweater—"to go around like a yiddlich pants presser from the Lower East Side, which your immediate forebears no doubt were"—how did he guess?—"but at least to make an attempt, doubtless doomed from the outset, at improving your class facade if not position."

With faintly curled lip, he examined me from head to toe, sighing and humming to himself and treating me with the affectionate contempt normally reserved for *Vogue* models. "Hmm ... perhaps, well, maybe not ... a possibility ... turn around and let's ..." His final verdict: "Okay, no more rough trade. Torn T-shirts à la Brando make sense only with the wet look. First, see my bootmaker in Jermyn Street and have him put it on my bill, I hardly ever pay it. Then schedule an appointment with my tailor, Tom Gilbey, he does for Ringo and John as well as Mick." Who were they? I was too ashamed to ask. "But you'll have to fork over for that yourself. And mind, none of that suburban Savile Row tat—that's for Nebraska Anglophiles. Above all, remember, angry young men are out." What's in? I asked. BenGy smiled like a cat over cream. "We are, fool."

I studied BenGy hard for a clue to who "we" were. In his off-cream suits and near-white shoes, red silk cravats and knife-edge creases and Palm Beach fedora, he looked like a Park Lane version of his friend and competitor, Tom Wolfe, "except," BenGy noted, "that Tom occasionally has an attack of ethics, from which I am refreshingly free." ("Morals," BenGy liked to remind me, "are just bad taste elevated to a political principle.") His own politics, if they existed, were midtown Manhattan Nietzschean-survivalist. Ejected from a string of private academies like Choate and Groton for

offenses BenGy hinted were too depraved even for my ears, scorn-
ing university—he'd begun writing professionally at seventeen—he
liked to give himself a wholly fictitious association with Princeton
because that was F. Scott Fitzgerald's alma mater. However, unlike
Jay Gatsby, BenGy made no pretense, when pressed, of actually
having attended classes—"which is what would have happened anyway if I'd enrolled," he said.

BenGy claimed to adore women; on the evidence, they certainly
adored him. In his presence even the most arrogant-seeming *Vogue*
models stammered and pulled at their miniskirts. "My secret," he
told me, "is that I take them seriously. But I don't respect them
because they're women. That's bluestocking bullshit. You can kick
any woman around if you take her seriously enough."

Now he tells me.

Despite BenGy's "sexism" (a word not yet invented) and the
aggressively male atmosphere of the print world called Fleet
Street—even today, its favored watering hole, El Vino's, denies
admittance to women at the stand-up bar—I quickly saw that a very
large difference between my New-Old Left and London's freelance
subculture was that on capitalist Fleet Street there were more
women whose writing was regarded with the ultimate respect: editors paid for it. Though at BBC and in the mainstream media, in
pay and conditions and attitude women suffered real discrimination, female journalists, if they survived at all, seemed to have more
autonomy and less smoldering resentment than Arnie Robin's lady
comrades or the wives of Basil Bullock and his New Chartists.
Maybe it was because, by a natural selection, only the most enterprising of iron-skinned women made it into BenGy's world, where a
good magazine piece was saluted as respectfully as a novel.

After my experience with the left, with its collectively edited
journals where decisions, endlessly delayed, got lost in a murk of
comradely obfuscation, it was a relief working for a magazine run
on strictly patriarchal lines, even if "he" was a she. Despite the magazine's frantic scampering after trends by definition obsolete once
they were set in print, and its implicit emphasis on "art" (photos
and layout) over words, the editor trusted the hands she hired.
There were few second thoughts, no editorial ifs and buts. Lines of
authority were clear, commands crisp. By comparison, the left's fer-
tile chaos suddenly seemed a bit of a drag.

* * *

Rose surprised me by not disapproving of my *Vogue* job. She had always been an avid reader while muttering that nobody human had bodies like that; an issue made her wait impatiently to buy cheap copies of what she saw in its pages—*Vogue*'s reason for existence. "But," she now complained, "could you tell your masters it's the shoulders they get wrong—there's not a British dressmaker alive who understands the thousands of round-shouldered women like me." I promised.

Women's magazines had been around for ages, of course, mostly crochet-and-garden jobs with an occasional blissed-out interview with a safe celebrity. Sex *verboten*, risk invisible, do-it-yourself about as avant-garde as *Women*, *Women's Own*, and *She* ever got. But in the early sixties something changed. *Vogue*, *Harpers*, *Queen*, and their imitators woke up to new markets of bored women whose prefeminist passions were building up into an explosion of style. The women's glossies were what *New Commitment* and *Chartism Today* had been to the left, a sort of *Guide to the Perplexed*: oddly political in their way, or so BenGy kept insisting.

"The punters out there"—he referred to *Vogue*'s readers—"could care less what's between the pictures. But I do. Doesn't it give you a kick, knowing you're helping me educate the next ruling class?"

Sure it did. But was this really why I'd come to England?

Slowly, unnoticeably at first, the iron mask of class slipped over my face, twisting my tongue into a new orthography. "I daresay" and "dear chap" replaced "luv" and "What's oop, then?" Thinking it might give me "culture" and polish, I absorbed my enemy's patois. My hard, nasal Chicago bark, which until now had placed me outside class and therefore immune to its wounds, began inflecting a sort of low-caste Oxbridge with a trace of BBC Standard Pronunciation that BenGy called "fake Anglo-Saxon." The BBC, a huge casting agency masquerading as a public broadcast corporation, had begun throwing patronage my way, training me in its superbly equipped Portland Place studios to give unscripted talks to half-million-plus audiences; but first I had to be drilled in how to avoid popping my *p*'s into the ultrasensitive studio microphone and how to operate the cumbersome shoulder-borne Ewer portable tape machine to record the battle sounds of my own peculiar frontline—the streets, alleys, mines, and mills—which I reported, in an absurdly clumsy copy of Edward R. Murrow's Blitz dispatches, without censorship, in a weekly program, *Black's Britain*, as an unremitting class war. BenGy, amused by my double life, on *Vogue* and haunting side streets north of the Wash with my BBC Ewer, called it "making the most of your master's long leash."

But as BenGy well knew, my new master was a mistress, Billie Stoutheart. I taught her how to read books, and she taught me how to use my eyes and ears as radar rather than mirrors. Every Saturday night, before she went out on her Chester le Prudhoe–inspired dates with "proper gentlemen" (rich twits), Billie sat me down in front of a TV program called *Ready, Steady, Go* and forced me to listen to the loathsome sounds of Billy Fury, Dave Clark Five, Marty Wilde, Eddie Cochran, and Joe Brown. Waa waa waa. "But look at those funny haircuts," I protested. Billie, dancing ecstatically by herself to the Beatles on my thick pile carpet, went, "Mmmm mmmm, dishy, aren't they?" "You're just a bloody gormless teenager," I shouted. "And you"—she whirled happily on me—"are joost a bluidy middle-aged deaf doorpost. Can't you *hear* what's happening?"

No, I couldn't, but at least I knew it was happening.

With BenGy's training and Billie's antennae, I now came back from trips up the British Zambezi, to Sheffield, Nottingham, and Runcorn, with notes on what the kids were wearing and the music they listened to, as well as their alleged politics. The north, Huddersfield and Tyneside, was where all the exciting new stuff was happening that eventually made its way into *Vogue* and onto album covers. Albums. That was entirely new; until now the kids could only afford cheap 45's. Where was all the money coming from?

Billie swayed in front of me to the Shirelles, waving a hundred-pound note tantalizingly under my nose. "It's around, Gus, like muck. You just pick it up. How come you haven't noticed, luv?"

Some reporter I was.

But at least I dressed the part. As usual when uncertain, I reinvented myself from movie heroes, this time not Brando or Monty Clift but London blades: Stewart Granger in *Beau Brummell*, Leslie Howard or David Niven as the Scarlet Pimpernel. Guided by BenGy, with nods of approval from Billie, I ordered several suits from his tailor, Tom Gilbey; a blackthorn tweed jacket from Grayson's of Old Bond Street; my shirts from Turnbull & Asser (where else?); and of course a splendid trench coat from Peabodys of Picadilly. "Don't I look just like Joel McCrea in *Foreign Correspondent*?" I enthused to Billie. "Who's Joe Mackrey?" she asked. I even thought of becoming a British citizen, but my solicitor—I had one now—advised, "Forget it. I rang the Home Office and they have your FBI file."

You know the type of American Anglophile who devours the *Times Lit Supp* and keeps Stratford going with "alternative" productions of Shakespeare. ("To be or facking not to be, that is the facking question.") This was different. I transformed myself into a Yank reporter disguised as Murrow-McCrea pretending to be a Regency buck: a total fantasy that BenGy judged crazy enough for a laugh. Having reimagined his own Americanness out of a Gissing novel by way of Henry James once removed from Ford Madox Ford, he felt infinitely superior to my film fantasy. "It won't do, not even remotely"—he scrutinized my first five hundred quids' worth of new gear—"but I fear that a sartorial hodgepodge like you may be the wave of the future. You look suitably grotesque, Black. Now go back to work."

It wasn't that simple. BenGy, who defined himself by other writers' best work, insisted as a condition of employment that I start on a second book, even if I did not yet know what it was. "I refuse," he said imperiously, "to be surrounded by one-book novelists. The real stuff, Black—the real stuff."

I was all set to do it again—until I read my reviews in the left press. Uff! Right in the breadbasket. *Commitment Past & Present* (the title of the two merged journals) tore my flesh off. In a venomous front-page review-essay, Basil Bullock added the mining book to my long list of crimes against socialism and accused me of "failing to approach a complex subject with an appropriate sense of historicity and social dialectic." Basil particularly disliked the scenes of miners drinking, fighting, and screwing as "a cheaply sensational distortion of the solidaristic values and traditions of communities that enjoy an organic wholeness alien to quick-fix journalists whose frame of reference is a disintegrating North American bourgeois culture," etc. When I complained to Arnie Robins, the real editor of the officially editorless *Commitment Past & Present*, he looked, as always, stricken. "Personally"—he shook his head as if trying to clear it of water—"I admired your book. But some of the comrades think you're poaching on their territory. Mingling with the working class without footnotes strikes them more as gutter journalism than responsible socialist scholarship."

That old gutter again. Why hadn't Rose warned me? Rose sat me down in a kitchen chair for my first lesson in postpublication martial arts self-defense. "You forget, darling—I *did* warn you. Anyway, Basil would have rubbished your work even if you'd delivered me naked to his baronial estate. His sort, remember those clergymen genes, don't easily forgive. And apparently your Young Left is as philistine as my dear Old Left—which until I learned better I too thought of as 'family.' Families are poison for writers, and political families are doubly lethal. They *hate* writers. Puritans like them think in neat little packages. At our best we don't. We blur edges, slop over neat lines, muddle things. Above all, we're unpredictable. Our stuff arrives on their scrubbed doorsteps with a great big messy thump. They dislike the surprises we thrive on. By the way, before you became a writer, what would *you* have thought of your book, eh?"

She had a point.

"Eat it," offered BenGy as my resentment at the left reviews boiled over, "and stop whining. We the bourgeoisie welcome you with open arms. Or haven't you read your reviews in the capitalist press?"

Oh sure, they, the class enemy, *The Spectator* and *Times* and that CIA front *Encounter*, gave me space and praise, but who cared about them? A book about miners that discredited me with the left but gave me cachet on the right—good God!

Unnoticeably at first, I had become part of the system I'd come to change.

Once launched as a writer in England, you can walk a high road to literature or a low road to journalism. Literature is serious, Fleet Street anything but. They are essentially two different writing camps, with only minor crossover, though writers from Graham Greene to Martin Amis take their journalism nearly as seriously as fiction. For so long I'd ached to be a "real" writer like Rose, E. M. Forster, and Colin MacInnes. But Grub Street paid me handsomely for what came most easily, which I was learning not to despise, and in a kind of blood selection, other Grub Streeters, unlike Rose's circle, made room for me. I got a huge kick out of being, for the first time outside the coal villages, accepted.

So I became a British journalist.

Accommodation to success was easier because of the unsubtle class character of the British press. Each major national newspaper spoke for a vested interest, mainly the Conservative Party. Most papers—*Times*, *Telegraph*, tabloids—were out-and-out Tory mouthpieces. In a country where half the electorate voted Labour, and half of them were socialists, there was no mass-circulation radical paper, and only one—the *Daily Mirror*—pallidly pro-Labour. No Yankee-style nonsense here about "impartiality" or "balance."

Of course, Fleet Street had its own anti-ideological ideology posing as bemused detachment, its own badges of honor awarded for low lives and high expense accounts. Few of the strenuously jaunty writers I now spent so much time with appeared to take seriously much beyond their girlfriends and heavy, steady drinking, which only Americans labeled alcoholism. Apoliticism was proudly displayed as a sign of the grace of talent. This masquerade where politics paraded as an absence of it bothered me. Say what you will, Marxshiremen, with their self-conscious and hard-won "links to the working class," at least imaginatively participated in the workers' world they championed. From afar, it was easy to mock the comrades as armchair socialists and pub proletarians, but at least they stuck their necks out. Whereas BenGy's lot, now mine too, made for a smaller target of satire; indeed, their (our) function was to target others with arrows tipped in malice, rarely pity.

For all their boozy sangfroid and professional detachment, my new clique, I had no doubt, would be on the scab side during a strike. The British press, taken as a whole, was violently anti-labor even though (or because?) reporters and pressmen were tightly organized in unions. BenGy's old, my new, Fleet Street friends were too clever to be outright Tories and too hip to be seen as earnest world changers: either position was "a dreadful bore." So we wore shoes light as gossamer and opinions of the same weight, skipping along the tips of the waves, enjoying the lash of the water at our ankles, and proud of our refusal to drown, swim, or help others struggling in the water. I couldn't remember when I had enjoyed people's company so much.

I was having the time of my life laughing at a world I was fully involved with. Dividing myself between Rose and Billie Stoutheart, wallowing in the sheer sensual pleasure of making words into print into guineas per article, surrounded by physically beautiful people and dressed to the nines in the best pre–Carnaby Street gear (dig that alpaca jacket), suddenly I collapsed like an old balloon. My imagination gave out—poof! like that. I'd outlived the fantasy. The little Chicago yiddlach had captured his Mrs. Miniver, bored himself rigid at All Souls' high table, retraced Jack London's steps in the East End, been down and out now up and coming in Orwell's London, ferried across the water to Birkenhead just to catch a glint of the golden Liverbird at sunrise, put my hand on a Royal knee, fought fascists to avenge Ridley Road, stayed with the Oliviers, and had unlimited access to a BBC microphone. What was left to do?

The left.

But the British Young Left had been devastated by the Cuban missile crisis in October '62. For once not knowing who to blame and where to protest, we Marxshiremen poured into London's streets by the thousands, milling indecisively in front of both the Soviet and the U.S. embassy. Our illusion, our hope, that Britain was capable of giving an independent lead was destroyed by the reality that the only decisions that mattered were being made in Moscow and Washington. Just when I thought Rose and I were all quarreled out, we had a bitter tangle over Cuba, when I said you had to do something about the missile crisis and she replied that sometimes it was best to do nothing, then added, "It's time for us to grow up, Gus. It's all gone, everything we believed. Our truths have come back to haunt us. Now we're pygmies in the fists of the Masters of the Apocalpyse."

"Rose," I said, "this isn't a *Dr. Who* episode. Where's your fighting instinct?"

She got up from the table to mix some hotcake batter, her way out of anxiety. Over her shoulder she said, "It's over, don't you see? Us. The Third World War is already here. All we can hope is to survive it."

Was this my battlin' Rosie O'Malley?

"Who is he?" I demanded.

"You are a Neanderthal." She dug even more furiously into the bowl of batter.

"Yeah, but who *is* he?"

She bent to blow the cooker into flame. "If you must know"— she didn't look at me—"it's Ibraham am Abraham."

She had to be joking.

Rose stiffened, slapping the batter into the fry pan. "Yes—but not the sort of joke you mean."

Who was this Ish Kabibble?

She started building a mountain of hotcakes on a plate in front of me. "He is an Afghan holy man. Except that he doesn't believe in anything so banal as 'holy.'"

"What's he look like?"

"He'd like that question," Rose said. "First things first."

"Rose," I said, "one of us is going out of our mind."

"At last," she said triumphantly, pouring thick, imported, expensive Canadian maple syrup over the buttered cakes, "you've got It."

Got what?

Rose's new guy—she actually called him Teacher—was an oily beauty in a white turban and knee-length Nehru jacket who claimed to be a wise man from Kabul. For the first time I had real competition in this androgynous seer who fed Rose morning glory seeds and tracts on Subud to help her explore "new psychic frontiers," as Rose called their dates. I should have seen it coming. All of us were getting bored with "the old stuff" of politics, which had led to the paralyzing indecision of not even knowing which embassy to storm. Of course her sudden turn to mysticism was a symptom of the fright we all felt during the missile crisis, but what good was knowing that? My way of coping was less imaginative: eight hundred of us joined Bertrand Russell in getting arrested in a violent Trafalgar Square sit-down. And I enlisted in the Committee of 100, to foster civil disobedience—both the U.S.A. and Russia had resumed H-bomb tests—and sat down again, this time with fifteen thousand in front of the Ministry of Defence. It was nonsense but necessary.

Still, I couldn't help wonder what Rose was up to with those morning glory seeds.

The sixties was a lie. Sgt. Pepper, Woodstock, love-ins, Haight-Ashbury, and Jimi Hendrix happened in front of the cameras. Here's what happened behind.

Scene: A suite in London's Park Lane Hilton. *Time:* 1962. Eleanor Roosevelt and William Faulkner are dead, Eichmann is hanged. There are race riots at Ole Miss, and in Britain half a million jobless, a new record. At Easter, a revived CND rallies a hundred and fifty thousand. British fascists, too, have a rebirth after Parliament passes a racist, restrictive immigration act; London Nazis march on Dalston, a once Jewish, now black district. De Gaulle threatens to veto British entry into the Common Market. The popular press is full of the Cuban crisis. But in this hotel room all that is absurdly irrelevant. Several men, bare-chested and stripped to shorts, sprawl on the bed or floor, high on LSD or mescaline. Only one of us, a conservatively suited doctor, William Maxton Last, is sober. Upright on a chair, he smiles bleakly at the goings-on. His favorite disciple (for the moment), Gus Black, is busy turning on some star tourists with vials of pure Swiss-originated Sandoz-made acid. In various states of mental and physical undress, Timothy Leary, Jean Genet, Bill Burroughs, Allen Ginsberg, and—no, it can't be, is that a Beatle in the corner?—giggle, frown, and deeply analyze the wallpaper. Like a verger of a Very High Church, Gus passes among them with a tumbler of distilled water provided by Willie Last to wash down the hallucinogenic cocktails. Each man is into his own buzz.

Strained but happy, I slumped at Dr. Last's feet. "These guys kill me," I said, pointing to our guests. "They're still into *Om*. Don't they know that went out with the Hula-Hoop?"

Last smiled patronizingly. "Americans. What c'n ye expeck? They're so—unborn."

"I'm American, Willie," I reminded him.

Last fondled my head. "Ah," he said, "but ye *know* ye have nae soul."

It was party time.

And, competitive to the Last, I had found somebody even niftier than Rose's crystal-gazing Sabu: Dr. Willie.

Gaunt and intense, vaguely resembling Henry Fonda's Tom Joad in medical pinstripes, Willie, as he insisted his patients call him, managed somehow to look like a prosperous Harley Street psychiatrist (his trade) while signaling that he was still the tough Dundee working-class lad he once had been. For street cred, he said "fuck" and "shit" as often as possible. "What are my credentials?" he repeated my first question to him in his large, dark consulting room overlooking Marylebone Road. "My divided self, mon, my split soul, same as you. If I'm as fucked up as you are and I can get you to see you're not fucked up at all but I'm fucked up for believing you are, then maybe I can stop myself being so fucked up," he announced.

He appealed to my class solidarity. "We're both street boys on th' con, right, Gus? We'll *kick* those bourgeois bastids square in th' nuts and then get down to th' only question worth askin', Why don't I kill meself?" I stared at this guy, who was smiling grimly down my throat. Holy potatoes, he was dead serious.

Uh, gee. "Why should I pay you to save your soul when I'm the one who's sick?" I asked.

"That's for me to know and you to find out." He leaned toward me with a twinkle. Beware twinkling doctors.

After much trial and error, I'd found Willie Last when I couldn't get going on a second book and BenGy Tyler stood firm on his threat to fire me unless I did. "Try drink, try hashish, try women—I don't care how you do it, but I won't have has-been first novelists in my office. Understood?"

Until I casually mentioned the Rockets A.C., Willie Last seemed awesomely bored with my anxious whining. Suddenly he perked up. "Yes, of course," he nodded, "a band of brithers blind to their mission of rescuin' th' Pearl of Wisdom from the Infidel." Huh? He reached under his black overstuffed couch, dragged out a small wooden box, reverently opened it, and produced a vial of clear liquid. "It's better than Murine for washin' yer eyes of th' astigmatism that's makin' ye miss It," he promised. Willie often capitalized certain words in conversation.

Rose talked about It too. I felt absolutely stupid not knowing what, er, It ... was.

But It was all the rage, including in *Vogue*, which tuned in to schizophrenia, Dr. Last's chosen field of practice, as to most other fashionable currents. I'd made a choice between increasingly chic radicals and radical chic.

Under Willie Last's tutelage, I embarked on a "schizophrenic voyage" that he assured me was the ultimate test of a serious revolutionist. Nor was Dr. Last a general who led from the rear. We Band of Brithers—I was now a leading member of Last's inner circle of "antipsychiatrists" dedicated to obliterating the egoic-biased minds of themselves and their patients on the sacred road to healing—were in it together. Only, as usual, somehow I found myself a wee bit more overextended than they were.

I spent too long with Last and his more florid patients; imbibed too much of too large doses of the acid he copiously provided; identified too closely with the institutionalized schizophrenics in a local state hospital that had become my weekend retreat; and tried too zealously to find a politics in the complex sadnesses of mental health work. Predictably, I went mad.

My madness, which would have been the final straw for *New Commitment*, didn't even cause *Vogue* staffers to blink. So what if I came to Hanover Square in a moth-eaten monk's robe Rose had sewn together to keep me warm on cold November nights, which I now turned into a religious raiment? So what if my magazine copy was larded with a mixture of Marcuse and Gibran and I kept dropping lead-weighted hints over expensive lunches at La Terrazza about the Gnostic roots of my present exalted state? Upstairs at *Vogue* the editors assumed, as did the models, that I was simply trying on a new fad to see if it flew. Only BenGy's nostrils twitched.

"You may think"—he eyed my weird getup—"you're breaking new psychic ground with all this speaking-in-tongues shit and that malodorous garment you insist on wearing in the office. To me you're just another scandaled vegetarian fruitcake of the sort Orwell despised. Good God, you smell as if you don't even bathe anymore. Afraid of washing away all that holiness?"

Right in one, BenGy.

Rose, too, warned me that I was losing too much weight on a diet of cabbage hearts and distilled water (the acid hit harder with pure H_2O). "You need a little more ballast on this barmy trip of yours," she cajoled, whipping up one of her miracle meals. "Keep your infidel food," I sneered from a great spiritual height, springing up and grandiosely flinging my monk's cape over my bony shoulder. Rose looked startled. "Good heavens, Gus, refusing food? You *are* serious about it."

It, again.

Suddenly England was changing so fast that schizophrenia seemed one of several appropriate responses. The style revolt—or what I was forbidden to call the swinging sixties—was, in purely Marxshire terms, a superstructure held by a base that was both eroding and modernizing at the same time. Prices were still low, while wages climbed to a level Britons miscalled "affluence." Fueled by North Sea oil revenues, there was a widespread hunger for anything untried. Even those permanently permed priestesses of British high-street culture, the bargain-shopping mums and Aunt Ednas in their Silverwoods macs who stood in bus queues all over the country, started to sport swishier hairdos ... and makeup! Hail, Mary Quant.

Vogue and magazines like it set the commercial tone for this change in taste and economics, which at its most vulgar was simply the rest of the country catching up with New Left "cultural" priorities minus the radicalism. To an extent hardly remembered now, magazine writers like BenGy and me called the shots, or rather, our photographers did. Their lens puppets, Billie Stoutheart and Twiggy, frieze actresses really, seemed to challenge what a woman should look like and therefore a man's response to her. They were part of a "satire scene" that loathed gentility and exalted brittleness. "Romantic" was redefined to include the Great Train Robbers, a gang of East End villains who smashed the engineer's skull for a few million pounds, and even Kim Philby's defection to Moscow—

we needed a bit of dash, preferably tainted by blood or treachery. In fashion, the "black thing" paralleled with passage of the little-noticed Commonwealth Immigrants Act, designed to "control" the flow of "foreigners" into Britain, where a racist scholar, Enoch Powell, had become the new, unelected, and unofficial prime minister. Until now, Britons thought only Mississippi and South Africa had blacks. Christine Keeler and her chum Mandy Rice-Davies had always known better; blacks were lovers, not trash collectors. Christine—we all knew her, through a friend of BenGy's named Stephen Ward—did more to discredit Conservatives in government than I ever had, as BenGy noted acidly. "She might," said BenGy, distilling the real point of the Profumo scandal, "almost be one of our models except for that bit of fat, and the teeth, of course." He brooded. "Hmmm, maybe we could even make a thing of plump floozies with an inviting space between their teeth ..."

It was fun imitating a nation splitting itself into multiple parts for that new goal, pleasure. By the numbers I was: (1) for Willie Last, the front man for a paper organization, the BrotherHood of Helpers, whose private purpose was to redeem our damned souls in a dank Brixton warehouse we called Meditation Manor, ostensibly a hospice for schizophrenics; (2) for BenGy, *Vogue*'s main man-about-town, charging about in my new Morris Mini like a rat up a drain-pipe in and out of art galleries, Covent Garden operas, West End theaters, private film screenings, book launchings; (3) for the latest revolution, and because it was the only place I could truly relax, a "participant observer" on an experimental ward for schizophrenics at a Hertfordshire hospital run by one of Last's BrotherHood; and (4) for myself I hardly remembered anymore, in my old Zorro gear (combat boots, jeans, cable sweater, navvy's knit cap), a street prowler with BBC microphone in hand and Ewer over my shoulder. As Ronald Reagan once said, where was the rest of me?

Now I know what I did wrong: everything. A drunken driver always thinks he's an ace behind the wheel. What was left of my brain was neatly split between two impossibilities, a sixties search for satori at 750 mikes a day (a late-blooming Dharma Bum's rush), and a belief that the "politics of schizophrenia" could be taken literally, i.e., that madness per se was a useful analytical tool in any practical activism. At the time, this was not generally regarded as unduly odd.

Willie Last said, "The yew lookin' for yewrself is yewr yew-ness wonderin' why yew cannot find yew, understand?" BenGy was slightly more succinct. "We'll make a shoot of it, Black."

BenGy's notion of a shoot was to pose Billie Stoutheart next to "some of your miner chums. Mills, moors, all that *How Green Was My Valley* stuff ... and Billie's marvelous flesh tone alongside their black, really black, underexpose if you have to, skin—Tony [Armstrong-Jones] will love it!"

I objected that BenGy was trying to make the north look like Chelsea.

"No," he contradicted me, "you are."

And so I went back up north, this time not with a U.S. infantry half pack and no money but in BenGy's XK6 Jag with Billie at my side and a *Vogue* stills photographer and his assistant, the Foreign Secretary's daughter, in back.

Money and sex were in the air. Even the coalfields felt it.

But first ("for journalistic contrast") BenGy insisted my little caravan stop at the Northamptonshire estate of Lord Ranulph de Carteret Gore-Templeton, who had agreed to let *Vogue* ramble over his grounds because he owed the editor a favor. (She'd hired one of his deb daughters.) BenGy's gimmick was to call this part of my piece "From Peers to Pits: A Romp Through Britain's New Classlessness." BenGy said, "F. R. Leavis wouldn't like it, and Richard Hoggart would call it a sickening example of 'shiny cultural barbarism,'—so there must be merit in it." Guiltlessly, he liked to invoke, if only to mock, the strictures laid down by the Leavisite literary critics, most of them, like Hoggart, Raymond Williams, and Leavis himself, working-class born; with puritanical rage, they denounced the flashy new cheapness (code: Americanism) of British society, which they loathed with an almost messianic fervor. BenGy actually read Leavis for pleasure; for myself, I perused F. R. and his wife/partner Queenie only when I needed more lashes on my back.

Billie adored the Gee-Tees, as Lord Gore-Templeton and his family casually referred to themselves, as if they were a rock band. Draping herself sensuously for Armstrong-Jones's lens round the marble statues in the lavish Palladio-copy garden landscape, she happily chattered with the good lord himself, his "dear lady wife," and several sons, all of whom seemed to be named Nigel and were awestruck by Billie. Only the butler and gardener frowned on this cross-class mateyness. Naturally, Billie and Lord Gee-Tee were totally at ease with each other, a phenomenon of the British class system I'd noticed before: it was the middle class that was uncomfortable with both.

Lord Gee-Tee was a former mine owner who spiked my ideological guns by instantly agreeing that nationalization of coal had been in everyone's interest—including his own, because the government was still paying him handsomely for his ex-holdings. (That crushing debt to previous owners was one reason the British coal industry had no money to pay better wages.) Indeed, "Call me Ranulph, almost everyone does," was practically pro-Labour. "Why not, dear boy?" he mildly inquired over port as we both eyed Billie swanning in front of *Vogue*'s cameras. "My lot hasn't done too well recently, and your lot seems to have all the answers. Just do leave agriculture alone. I've yet to meet a socialist farmer." He had me there. The only hint of ruffled feelings came on the morning of a shooting party when I wasted fifty cartridges without winging a single pheasant. Huddling together in the rain-heavy gorse, Lord Ranulph and I broke the shotguns as the beaters went ahead of us in search of more raw aerial meat. "Poor shot, or no stomach for it?" asked this seventy-year-old owner of an ancestral home that went back to Henry VIII. "Grouse makes me belch," I lied. He laughed and lent me his brandy flask.

It was hard not to like the English upper class. They were superhumanly tolerant in matters from which they were so insulated they simply weren't touched in any of their vital organs. I admired their "civilized" detachment, their good manners, their sense of occasion (those state funerals, those royal weddings). Unlike the Young Left, they laughed at my jokes and didn't judge me. A long weekend with the Gee-Tees persuaded me that the sixties had, for them, changed nothing except that they looked upon class and the class-ridden in a slightly new way. "Oh, the country's transforming all right," Lord Ranulph told me at our last breakfast, served in silver salvers by several maids. "The grammar school boys are in the saddle now. Brainy sorts, not like us, no, not like us at all. We're wonderful owners—" ha!—"but often bloody awful managers. Trust your lot does it better. Pity so few of them ride, but then I suppose, oh, you know. Growing up on a horse the way we have, and in a council flat as so many of them have, does create a certain problem in communication, but I daresay it will work out in the long run, wouldn't you agree, Gus?"

How different were the Gore-Templetons—so open, so charming—from Yorkshire miners. Maybe the academic sociologists were right and Thurcroft was a "throwback," mean-minded and provincial in the worst sense. Who would want to live and work in a changeless, featureless place like that—did I say changeless?

Since I'd last been to the village, Noreen had left her collier fiancé to marry a Barnsley pub keeper, a big jump up for this miner's daughter. Len Doherty finally escaped the pit to become, of all things, a reporter for the *Sheffield Star*. Len's mentor, Bradley, the local union president who had run the political side of the village for a thousand years and trained Len to fill his throne, lost heart when his "son" left mining—and also lost a union election to a whole new slate of younger militants unimpressed by his "what Ah've done for this village" boasts. Unlike Bradley and Len, these new union guys owned cars and had been on Continental holidays, and they were indifferent to my previous Thurcroft history. "I'm a friend of Len Doherty's," I'd introduce myself to blank stares: wrong move, because Thurcrofters acquainted with Len did not forgive him for leaving work underground. Though he continued to live in the village, he was not part of it anymore. "Ah'm just lahk thee now, Gus," he said over a pint in Welfare Hall. "What did Khrushchev call you Jews—rootless cosmopolitans? Ah've at last joined the Jewish race, tha'll be glad to know." Of course he saw the village differently now. "It's so small, so narrow. Ah honestly can't believe Ah once thought Thurcroft was th' capital of the world." "But it is," I said. He ruffled my hair. "Tha daft Yank—tha'll go anywhere to stop time, won't tha?"

Fat chance of slowing history down in the 1960s.

The *Vogue* crew, notwithstanding Billie, who was a sensation among the colliers, was not welcome in Thurcroft. We were part of the despised media. "If you like," advised the new union president, "leave the girl but get yourself and those others back to London, okay? We prefer being lied about from a distance, if you don't mind." (Younger telly-influenced miners were losing their archaic Yorkshire accents.) I told him that *Vogue* wasn't interested in a wildcat strike that was brewing up at Thurcroft pit. "That just makes it worse," he said with finality.

In the pub I had a last drink with Len, who looked over at my *Vogue* friends, including Billie, getting tipsy fast in the center of a throng of coal hewers. "If she's what tha're gettin' used to, Gus, Ah'm coomin' to Lunnon to get soom of it." He smiled. Then he got serious. "Tha'll be goin' back to America soon, Ah reckon. The thing that brought thee here has changed so much Ah don't think it even exists anymore."

Next morning, we rode the same goodbye bus into Sheffield, he to his new job, me to scout the north for new Thurcrofts. Had A. E. Housman ever gone back to the villages he wrote about?

As Len got off the bus, he unpinned from the lapel of his new blue serge suit a hammer-and-sickle badge that a visiting group of Soviet Don Basin miners had given to their Thurcroft counterparts, and stuck it on my stylish angora sweater. His last words to me were, "Guttersnipes of the world—unite!"

The north, my north, was changing, had been evolving, even when it seemed most static and immobile. Down below, there was a whole new breed of miners who had little memory of World War II, even of stoop-seam labor now that mechanization was starting to bite. Up above, in the Yorkshire/Lancashire "cotton belt," the mills of Bradford and Huddersfield now employed Gujarati Indian immigrants recruited to replace traditional English loomwatchers and keep the machines going three full shifts a day, and I didn't speak Gujarati or Urdu.

Immigrants, mechanization, younger less war-weary workers, demographic changes: my escape hatch to the north was closing because I had given my heart to an older generation of workers on their way out. Gradually, I left London less and knew Britain more from newspapers and TV, which means, not knowing. It was slipping from my grasp. My psyche, which had identified with the northern working class, seemed to be disintegrating as they were. "Not," pronounced Dr. Last, "a bad definition of schizophrenia. Welcome to the club."

I'll join any club that will have me.

Between us, Dr. Last and I cooked up a scheme that either would kill or cure me of the schizophrenia he insisted was causing my fevers and stomachaches. Now was the time for me to return to the United States of America, "tae enter th' belly of th' whale, be devoured by it, and if ye emerge alive it will be tantamount tae th' Tree of Life any Irkut shaman climbs as part of his routine job." Well, sure. The Lost Pearl of Wisdom, Last assured me, lay buried deep up the lunatic anus of the Big American Whale; my "project" would be to retrieve this pre-ancient jewel, which was really only a part of my forgotten, fragmented self. Dares are my weakness. I packed a large Gladstone bag, locked up my Bayswater flat, and booked a first-class sea voyage back to the only place I knew that stayed still in my heart.

□ □ □

It did not, in 1963, take a lot of brains to see that America was almost as fragmented as I was.

On my first trip back to the States in seven years—ostensibly on a tour for *Vogue*, actually looking for the Secret Pearl of Gnosis—I mainly rocked in the bosom of black Abraham, north and south, because whites had a problem with me. Without question I was accepted in black homes, churches, schools, and even by Malcolm X's Black Muslims, who had already begun to form a separate tendency inside the Hon. Elijah Muhammad's movement. In my self-delusion, with one part of my brain shut down like an iron gate and the other flapping crazily open on acid, I listened for the high, piercing note I had heard repeatedly in my sessions with English schizophrenics. Freedom, Freedom Now, FREEDOM NOW! I had to find and capture this soaring cry of liberation in the darkest, least liberated regions. Everything in the States I saw and heard I judged by how it tuned in to this impossible musical note.

Malcolm X, if you grant context, was the soul of reason. The voice, crisp and clear and in absolute control of his anger, shattered me. In the end, there is such a thing as character. Wherever Malcolm's voice suggested, there I tried to go. "No sellout ... no sellout." "The white man isn't as much of a devil as you are if you make yourself into a pale copy of this weak, devilish white man who makes you believe that you are *his* idea of the devil." "If the white man hits you, hit him back. If he shoots at you, shoot him. You don't have to have a college degree to protect yourself."

There is a reason white people sometimes follow black leaders, and it is that no white leader speaks to the injustice we do ourselves as well as others.

But sometimes it has to start with skin color.

On my first exuberant swing around the U.S. left, white student radicals booed me at Sarah Lawrence College, pitched bottles at me at a New University Thought conference in Chicago, and chased me out of a Minneapolis Revolutionary Youth Movement lecture hall with thrown chairs. Like Jesus—a comparison Willie Last encouraged—I'd come among them preaching the gospel of personal liberation through radical self-denial, but all they wanted to talk about was how did I come by the pure stuff, Sandoz Lab lysergic acid? In New York, I asked Michael Harrington why I, as a Resistance elder, had bombed so badly on the left Chautauqua circuit. "It may be Oedipal," he suggested. "We're their history and they're trying to exchange parents." For who? "Castro is the father and I guess Emma Goldman is the mother," he said. "Bad sex," I said. "Remarks like that are what get you slugged in Madison, Wisconsin," he said.

New University Thought, Studies on the Left, RYM-1 and RYM-2, RU, SPU, and Students for a Democratic Society—the American New Left—had a shorter history and were into longer battles. At first I could not believe we all were not fighting the same enemy. Surely it was just a question of semantics. Like hell.

Not even my own generation had time for me. They'd just begun to crawl from under the McCarthyite rocks and were working overtime to make up for the lost years. So it was, "Hiya Gus where ya been sorry I'm rushed got a business to run give me a call next time you're in town."

In Hollywood, I tracked down the original Committee of Correspondence, with whom I'd met behind drawn shades during the Rosenberg terror. Minus one who had committed suicide, they were inching back into the job market. A couple of the screenwriters were selling scripts half over the table, and our journalist, who had edited a small-circulation liberal magazine, was writing lead editorials for the archvillainous *L.A. Times*—and, like me on *Vogue*, loving it. "It's my first paycheck in ten years, Gus. They *need* people like us now." Several Correspondence members had dropped from sight; others had taken advantage of the decade-long black hole in their careers to retool. Even our carpenter was doing all right with a company he'd founded to market a new type of frozen-food locker. "I think I'm going to be rich, Gus," he confided. "It takes an idiot not to make money in today's America."

So I went looking for the idiots.

My first stop was the Student Nonviolent Coordinating Committee, a group of black—and some white—students who had kicked off the first sit-ins and now, based mainly in black colleges and churches, had spread all over the Deep South to teach poor black folks, often in their own families, how to vote. Have we forgotten that registering to vote in Alabama or Mississippi was the ultimate test of a black man or woman's courage? Riding backcountry roads with Charles Sherrod, Bernard Montgomery, and Bob Zellner in cars tracked by armed white deputies at midnight; sleeping on the old wooden floors of tiny black churches in bayous and cotton fields; holding hands with the bravest people I had ever met, homegrown black teenagers and white college students down from Oberlin or Berkeley, singing, "And before I'll be a slave/I'll be buried in my grave ..."; knocking on the unhinged wooden doors of share-croppers' shacks to ask haggard strangers owl-eyed with terror to risk their lives for a constitutional principle; making friends for life with young blacks who soon would despise the idea of working with the whites they had come to live and even sleep with; spending days and nights in small, sweat-hot parlors waiting up with a black family for the telltale scream of tires that might precede a paraffin bomb flung through a front window; learning from teenage blacks that there was nothing to be scared of anymore because fear itself was the worst death—all this told me I was a stranger among heroes. In Greenwood, Mississippi, Dick Gregory commanded me to get my ass out of where it didn't really belong and go up north where the real nigger haters were. So, in nine full U.S.A. months, which was the term recommended by Dr. Last to bring my soiled soul to full pregnancy and return to England a triumphant Gil-gamesh-Ulysses,

1. I broiled for a hot July month in a tiny, windowless, un-air-conditioned demi-room in Manhattan's Piccadilly Hotel while I commuted to a series of jobs: worked in a Queens plastics factory that made airplane instrument panels, drove a school bus in Forest Hills, operated a wood-sawing machine in a shop under the Tribor-ough Bridge. In each of these jobs I was the only white, sometimes the only English-speaking worker. Where was the white, American-born working class?

2. "Making a better living than you, chump," said Jimmy Hoffa, leader of the Teamsters Union. Through a socialist intermediary, Teamster VP Harold Gibbons, Hoffa had invited me to Washington, D.C., to write about him. "Sit you down, kid. Watch me work. Examine my whole operation," he promised, "then do an article telling Bobby Kennedy to jam it up his keester. Deal?" The Kennedys were directing an antiracketeer vendetta against benefac-tor-tyrant Hoffa. Reporters, I piously told Hoffa, didn't make up sto-ries before they got the interview. "Oh yeah, I forgot," he cracked, "they make 'em up afterwards."

After office hours, with the Teamster building almost dark, Hoffa liked to reminisce about his mentors, the Dunne brothers of Minneapolis and Farrell Dobbs, now head of the Socialist Workers

Party. "The Trots taught me everything I know about union organizing. Farrell was like a father to me, write that down. There was only one thing wrong with him: he never wanted anything for himself. Any man who don't want to provide for his own family is going to be one helluva lousy negotiator with the bosses." When I argued, he cut me off. "I hate idealists. Can't trust them. A guy who'll do something for himself and his family first, you know which way he'll swing. Altruists are a wild card. Unions are stable institutions in the end. Wild men we don't need." Uh-huh, I said, what about those porky piecards with pinky rings in Hoffa's outer office? "Didn't Harold teach you anything? Some of those guys built the union. If they didn't want nothing for their families, *then* you'd see a lousy crooked union,"

3. which I did the sweltering afternoon of the two-hundred-fifty-thousand-strong civil rights March on Washington, which I witnessed from the Italian marble steps of the D.C. Teamsters headquarters, but when Hoffa's guys in their two-thousand-dollar suits began catcalling and jeering at "Martin Luther Queen," I broke away to join the massive church-labor throng, a festival of the best. In the crowd I bumped into a friend from the L.A. Committee of Correspondence, Frank Wilkinson, who had just come out of a year in prison for refusing to knuckle under to HUAC, and he introduced me to actor Sterling Hayden, a Hollywood Red turned informer turned anti-informer, who was in D.C. to help make amends to people like Frank. Hayden said, "I hate marches on a hot day, I had enough of them in the service," so we went back to his room at the Mayflower Hotel and got enjoyably drunk watching Reverend King on TV. Somehow, Hoffa found out where I was, and much to my surprise he walked in on us. Both Hayden and I wanted to know if he didn't have better things to do with his time.

Hoffa said to Hayden, "Hey, you got some kind of war record. How come you became a stoolie?"

Hayden, a World War II OSS paratrooper, switched his bleary gaze from the TV screen, where King was delivering his "I Have a Dream" oration at the Washington Monument, and looked at Hoffa as if he didn't know who this square-shouldered, crew-cut pint-size was. "Oh yeah, you're Jimmy the Gyp. Tell me, Jimmy, is that bulge in your jacket a gun or just a wad of dough you stole from honest union members?"

Hoffa gave his dreadfully expensive blue pinstripe suit a quick glance in the full-length closet mirror, then drew up a chair and straddled it facing Hayden. "I know guys they would crap in their pants before talkin' to me like that. You a Commie like the kid here?"

Hayden took a drink and said, waveringly, "You can't insult my guest."

Hoffa laughed. "He spent the last couple of weeks with my Teamster guys. The kid is insult-proof by now."

I asked Hoffa why, when swarms of freedom marchers paraded past his building, the Teamster executive board had to stand out there on the steps and jeer insults at them.

"'Cause," replied Hoffa, pouring himself a paper cup of Jack Daniel's from the bottle on Hayden's bureau, "you and Reb-er-end King are troublemakin' radicals, is why. I hope you noticed some Negro teamsters up there with our guys. Our Negroes know more about discrimination than Reb-er-end King ever will know."

"Stooges," I said, not sober.

Hoffa took no offense. "Look at you guys. Two old Commies sobbin' in their beer."

Hayden stared down at his cup. "Gus," he bawled, "this isn't beer, is it? You said it was bourbon."

"And alkies besides," added Hoffa.

Hayden got up with some difficulty and stood over Hoffa, who calmly looked at him.

"Don't even think about it, Mr. Hayden—there's no stunt man to double for you now."

"Right you are," said Hayden, and walloped Hoffa off his chair.

Hoffa didn't fall, just grabbed Hayden around the waist and began hammering him. Hayden, in slow motion, picked up the chair and crashed it against the wall, breaking off one of the legs and clubbing Hoffa with it. There goes my story, I thought.

The bellboy knocking on the door was like a gong sounding Hayden and Hoffa to separate. They began straightening their clothes and unmussing their hair. Hoffa seemed especially worried about his suit, searching it for rips.

"I paid more for this than you ever took in blood money from the congressional committee—I can give you lessons in how to be a man in front of those cocksuckers," Hoffa said, inspecting himself closely.

Hayden slumped back into his chair. "You're stupid, Jimmy. I never took money. I talked because my ass was in a sling. No money changed hands."

"Well, I'll give you that," Hoffa said equably. "Hey, kid," he said to me, "comin' by tomorrow? I'll show ya how I negotiate a sugar haulin' contract." He straightened himself up a little like James Cagney and sauntered out.

I apologized to Hayden for Hoffa's intrusion. He gave a little laugh. "Just tell yourself it didn't happen, Gus. I don't believe it—do you? When you're through with all this Teamsters b.s., come sailing with me," he said, but I said I had business elsewhere ...

4. which wasn't quite true since my only business was to fill up time on Greyhound buses everywhere Trailways didn't operate, stopping off

5. to make personal calls on my private *Who's Who* of notable Americans I'd been compiling for the seven homesick years I'd been away, including Bruno Bettelheim in Chicago, the Catholic worker-priest-hobo Ammon Hennacy in Salt Lake City, and my father, Jake Schwartz, in a tiny apartment on Nelson Avenue in the Bronx. I liked Ammon Hennacy best because he asked me to stay. My father, whom I had not seen in twenty-three years, was cordial, like a man afraid to tell you he was not, after all, going to buy your vacuum cleaner. His second wife, Fannie—I got confused, because he and Polly never married, was this number two or three?—hovered in the background, serving marble cake with tea anytime Dad's temper looked bad. Dad could not remember my name. "Listen, Bernie ...," he'd say. "Pop," I'd interrupt, "my name is Gus." "Oh yeah, Bernie is your brother." What brother? He looked at me with helpless anger. "Leave it alone, kid. Your mother and I passionately loved each other, but she was hell on wheels to live with. I never even told your sister about her." What sister? He was getting in deep. He gave me one of his hard smiles, Paul Muni in *Scarface*, feral and shrewd, and without further ceremony took me down to the subway, his small jungle eyes mau-mauing the black and Puerto Rican kids on the street. "These punks," he bragged at seventy-four, "know better than to mess with me, Bernie. I took one of them out with a jack handle last week who was trying to steal my tires." Wiry little bastard probably wasn't lying. "Don't come back." He shook my hand at the subway entrance. "I have no money." And then he was gone. If Daddy rejects you, you can always

6. turn to Big Mama, Chicago, except there is no "Chicago," only the neighborhood, Lawndale, the west side, now black and unyielding. Talk about white flight. In 1945, eighty percent Jewish; in 1963, ninety-nine percent black. Not Sixty-ninth and Stony

Island South Side Chicago–wise black, not blacks who had been around since the 1919 race riots when the stockyards still had jobs for low-wage cow killers. (Once, when Jake was organizing meat-packers and took me along, I'd seen his Ukrainian bodyguard, Alex, a gut-ripper, drink a quart of steer's blood from a tin container, an Old Country way of warding off TB, which made even the black butchers in their blood-smeared aprons look queasy.) These new Twenty-fourth Ward residents were rural Mississippi and Alabama blacks pushed off the land as machines replaced field hands and white plantation owners abandoned "their" blacks they had exploited for generations. These were the poorest of the poor, in front of my old graystone, glaring at me in a way that not even Neshoba County white deputies did when they saw me walking down a dusty street hand in hand with a SNCC teenager. No point looking around here for "Negro" equivalents of the Rockets A.C., so I drove over to the old Pulaski Road police station and lied and said I was doing a story for the BBC on my old neighborhood, and the desk sergeant laughed. "I knew we had every crazy type sono-fabitch, but you're the first Englishman from around here. Sure, we give ride-alongs."

So for two weeks I rode along with two black Chicago police-men each personally carrying (forget what was in the squad car) a .45, a .38, a knife, and a .25 strapped to the ankle. They taught me the new rules of Lawndale. Boiled down, get the drop on them. We mainly prowled my beloved, stinking alleys between ten p.m. and eight a.m. One night I nearly got blasted out of the back seat by a band of Blackstone P Rangers who coona care a fu' 'bout po-lice, to the delight of my guides, Officers Danny and Gregory. Immediately after the firefight they retaliated by raiding a Kedzie Avenue bar, lining the patrons up against a wall and clubbing anybody who looked over his shoulder. "Here," said Officer Danny, shoving his .38 into my hand, "make 'em feel nostalgic." He insisted I hold the piece on the crowd while he and his partner went up and down the line frisking and punching.

Later, in the car, they told me I done good. "We just initiated you, Gus. How does it feel to be one bad nigguh?" And they nearly died laughing. An hour later we all stood over Bonnie, a fourteen-year-old spraddled on the Pulaski Road streetcar tracks with a small bloodless hole in the middle of his white T-shirt, and pondered if he'd make it to ER. "You'd be surprised at what nigguhs can live through," Officer Gregory philosophized. (Bonnie was DOA.) We ran through the streets looking for his killer, a fifteen-year-old named Dragon, but never caught him. At shift's end, in the doughnut shop on Independence and Roosevelt Road, I asked Officers Danny and Gregory why they were so tough on other blacks. "Because," Officer Danny said, "we got out and they won't and somebody's gotta punish the sonofabitches for dragging us all down." We said goodbye, because they were going on day shift, and later that afternoon I

7. went on Studs Terkel's WFMT radio program to plead with the two surviving Rockets, Joe and Bobby, to contact me, but they didn't. "Your kind of corner punk," said Studs, "is not an FM guy." So, back on Greyhound, to

8. St. Louis, where I had a reunion of sorts with an FBI agent who, on his own time, for kicks, had spied on me during his London holiday. Herbert, who retired young to teach police science at a local college, showed me a copy of my latest raw FBI file, which demoted me from "Comsubver" to "Comsymp." This depressed me as a sign of aging, and I

9. got lost on the highways to burn up time and crashed a rented VW in Bloomington, Indiana, and got into a poolroom brawl while I waited for it to be fixed. What I most remember was a farmer passing in his tractor who looked down into the gully where I was clambering out of the upside-down Bug. "Had an accident, eh?" Pa Kettle asked, and drove on, so so did I and

10. got stranded in same repaired VW in an unseasonal snowstorm on the Pennsylvania Turnpike and had to pay a highway patrolman to lend me a pair of new wipers. "Back in Chicago," I told him, "there's a new police commissioner, so the cops are temporarily off the take and it's making everybody neurotic," and Smokey Bear said, "Well, we're not very neurotic around here," and asked me for twenty dollars more, which persuaded me to head for the sun

11. in LA (again), living in a grotty un-air-conditioned room next to Hollywood Freeway while I brooded about trying the film biz again. My old boss, Bess Maree, met me at Scandia and said, "It's no longer an option, kid. You're too old—and anyway, you look like hell, Gandhi in blue jeans, they won't buy it in this town. But I like your English accent. Want to open up a restaurant with me? That's where the real action is now."

The real action? I had lost touch with the idiots.

* * *

Music up—James Brown belting "I Feel Good"—and over an angry preacher's soaring curse:

"They won't train us, they won't educate us. Soon we gonna have everything. The white folks is running. EVERYBODY'S gonna have second-class education. That's equal! That's America!!"
—REVEREND WILLIAM CLEAGE, DETROIT

If crime is Chicago's secret export, radical factionalism is Detroit's. Motown is America's most political city, its blacks the most ideologically sophisticated. The bones of many an infighter—Int'l Workers of the World, SWP, CP, SP, IS, Proletarian Party, you name it—litter its doctrinal alleys.

In late summer 1963 I walked up one of those alleys.

Freud says a mature mind believes in coincidences, but I believe in contacts. SNCC's Bernard Montgomery had pushed me to go on the March on Washington, where I met a UAW Dodge Local 3 shop steward who passed me on to a retired Ford worker who guided me to Detroit's Joe Hanson, Leon Trotsky's former bodyguard/secretary, who introduced me to two of the smartest, nicest American radicals I had met in years.

Henry Doolin, a black Chrysler auto worker, and his wife, Nellie Cross, a Trinidad-born Vassar graduate, were like Hepburn and Tracy in *Pat and Mike*, a class mismatch that worked brilliantly in practice. They were Red bluebloods, with different lineages. Henry came of runaway slaves who had won their freedom with their rifles by enlisting in the Union cause; there was a century of northern city choices in his blood. Nellie, daughter of a judge who was part black, part Scottish, and his part Venezuelan, part Indian wife, had the easy arrogance of Caribbean gentry. Henry and Nellie—never "the Doolins"—reminded me of my mother, Polly Black, in the way they carried themselves with the effortless pride and natural superiority of labor aristocrats.

Henry and Nellie—he large and protective, she small and well spoken—were part of a split from a split from an original founder, Trinidad-born C. L. R. James, who along with the nearly forgotten George Padmore had been one of early black nationalism's leading strategists, and not incidentally, a cricket correspondent of genius. Deported from Ellis Island, C.L.R. left behind a small Trotskyist movement, the Johnsonites, including Nellie and Henry, who eventually broke away from him but in an unusually friendly, even creative way. The Doolins (sorry), although serious students of Mao, Raya Dunayevskaya, Rosa Luxemburg, and Victor Serge, had done a rare thing, used their world-embracing ideology to help them understand, and to fit in with, the street-level needs of their own Detroit neighborhood; as radicals, they were uniquely committed to Motown in its particulars. Somehow they had reversed the law that the harder left you are, the stupider you have to be. They had taken Marxism as far as it could go rationally.

A dope addict will find an opium den even in Disneyland. Until meeting Nellie and Henry, I had not taken "factionals" seriously, but in the early sixties smaller voices were being heard on the international left. Nellie and Henry gave me a chance to examine the limits of black militance in action.

For an excuse to hang around Detroit, I became a temporary writer in residence at Monteith College, a subschool of Wayne State University, which took in working-class dropouts. I was no proper teacher, which takes genius or time, but Polly and Jake's platform genes got me through. During an early fall trimester I winged my lectures, a bluff bought by everyone but the department secretary.

Mildred—"not Mil or Millie"—hated me on sight. Black, pretty, and efficient, she introduced herself the first morning thusly: "I come at nine, I leave at five. I take a forty-five minute lunch, not forty-four or forty-six. I'm a fast typist and can do files. I won't make you coffee or do any shopping for you. Understood?"

"Hey," I said, "if you're unhappy here maybe you should ask for a transfer."

"Are you objecting to me already? I'll file against you with the state of Michigan."

"What for?" I asked.

"I'll think of something," Mildred said.

I asked the department head to move her elsewhere. My boss, a gentle Catholic scholar, cringed. "Gus," he confided, "the racial situation here is very complicated. Our black nationalist students nominated Mrs. Mayberry—er, Mildred—as their 'employee representative.' It's an experiment in worker-employer democracy."

I went to the department's only Marxist with whom I could talk the Old Language, but all Ray Slovick said was, "When the oppressed-oppressor nexus becomes personified, a Hegelian interaction of dynamic opposites obligates cadres like yourself who inhabit the superstructure to draw upon the strengths of the base in whatever form they manifest themselves." How about if I made a pass at her? I asked. Ray, himself a former auto worker married to a Fisher Body foreman's daughter, winced. "She's packing—like half your students. You want a thirty-eight slug through one of your balls?" Under pressure Ray could speak English.

Ray was exaggerating, a little, about how many of my black students carried weapons. The next day I called my class together, dismissed the whites (I'd hear about this later from the department chairman), and polled the blacks: How many of you are packing? Of the nine youths, four raised their hands and volunteered to show me their arsenal, which I politely declined. The next day, when several of them came to my office and asked me, in the nicest possible way, to teach them a course in the history of black America, which was not yet fashionable, I nervously assented.

"But I'm white," I reminded them.

"We noticed," was all Mims, their leader, said.

The class was a roaring success. Full attendance (open admissions for street kids), prompt starts, plenty of discussion. The problem was, halfway into the lectures the black kids asked me if I, as an ex-GI, would hold a practical seminar on how to break down, repair, and fire a whole range of weapons, from M-1 Garands to rocket launchers, which they'd just expropriated from a National Guard armory. I begged off. Mims smiled and said, "Fanon and Che, which you got us reading, say yes." But I also had on my reading list DuBois, Frederick Douglass, Zora Neale Hurston, and Langston Hughes. Mims winked. "James Baldwin says, the fire *this* time. We'll bring the stuff to you."

It wasn't one of my finer moments. My excuse is that a few days previously the KKK had bombed a Birmingham, Alabama, church and killed four black girls, which put my black students in a cold rage. So, in Mims's house on Six Mile Road, against my better judgment, I taught seven of my nine black students how to strip and reassemble their armament, and nothing more was said. "Don't look so glum," Mims smiled afterwards, "you didn't have a choice. After what we told you, if you hadn'a helped, somebody would have taken you out. This way you get to save one life—yours."

Mildred had the last word.

Until now she and I had cobbled a cool, distant truce that constantly threatened to break down but didn't because we both bit our tongues. Back home at Henry and Nellie's, where I rented a side bedroom that during the day they used to cyclostyle and mail their weekly *Workers' Voices*, consisting entirely of letters from the shop floor, Henry said, "Kick her ass outta there, Gus. Four hundred years of slavery is no excuse for incompetence." But she wasn't incompetent, I said, just angry. He bridled. "Shee-it. I'm angry too. Been pissed off all my life. But doin' good work is the start of rationality. Fire the bitch." Nellie temporized. "Whites like Gus have to learn to cope with black anger. Firing her won't solve anything. Maybe he should try being reasonable with her." Henry snorted. "He tried that. She don't want to negotiate, Nellie. She wants his dick in a grinder." Nellie made a face.

Next day, for the first time, Mildred asked to see me on her lunch break. She closed the door firmly and said, "Your student Mims is my auntie's boy. I know what you're training our black youth for. He was going to be the first in his family to graduate anything like college. Why are you writing him a one-way ticket to Jackson, Mr. Black?" Jackson is a high-security Michigan prison. Since she had me bang to rights, I lost my temper.

"Fuck you, Mrs. Mayberry." I got up, leaving the office door open and my back unprotected. She let me make it out of the building. When I got home, cursing my foolish racist paranoia, Henry Doolin heard me out in silence. Then he said, "What do you think, Nellie? Think she would have got off a round?" (Henry had his own .38 behind a mantel bust of Kwame Nkrumah.) Nellie pondered a moment, then shook her head. "No, probably not." But it was a long moment.

"Henry," I inquired a few days later, "what's it like in America these days? Is there any chance for a black person and white person to make it?" Henry asked, "Without sex or politics bonding them?" Just as human beings, I insisted. "Black and white, unite to fight, that sort of thing, huh?" Yes, I said. He put his arm around me. "Why, baby, that's what we're all about, and no fooling. But I wouldn't bet my last dollar on it."

A little later, after the weekly meeting of *Workers' Voice*, Henry and I sat in the kitchen drinking beer. He suddenly said, "All revolutionists are sick people. Otherwise, we'd just be defeated like most folks. But we can't ask them to cure us—that's a fool's task. We heal ourselves and pass on the remedy, and if they don't buy it piss on 'em, right, Nellie?" But, unhearing, she was still in the front room going over subscription lists: *Workers' Voice* had a readership of a hundred and fifty.

I stayed awake all night thinking. Downstairs, Henry, Nellie, and their closest collaborators—who included Wilfred X, Malcolm's brother—were putting the finishing touches to the paper. I felt alone. Only black people, south and north, had welcomed me back to America. That should have been good enough, but wasn't.

For nine months I'd fought for a place in a country I did not know anymore. But I wasn't black, no matter how warmly Wilfred X shook my hand, and anytime I thought I was, there would always be a Mildred bringing me back to racial reality, a piece in her purse. Any way I looked at it, home was now a foreign country with an unspeakable climate, uneatable food, coins so heavy they tore big holes in my pocket, and a mistress/companion with whom I now had a totally English relationship, past troubled waters into passion spent, ardor composed, Beauvoir and Sartre without the garlic. What more did I want?

That morning I came down to breakfast and told Henry and Nellie I was going back to England. Henry put his hand on my shoulder. "You make me very sad, boy. If we can't keep people like you, what then?" I laughed. If I was the best they had, they were in trouble. Nellie chipped in, "I'm getting tired of tourists. Let him go."

They didn't press me. What a choice: revolution in Detroit or a desk at *Vogue*.

The iron butterfly I kept locked in my little wooden box of Sandoz vials with the leather straps flew me back across the Atlantic.

BOOK 3

THE MASKED AVENGER STRIKES AGAIN

Time: 1970. Seven years after my return from Detroit. *Scene:* Ruskin College, Oxford. An historic occasion. Four hundred shouting, arguing, passionate women attend Britain's first Women's Liberation Conference. The hall is ringed by pedestaled busts of former Oxford scholars who stare down at us like Maltese falcons. It has the excitement, and threat, of a Soviet mural of the 1917 storming of the Winter Palace. I slump at the rear of the noisy hall, hoping not to be noticed. What mad urge drove me here? As the angry, hopeful, violent speeches flow and swirl around me, I scrunch down under my Old Bond Street county-style cap.

"Are you ill? Or just scared of us?"

I peeked out. First, the red hair caught my eye—just like Mom's—then the strong, slightly sulky, almost too perfect face, then the full picture: a black bolero-tight jacket flaring snugly over the hips, a flowered Liberty's silk shirt open at the throat, a nearly ankle-length skirt covering the tops of her smart Italian boots. Criminy. I couldn't improve on this one.

My heart racing with fear and lust, I looked around. Was she talking to me? No, God and I were not on that good terms. So I pulled my cap down tighter as if to shield my eyes from the blasting force of the militant hecklers all around us. In the large, crowded hall there were only a few other males.

I could feel her amused eyes on me. I peeked again. "Friend or foe?" I hissed.

She laughed, throaty, deep, from her gut. Yeah.

111

"Friendly foe," she answered. She too looked around, as if nervous about being seen talking to me.

I leaned across the two metal folding chairs separating us and muttered, "I feel"—sliding into the chair next to her—"like the only Jew at a gentile nudist camp."

She nodded. "We're not exactly the Gestapo—though I admit we're in a mood to round up the usual suspects."

A *Casablanca* fan too.

"You, er, with anyone?" I asked. Again her low, sexy laugh.

I took off the cap and wrung it in my hands. It was cold in the hall—or were those revolutionary gusts? "Listen, don't get me wrong," I quickly added, "only a guy with a death wish would try for a pickup here." She wasn't buying it, but also she wasn't screaming for the cops.

She suggested, "Don't be put off by our rhetoric. It's mostly symbolic—"

"—Ha!"

Now she examined me seriously. "Believe it or not, none of us here is interested in you one way or the other. That's the point of all this." She cocked her gorgeous head, letting her amazing hair tumble below her shoulders. "What *are* you doing here, by the way?"

I lied and said I was covering the conference for the *Manchester Guardian*, which sounded less inflammatory than *Vogue*. "Tell anyone who asks," BenGy Tyler had grinned evilly on assigning me, "that you're doing a fashion story on revolutionary chic. We'll pay funeral expenses."

"You're a spy." She stared at me.

"How'd you guess?" I smiled brightly. "From the bourgeois media. They can't wait to get my copy about all you wacko lesbian bitches."

"Hush, you foolish man." She seemed genuinely concerned. "Not everyone here can take a joke."

Tell me about it. C. L. R. James's wife, Selma, a Flatbush Avenue broad if I ever heard one, had the floor and was denouncing me—okay, "patriarchal fascists"—so graphically I could see my head on her pike. A year's pay I'd give C.L.R. to discuss mutual sexual problems. Better I should have stayed in Detroit and dated Mildred.

Emboldened, I sat up and frankly scanned the redhead's figure. All *right*. I told her she had a terrific—sense of humor.

She got more apprehensive. "You must really like taking risks."

I put my arm around the back of her chair. "They don't," I said, "call me the Masked Avenger for nothing."

When BenGy read my story he tore it up. "I can't use this garbage," he said mildly. "What happened to your objectivity? Your impartial detachment? Your keen sense of who signs your paycheck?" Then he caught himself, nodding his head slowly over my copy again. "Hmmm. Those sharecroppers' overalls you say some of those women's liberationists wore. By any chance catch the label?"

Multiple choice question: I went to the women's liberation conference to (a) get laid, (b) find a wife, or (c) breathe fresh air on the left? Answer: all of the above. By definition the grind of politics is extremely boring. The typical mix of long agendas and inflated blabber usually means only a special race of hardheads feels qualified to run the show. Nonpoliticals with something original or fresh to say often don't say it because they're intimidated by the hardheads, whose specialty is scaring away newcomers. Hence, most meetings are usually populated by apparatchiks, senior or apprentice bureaucrats one normally would not want to spend time with. However, I was a pro. I know that if I left the meeting early, or worse, failed to show up because I had less irksome things to do, the hardheads wouldn't even have to sweat to win the crowd to their (usually absurd) "position." So I trained myself to sit for hours listening, watching, waiting. Unless fanatic, you find ways of amusing yourself during the tedium. E.g., doodle, daydream, check out the opposite sex. To a mind inflamed by bone-devouring boredom, all possibilities exist—to be a new Picasso, or to find the woman of your dreams.

Was I out for myself or the cause? It's moot. Politics, as I understood it, was like a jewel (defiance) mounted in a setting of dull rhinestones (dreary rhetoric). I figured the trick was to pluck the jewel from the setting without triggering too many alarm bells.

The above, known as Black's First Law of Thermopolitics, applies also to business, academia, and the military—anywhere the politics of power is practiced.

What's time? It had taken me a mere seven years to recover fully from the virus of schizophrenia I'd caught from Dr. Willie Last and his colleagues and disciples. Easy to go mad, I found, hard to come back. It helped that Willie was off hunting another snark: not the emancipation of the mentally ill proletariat, a goal I shared, but a version of Rose O'Malley's cosmic quietude, where one's Inner Eye boosted It-self over not-self—that is, a naked, unruffled narcissism that clearly implied civil politics of any sort was the grubby business it really is.

At a hundred sixteen pounds, down from one seventy, I no longer had the luxury of snark hunting. If I wanted to pursue human quarry like Helen Hadley, I had to put some weight on my bones. Madly, after the women's liberation conference, I did a crash course of English breakfasts thrice a day at my corner caff—fried eggs, bacon and sausage, baked beans and fried tomatoes, mushrooms on toast dripping with butter, and Camp coffee. On the same day, I hit my old weight and Helen Hadley's bell in Covent Garden.

My first date with Helen (to see Godard's *Weekend*) was pure formality. We kissed, fought, made love, and closely compared genealogical dowries. Helen, a steel ladler's daughter from Sheffield, just south of Thurcroft, was practically out of a socialist *Debrett's*. Her father was a union shop steward, Trades Council delegate, Peace Pledge Union activist, and Labour Party councilman; her mother, in the old way, stayed at home pretty much under Husband's thumb. Two uncles had fought on the Loyalist side of the Spanish Civil War.

When I told Helen about my mom—her flirtatiousness, self-sacrifice, organizational smarts, and neurotic willingness to accept men's low estimate of her talents—she was fascinated, even fixated. Wistfully owning up that her mother was a conservative, indrawn woman, Helen said, "I wish I could adopt your mother as mine."

"Take her, she's yours," I said lightly.

In giving Polly to Helen, I sealed our fate.

"What about Jake?" I asked as an afterthought. "I'm his son, too."

"We'll soon fix that," Helen said, opening her arms to me.

What do politics have to do with love? A lot, if you're a prowling Marxshire cat.

When I met Helen Hadley, Labour had been in power six years, sufficient to demoralize any socialist. Instead of the pseudoaristocrat Tory Harold Macmillan, who calmly joked his way through crises, we had Harold Wilson, a plebeian "socialist," as prime minister. A shrewd, conscienceless, pipe-smoking Yorkshireman, he was, like the politician he gave birth to, Margaret Thatcher, a "grammar school scholar," that is, a bright lowling brought in from the scullery to clean up the rat-infested house.

Smarter than any of his political enemies, Wilson had a clear shot at renewing the nation. His excuse for not doing so had a tired ring: "The world economy," whined successive Chancellors of the Exchequer, "of which we, as a trading nation, are an inseparable part, places constraints upon this year's budget that, regrettably, force us once again to tighten our belts...." That old belt, kept on a nail in a back bedroom for use in perverse sex and Whitehall economics. But Wilson, a pygmy Prometheus self-bound by his own balance-of-payment dogmas, needed to prove to his Labour left, who despised him for actively backing the U.S. in Vietnam, that he still had balls. So he set about "improving" Britain by tearing down most of its city centers, with the demolition contracts awarded to a few, very few, of his chums. This reduction of the country to the architecture and color scheme of a Howard Johnson's restaurant the Prime Minister dubbed a "white-hot technological revolution." Labour bureaucrats, Tory placemen, and Fleet Street pundits were crazy about this orgy of self-destruction. The rest of us, including remnants of the New Left, were so eager to be swindled by one of our own we bought it too.

But not everybody did. As if in response to this "socialist" rape of tradition, a British youth revolution began busily disrupting art colleges and universities with sit-in strikes. Soon the "socialists" would depart office, when they were seen as incapable of controlling unemployment, the unions, and the Jimi Hendrix/Janis Joplin "fuck you" syndrome. But Helen and I went right on making our own revolution.

Time: Spring 1970. Scene: Embankment Gardens, between Waterloo and Charing Cross bridges. Elsewhere four Kent State students protesting Cambodia are shot dead, and John Lennon announces that "the dream is over." He doesn't know about Helen and me. To catch some unseasonal sun, we're lying lazily on a soft patch of buttercups, deaf to the roaring Thameside traffic. Helen wears a rough crown of flowers I've woven for her. She gazes down at me, dropping buttercups on my new revolutionary beard.

"You're a fool, you know," Helen said.

Self-satisfied, I scrunched around for a better fit of my head in her lap.

"But I love you," she said. "In love. Falling in love. It's wonderful to be able to say that."

"What's the big deal?" I mumbled.

She showered my beard with flowers. "This, you big lump. It's so amazing, so unpredictable."

This wasn't like my cool, unflappable Helen. As usual when nervous, I became big-bellied, bellicose Mitchum.

"Don't analyze it, honey, just enjoy it," I yawned.

"You really do wish I were a stupider woman."

"Yeah, sometimes."

"Rose O'Malley wasn't stupid."

"Sure was. She let me go, didn't she?" I said smugly.

Helen was like Rose only in one respect: she was secretly pleased with the naked male ego.

I turned to look up at her. "Have you been reading Rose's novel again?" Helen had begun leaving *Loose Leaves from a Random Life* around the flat we now shared.

"Did you really do all those things Rose says in her book?" Helen asked.

I dismissed the question. "Would it matter?"

She started to shake her head, then paused. "I know it shouldn't count. It's her fiction."

"But you believe it, don't you?"

"I don't want to."

"Don't let Rose interfere with us. She'd like that. And don't nail me up on a cross of a few steamy paragraphs."

"You don't know what she means to the movement."

I laughed. "You broads are crazy. She generalizes from the experience of one injured woman. Personal testimony, sure. 'A Guide for the Misguided'—forget it, baby."

Timidly, "Did you like making love to her?"

"Only when she—" And here I pulled Helen down to whisper into her ear.

She recoiled, making a face. "What sensitivity. What an elegant choice of words."

"So I'm a primitive. Arrest me, officer." I offered my hands to her imaginary manacles.

She pushed them away. "No need. You're sufficiently arrested as it is."

"Be fair. You got me doing dishes when Rose O'Malley never even came close."

"You're quite proud of your manly stupidity, aren't you?"

"Just my way of being sexy."

Helen studied me. "Don't you understand? This is 1970. Being macho and brainless isn't sexy anymore, just cloddish."

"Tell me about it, Germaine." That always got a rise out of Helen, who had fiercely debated Germaine Greer at the Women's Liberation Conference. Raised in a strict Wesleyan home, Helen would sooner have died than talk dirty in public like Germaine (e.g., her platform boast that she would rather "fuck a lorry driver than an intellectual" any night).

Helen kissed me to shut me up. Then she pulled away. "We're incompatible, you know."

I half wrestled her with kisses on the neck, breast, and shoulder.

"Lucky old us," I sighed.

Lucky old us, a princess and prince of the international left. If Rose (b. 1920) and I had shared a language of disillusioned Communism, Helen (b. 1940) and I embodied an unprecedented hope, called feminism, which aside from what it could do for women, opened up a possibility of deep-down amity between the sexes. Naturally, Helen and I were too hip, too self-aware, to try to personify anything as dumb as the New Woman or New Man. No, this time no Stalinist heroics hiding the corrupted heart.

Helen actively encouraged me to keep seeing Rose—out of bed—because we were doomed, she said, if we became A Couple losing our personal histories in each other. Being trusted was a new experience for me. And so was Helen's tribe of wild Comanche women, of which I was now an adopted white child.

Time: Summer '71. *Scene:* Helen's small bohemian flat overlooking Covent Garden market, a year after I moved in with my exercycle and dart board. Anybody who's seen Hitchcock's *Frenzy* knows the area. In Helen's tiny, raftered kitchen, an oilcloth Union Jack apron round my middle, I'm pretending to wash dishes but actually eavesdropping on the whispers and giggles behind the firmly closed door of Helen's bed/sitting room, where her women's group meets every Friday night. I'm used to being excluded. Itching with curiosity, I hold a water tumbler to the wall, cupping my ear to it. They're talking sex, as usual.

"Oh, come *on*, it does *not* look like a raw carrot," I muttered to myself, involuntarily glancing at my crotch. For the ninth time I absentmindedly washed Helen's fry pan, straining to hear.

If Helen talks about us, I'll kill her. But mostly it was her best friend, Emma Gore-Templeton, of *the* Gore-Templetons, pontificating tonight about the politics of vaginal versus clitoral orgasm. Emma was the movement's Senator Phogbottom.

"Stupid cow," I said, but was back at the sink when the door opened and the Sisters trooped out, giving me hard glances and saying goodnight to Helen without a word to me. Helen, raised properly, apologized later for their bad manners and said that just because male lefties had always treated women similarly was no excuse.

With her friends gone, she leaned against the stove watching me dry up ostentatiously. She smiled. "You're so obvious. A real scream. We all heard you snooping."

"Tell them it's termites. Now give."

"You're only interested in the spicy parts," she objected. She said they'd also discussed the Ford women workers' strike, support for the locked-out West End office cleaners, and a reception for Madame Binh, the Viet Cong representative in Paris.

"Uh-huh," I said.

She gave one of her throaty laughs. "Orgasms is all you ever want to hear about."

"Let's start with that."

Helen tossed her beautiful red hair in mild exasperation. "That's just what we talk about—men who insist on pinning us exclusively to our sexual functions."

"Ah, men. Brutish, self-centered, violent."

"And infantile."

I threw down the towel, singing, "It seems to me/I've heard that song before/It's from an old familiar score ..." Dear Rose.

Helen came over and nuzzled my neck. "You Old Lefties are the worst. You think being a socialist inoculates you against sexism. It's why we started our own groups."

"I wonder," I mused as I writhed under her touch, "if Lenin and Krupskaya got into wrangles like this."

"They did"—Helen turned me around for a full kiss—"if he made such a big deal of washing a few dishes."

Helen and I were still in our idyllic phase—a matinee idyll. Movie fanatics, if left to ourselves, we'd have stayed forever curled up in each other's arms in a back loge of the Scala's tiny cinema watching *Top Hat* or *Nothing Sacred*. Sometimes, impelled by a strange compulsion to be more intimate, we'd even playfully act out scenes from our favorite movies. Our all-timer was *Klute*, with Jane Fonda as the troubled hooker and Donald Sutherland as the honest cop. We invented, with improvised dialogue, what happened after the fadeout.

All it needed was for Helen to say, "Action!"

Time: 1974, in the midst of a national miners' strike. The ideas and enthusiasm of the '68 student movement have fed into a rising arc of labor militancy unknown since the 1920s, and the miners are holding firm. I've been doing picket duty at Battersea power station, and Helen's kitchen in Covent Garden is open round the clock to strikers. During a lull, we treat ourselves, yet again, to *Klute* at the Mayfair, on whose couches we've done so much courting. Now we're back in her flat, crammed with miners' sleeping bags. And "into" the characters of John Klute and Bree Daniels.

"God," Helen-as-Fonda-playing-Bree said, putting down a string bag of groceries we got on the way home, "it's so wonderful to be a child again. You permit that." She shook her head wonderingly.

Me-as-Sutherland's Klute, gruffly: "Now it's my turn."

"What?"

"Why should you have all the fun?" I complained.

Helen/Fonda's balloon burst. "I get it. Reciprocity. Now you want me to rock your cradle, is it?"

"Fair's fair."

Helen blazed away, just as Fonda had in her first fight with Sutherland. "You bastard. You're like all the other johns. You can't give without adding up the bill, can you?"

"There's no bill," I explained. "This isn't a business deal. I thought feminism was all about—"

Helen, angry: "Don't you dare lecture me about feminism. I've known guys like you all my life. Always looking for a woman's secret weakness, when her guard is down. Then, zap."

Me, gently: "You're not such a bad zapper yourself."

Helen, appealingly: "But I thought you … I don't know, you were different. That you embraced all of me, bad and good. But no, men always have to have an edge, don't they?"

"What edge?" I demanded. "You come along and show me a new way. I'd be a fool not to take advantage—"

"Of me," Helen cut in.

"Of us," I insisted. "What we're making together. A sort of space."

"A playpen, you mean."

"What's wrong with that? Isn't that what it's all about?"

"Goddamn it, Klute," said Helen, "I'm the child. You're the man-father. Can't you hold on a little longer?"

"I wondered," I said, "when you'd get around to sex."

Helen: "I didn't mean that." Then, bitchily: "Exactly."

I stood up, all six foot three of Sutherland. "I know what you meant. I'd be frigid too if I'd turned as many tricks as you."

Helen gave a tight smile. "Ah yes. Here we go." She looked at her watch. "I give you exactly two minutes before I'm a lesbian ball-breaker."

"You said it, I didn't."

Helen, bitter: "It didn't even take two minutes."

It was going wrong. The movie game was taking us over. Waking up, I leaned across to Helen and held out my hand. "Bree ... I mean, Helen."

But she was still in it, sneering, "Bree honey. Bree baby. Bree sweetheart." Then, icy: "Be a man, for Christ's sake."

I tried calming her. "I didn't mean to scare you, Helen. Honest. Let's stop pretending."

Helen, too, now saw we'd gone too far. Shivering a little, she took my hand. "Why do we do it? Other couples are satisfied with perversions like cross-dressing and S/M."

I shrugged. "I guess we just don't want to grow up."

We exchanged looks of real fear.

"Or else," Helen said sadly, "we're afraid of what will happen when the movie's over."

Our version of *It Happened One Night* happened one sleety spring day in 1975 when I decided to be Helen's Clark Gable.

Nobody is surprised by the weather on the thousands-strong march, for once celebrating rather than protesting: The U.S., ending two decades of military involvement, is evacuating its troops from Vietnam. The vast crowd, which probably has a thousand points of internal dispute, is a cross-section of the London left, which has been committed heart and soul to ending the war in Southeast Asia. It winds through a Sunday drizzle of light snow toward Marble Arch, with much chanting, sporadic songs, placards waving to a few puzzled pedestrians along Oxford Street. Helen looks gorgeous in a shiny black three-quarter Saint-Laurent raincoat, plastic rain hat, and those expensive Italian boots she splashes out in. I'm in my normal marching gear, grubby pea jacket stuffed with Mars bars, apples, almonds, even a magazine in case I get bored or arrested. (I hate waiting to make bail in West End Central police station with nothing to read.)

We're holding hands as if on a country stroll, which this is for us. We've been in some tough street battles together—Grosvenor Square, Red Lion Square, several of the Vietnam Solidarity Committee clashes—and this is a doddle amidst May snow flurries.

Suddenly Helen caught a reflection of us in a Selfridge's shop-window.

"We look ridiculous." She pointed. "Mr. and Mrs. Rent-a-Mob. All we need is a hammer and sickle in our hands."

"I like that," I said.

She nudged me. "What an exhibitionist."

"No, I mean the 'Mr. and Mrs.' part. Will you marry me?"

She tossed her head. "What, after all this time? Don't be absurd."

"I didn't want to rush matters."

She glanced at me. Was I serious?

"What's wrong?" I needled her. "Afraid the Women's Central Committee might expel you for bourgeois maritalism?"

That was no joke. Her group, including best friend Emma Gee-Tee, had given Helen a hard time when we began living together. Some of the sisters even stopped speaking to her, and one, an American radical lesbian, slapped her face. Helen didn't tell me about it for months for fear I'd kill the bitch.

"Man haters. Sexual nut cases," I said.

"They were my friends."

"Give me enemies any day."

We trudged along, wiping snowflakes off our eyelashes, under a soggy banner: CRICKLEWOOD WOMEN FOR CRECHES AT THE WORKPLACE.

"Well, how about it?" I persisted.

Helen looked slightly desperate. "You once said you'd never hook up again with a woman who'd been in psychoanalysis."

"Freud says a mature mind is capable of infinite flexibility. Or was it Ho Chi Minh?"

"How can I tolerate a man who makes up quotations to suit his mood?"

"Easy. Marry me, Helen."

She stumbled and I had to steady her.

"Are you actually proposing?"

"Hell no. I'm just askin' if ya wanna get married," in my best Brando/Stanley Kowalski voice.

Helen looked around. "On a demo? Well, I suppose it's romantic in its way."

I slipped my arm around her raincoated waist. "I'm hung up on ya, kid. Yes or no, I ain't got all day."

Helen's face mirrored her conflicts. Panic and hope struggled with resistance and surrender. The snow turned to rain.

"You are joking?" she asked uncertainly.

I covered us up against the driving wet. "Pay or play, baby."

"Yes. All right. I will."

It was my turn to glance suspiciously at her. But Helen's face, though full of doubt, was also vividly alive.

I went into shock. "You will?"

Now Helen stopped and burst out laughing at my woebegone expression. Marchers, some smiling at us, parted for us to embrace.

Helen hugged me and whispered into my shoulder, "See what you get for teaching me how to play poker? I outbluffed you."

Ours was a real New Left wedding.

Helen's parents, though average-looking working people, cast a long shadow. In their Sunday-best suit and dress, Mr. and Mrs. Hadley looked out of place amidst the baggy trousers, velvet open-collar shirts, saris, and Mississippi-SNCC overalls of our guests. Aside from me, Mr. Hadley, and my two best men—BenGy and a new pal, Hywel Morgan, a South Wales miner I'd met on strike—nobody had on a suit and tie. (I'd put in several calls to Len Doherty at his Sheffield newspaper, but he never rang back.) Helen's maid of honor, Emma Gore-Templeton, was in a sort of Laura Ashley miniskirt. Arnie Robins' only bow to the occasion was a clean shirt stuffed into his usual greasy cord trousers; did he ever bathe? And those of Helen's women's group who still spoke to her—some were furious at her for marrying—made their point by wearing dowdy day clothes and disapproving frowns. Even BenGy, ornamented in his usual off-cream suit, milk-white shoes, blood-red cravat, pale bamboo Panama hat, and gold-knobbed walking stick, and expecting the worst, was impressed. "I haven't seen such massed bad taste," he hissed in my ear, "since the Old Vic's last production of *The Lower Depths*."

But he blinked appreciatively at my bride.

Dear Helen, ambivalent to the last, was resplendent in a blazing white-and-gold nearly transparent knee-length wedding dress. Having made *her* point, sex triumphant over convention, she was palely sweating at the prospect before us, and clearly was scared of her parents' reaction. "First I chose black because weddings remind me of funerals," she'd told me, "then red to proclaim my revolutionary fervor, then I thought, to hell with them all, I'm still a virgin in my mind." I hugged her till she gasped: my Helen.

The marriage ceremony, in a side room of Holborn Town Hall, was a Buñuel comedy that only Helen and I seemed to take seriously. The officiating town clerk was a hulking, round-shouldered double for Boris Karloff in *Bedlam* who peered malevolently at me over his half-specs and, staring us all into silence, commanded in frozen italics, "You know, Mr. Black—curious name, Gustavus, ethnic is it? Americans, yes, oh well. As I was saying, we in the United Kingdom, unlike you Americans, tend to treat these vows seriously...." Helen stepped on my toe to shut me up. But Hywel, in the back, already two sheets over, roared, "G'wan, bugger the bourgeois propaganda and get on with it, vicar!"

The party at Helen's afterwards flowed all too logically from the above. Good thing Mr. and Mrs. Hadley had to take an early train back to Sheffield.

We'd invited a potpourri, and a brouhaha came. Including Archie Boylan, a beer-paunchy, bellicose U.S. Army AWOL Helen and I had rescued during my recent days as a stationmaster on the Vietnam-era underground railway. Asking Archie to my wedding was one of my dumber ideas.

But nobody behaved well. As champagne and guests mingled freely, Hywel, a miner as well as a former pro rugby winger from Cwybran, pounced on me. "What a mob you're marrying into." He slapped my back. "I swear I'd be afraid to have some of them playing in the scrum opposite me—especially the women." Overhearing, Emma first berated then pushed Hywel, whereupon my friend Harry (ex-British Army spiv and check-kiting artiste, just out of Pentonville prison) had a go at Emma, who crashed into bearded Syme, a Talmudicly bent Whitechapel tailor and seasoned street fighter I'd met at a Mosley punch-up, who upbraided Archie, who'd just put his hand up the sari of one of Emma's girlfriends, who slugged BenGy, who'd started laughing. I hit Archie, who punched me, Helen tried pulling us apart, somebody grabbed Helen's long red hair, and I piled in with Hywel on top of me, oof! I dragged

Helen under her prized purple velvet Victorian chaise longue, and together we sat it out sipping champers with a ringside seat at what had become a small riot.

I freaked out. How dare they defile this most supreme moment? "Relax." Helen kissed me. "Everybody is making their own statement. Maybe if we stay down here long enough we can deconstruct it."

"I'd like to deconstruct some of them," I said. "This is my wedding day."

"No," she corrected, "it's theirs. We'll have ours later, alone."

So, after two police visits, we abandoned the flat, now sprawling with semi-strangers, and spent our wedding night at the Dorchester, Park Lane, and were paying the bill for the next six months.

Forty-eight hours later, we returned to the Covent Garden flat, which was neat as a pin. There was a note on the marble mantlepiece: "Congratulations and bless you. I've cleaned up a lot worse than this underground. But drank all the leftover booze. Hywel."

All in all, not a bad kickoff, I thought. But Helen, surveying her cozy Paris-style garret with its angled roofs, said, "It's too small, isn't it? Let's do it right and buy a house."

Getting married had been my idea. I wanted Bree, I mean Helen, to bring me in from the cold. But she was so shaky I had to practically hold her up during the ceremony. (She had vomited all night.) Marriage made Helen feel as if she was betraying herself and the Movement. For this sacrifice of principle, even of self, I owed her, and tried to discharge the debt by becoming a Movement man.

It isn't hard once you get the knack. Put a lock on your vile sexist mouth; never stare openly just sneak a sidelong glance at a pair of good legs; rethink Marilyn Monroe from sex goddess to tragic heroine; don't laugh (openly) when the National Film Theatre runs a Doris Day season under a banner of "Premature Feminism" ("Saying no was the first stage in a raised feminist consciousness"); do your share of the housework (after grumbling); put out teacups and obediently leave room when Helen's women friends come round; learn to degenderize your vocabulary, "chairperson," all that. And scan without prejudice a whole new library of feminist periodicals, actually no worse than male equivalents and sometimes better. Spare Rib, Shrew, and Red Rag, in which theory took a back seat to "praxis," had a direct, often witty personal style that arose out of specific women's experiences and made old-line male left journals look pretty fusty. There was an angry, opti-

mistic jokiness I'd only seen in the best anarchist papers, like the Detroit Workers' Voice. *Feminism in the late 1970s still had that vital spark. Great to be part of it, even as a camp follower.*

But it was the Detroit problem all over again. I wasn't black—or a woman. I was a white male, not a good thing to be in Helen's circle unless, like so many radical men, you lived in a permanently apologetic mode, not my style. Anyway, women usually spotted the Chicago Rocket in me. Why couldn't they also see the scared man child?

Rose O'Malley always had.

They had to meet.

It happened only once. Thank God.

None of us really wanted it, but London's social machinery has a logic of its own. Rose had accepted my marriage to Helen in good grace, it seemed. She had said unconvincingly, "I must meet your new girlfriend one day." And I stupidly said, "When?" And so here we were, self-consciously studying our menus at an ironwork table at a Regents Park open-air cafe, in the summer of '76.

"In a way," Helen had told me as we dressed to go out, "I feel a bit sorry for Rose, the way so many women have turned her into a White Madonna. At least they buy her books, so she must be rolling in royalties. By the way, who's picking up the bill today?" My practical Helen.

"Well, my friend ..."

I could almost hear Rose's note-taking gears crunch into action. At least she had on the eye shadow I'd trained her to apply. Two women, twenty years apart, both wearing no makeup, only eye shadow to my taste. I sat back, pleased as a pasha.

"Hello, Rose, I'm truly glad to meet you," said Helen, who surprised me by reaching across to kiss the older woman. Rose blushed, then arched her neck to scan Helen, looking for a hostility she feared, or hoped, was there. But, bless her, Helen was as open and spontaneous as I'd ever seen her. I think she was trying to tell Rose something, woman to woman, that had little to do with me. And Rose warily responded with the side of her that always chose engagement rather than withdrawal. Anyway, she probably liked women better than men. For that matter, maybe Helen did too. God knows what we were all doing in heterosexuality.

All through lunch Rose squinted at Helen, who compromised between respect for Rose and self-assertion. I dreaded them wrangling over feminism; these days Rose firmly dissociated herself from the movement her writings had helped give birth to. But when it came it was surprisingly friendly, even comradely. At first.

As usual, Rose moaned about how feminists, especially Americans, got her wrong. Then, crisply: "Do you write, Helen? No matter. Once you get going, you'll find yourself cursed by two things: being placed on required reading lists in Dakota universities, and feminists who read you literally. Be warned."

My heart skipped. Would Helen rise to the bait? Rose knew perfectly well that most feminists yearned to write. But my girl rode gracefully over the implied condescension. "Writing's bloody hard work, Rose—as you know. I'm edging into it gradually. But I know what you mean about feminists rewriting the writers they say they approve of. If I thought as much about that as you do, I'd never sit down to a typewriter, would I?" Helen said it so sweetly Rose had to look again to see the flying axe. This was getting interesting.

Rose picked it up, tested the blade on her thumb, and flicked it back. "I have always told Gus," she said, "never to worry about his audience. Once he forgot them he began to write, didn't you, old friend?"

Rose hardly looked at me. Her small, slightly unfocused eyes fastened on Helen, who looked superb today. Helen had carefully dressed down, in a plain skirt just a couple of inches above her knee, sensible shoes, not sexy Milan boots, tailored silk shirt (of a sort I used to buy for Rose and now encouraged Helen to wear), tweed jacket conservatively cut but subtly emphasizing the swell of her hips. In private Helen bitterly complained of her "negative body image," but my god, she came through in moments like this. Rose, as usual, looked a mess, her hair twisted in a wrong-way bun, and wearing, or drenched by, a purple sack dress that hung on her like ... like a sack. Oh, Rose, I thought, you should have divorced everything but the Balenciaga in me.

"Yes," replied Helen, "Gus is always telling me how much he owes you as a writer. He says *Loose Leaves from a Random Life* released him from the death grip of autobiography to do his first book, about the miners—"

"Bloody good book it was," Rose shot in maternally.

My Helen asked Rose what she was working on.

"Oh, just another novel."

Grrr. Almost every time we met, Rose triumphantly brought me a fresh copy of a new book, followed by her usual lecture about why didn't I publish more. She liked giving media interviews proclaiming what a shy genius I was. Ha.

"By the way"—Rose bobbed and weaved—"how *is* Gus's block?" As if asking about my acne.

Helen told her I'd just completed my third novel.

"Oh yes?" Rose smiled cordially. "Of course. I always told Gus normal married life would suit him."

The big guns unveiled.

"Oh, Rose"—Helen gave her light cocktail laugh—"is marriage ever normal? I mean, you had ... how many?"

Rose's face turned to stone. "Well," she said through thinning lips, "I see you've made him into a proper Jewish husband. When's the baby arriving?"

Whoosh. Whiz. Bang.

Helen bent to her shrimp salad. "Gus tells me you offered to untie your tubes for him, Rose. That you'd do it for political reasons. Personally, I think he made a mistake not taking you up on it."

Rose observed icily that her son Alastair was such a handful she was glad I'd said no. "And Gus himself is such a baby I don't know if I could have handled two in one house. Or has he grown up since leaving me?"

Helen smiled back. "I would have thought," she said, "leaving you was his first sign of maturity. But he's always told me what an absolutely wonderful cook you are. Have you read Elizabeth David's latest on—"

Rose was in a rage. She didn't so much mind being got at over me as being patronized as a chef. I tried to get a word in, but both women looked so coldly at me I shrank back inside myself.

A long silence. "Oh well ...," said Rose. Meaning, Escape-Transfer-Save on her mental computer.

Helen saw it too. She burst into real laughter. "You two," she gasped, "are like runners at the starting block in some kind of weird race. Who's going to write about this lunch first?"

Rose stared at Helen, then me. A slow, commanding grin spread across her lined, lovely, Gene Tierney features. "It's not," she reminded Helen, "who writes it first but who publishes it."

Touché.

"Aw, c'mon, girls," I urged, "let's all relax." Both turned surprised glares on me, as if noticing me for the first time.

"Good heavens, Helen," said Rose, "haven't you done anything about his disgusting sweet tooth?"

Helen sighed dramatically. "I've tried, Rose. Honestly. But I think you spoiled him rotten with those cakes and jams you used to make for him. Look at the man, getting fatter by the day."

They gazed at me fondly now, a suckling pig roasting slowly over the flames of their newfound intimacy.

"Oh well ...," Helen and Rose said in tired unison.

At best, Rose's alliance with her "daughters" of women's liberation was uneasy. At one level, Helen & Co. were a sexual hazard, because being younger, they were too much like the "dolly birds" Rose had always feared men left her for. But the difference ran deeper. Rose belonged to a generation of rather old-fashioned, risk-all bohemians whose female ancestors were single shooting stars aiming at their autonomy in impossible circumstances: Annie Besant, Margaret Sanger, Marie Lloyd, Florence Nightingale, the Pankhursts, Rebecca West, Doris Lessing. Victorian toughies. Between such "grandmothers of the movement" and Helen's friends, even as the latter penned biographies and Ph.D. theses about the former, there was surprisingly little emotional contact. Few of Helen's generation were prepared to commit the sort of sexual suttee that, for example, Eleanor Marx had. George Sand? Forget it.

Rose, I knew from our talks, resented the academicism that had become such a part of modern feminism. She had gone for broke, why couldn't they? Not that Rose expected them to. Wasn't that why she had written, to save them a little of her agony?

Helen's respect for Rose was based on an instinctive understanding that Rose had genuinely flayed herself to become who she was. "But Rose as a model? Who in our right minds would be so masochistic as to love a man like Paul Blue?"

"Books aren't life, exactly," I warned Helen.

"Don't you think I know that, silly?" Helen assured me.

But did Helen know that something went missing in Rose's books? What Rose put into her writing was one thing; what she left out was also important but harder to identify. I wanted to tell Helen, Look, Rose splits herself into all sorts of people in order to write, and some of those people have to be strangled for the survivors to live. The "creative process" itself was a lie we agreed on. But I didn't want my Helen to be hurt by something left out of a former mistress's novel.

"Trust me, Gus." Helen put her arms around me. "I'm not exactly a fool, you know."

She was right. Why should I interfere? It was women's business.

Thank god, or the Black Madonna, Helen did not want to write. Yet. As a professional macroeconomist in a government department, she was absorbed in statistics, not words. "Anyway," Helen said, "real writing belongs to self-cannibalizing savages like you and Rose who would go insane without it." Uh-huh, thought I, I wonder how long it will take ...

How different from Rose, who once she smelled the fire dashed heedlessly into the burning building. You swoop early and fix your claws on the wildebeest in a struggle to the death, or you spend much of your life hovering aimlessly.

Rose once told me she would have killed herself in adolescence if she had not happened on Virginia Woolf's essay "A Room of One's Own." "Those last words of Woolf's, my darling, 'She will be born,' I was sure were addressed to me personally. And I *willed* myself to be born, again." Rose was referring to the author's invocation of Shakespeare's mythical sister Judith, who, had she not lived in the sexually repressive sixteenth century, might have surpassed even the Bard himself, Woolf thought.

Stirred by Woolf's words and Rose's childhood memories, I too had felt myself to be Shakespeare's sister. So it wasn't just a Middle Ages thing. For example, my mother, Polly—

Helen kissed me so hard it hurt that night after we saw Rose. "I could never love you if Polly Black wasn't your mother."

"But," I reminded her again, "I'm also Jake's son. I'm probably more like him than Mom."

"Don't say that!" Helen recoiled sharply. "How can you. He's a ... a ..." (We always spoke of my mother and father as if somehow they were more alive than hers.)

"A man?" I suggested.

"Yes, a man," said Helen.

"But that's what we're like," I said.

Helen was not angry with me. "You say that with everything, you know? It doesn't make sense."

"Sure it does. I'm a guy, that's who I 'identify' with. Men."

Helen got up from bed—I almost expected her to throw a blanket around herself violently in one of Rose's grandly disgusted gestures. Instead, she just looked at me in the half-light of the street-lamp filtering into our bedroom.

"Will it always be the sixteenth century, Gus? Always?"

I felt awful. For letting Helen down, just as I had Rose. Shake-speare's sister didn't have a chance against Jake's son.

But Jake's son may have been preferable to the "sensitive" males who had begun swarming all over the women's movement. Beware, I warned Helen and her best friend, Emma. These sensitive guys, for all their talk about "bonding" and vulnerability and the need to cry and learning to lose, are reptiles who will crawl up your leg like any other snake, including me. Emma objected. "Men," she declared, "have to start somewhere, just as we did. Why can't you be positive for a change?"

The most positive thing I'd done so far was to engage with Helen and by extension her movement. Did Emma want me to be a saint as well? Clearly she did. Helen, my translator, was more hon-est. "Look, darling," she explained, "we have men—okay, some men—on the run for the first time, and to be perfectly truthful there's something distinctly pleasing about the sight of them scat-tering for cover even if they're camouflaging it as 'men's groups,' 'maximizing masculinity,' or whatever. Who knows? It's a difficult road and maybe Emma is right, you shouldn't jeer from the side-lines."

Did that mean she wanted me to join a men's group?

Helen gazed lovingly at me across the dinner table. "If you do," she said, "I'd go straight to my solicitor and ask for a divorce."

Helen was kidding about the divorce but not about wanting A House.

For Helen, A House was the ultimate sanity, an insurance policy against class degradation—an attitude she had inherited from her parents, for whom the unnameable terror, descent from the work-ing poor to the gutter, was propertylessness. And sooner or later we'd have to move because Covent Garden was being taken over by property developers who were forcing out the vegetable market and would put the arm on us too. But I had a renter's soul and didn't want A House. And didn't Helen agree with the old anarchist slo-gan, "Property is theft"?

"No," she said, "and neither do you. You're just letting me front for your own desire for a little respectability." Oh.

So she got The House, I got The Depression, and we shared The Mortgage.

Across the river and into a treeless suburb that had no name but that I thought of as North Clapham/South Lambeth/East Stockwell/Somewhere Southwark, midway between the Oval cricket ground and Vauxhall Park, a zillion spiritual miles from the Seven Sisters dance halls and North Circular caffs that I, a Rocket A.C. in exile, thought of as my turf. In the taxi crossing Vauxhall Bridge Helen began to cry.

"What's wrong, honey?"

"You look so bloody miserable, Gus."

I wiped away her tears. She took my hand. "It's really a fast Tube ride to the West End," she promised.

The House itself—23 Vicarage Terrace—on one of those little squares that are London's glory, was a charm, a tall three-story job with front and rear garden, plus views, albeit of a gasometer in back and a public housing project in front. After showing me around, Helen read my face again. "You won't feel isolated. Lots of our friends live around here."

That was part of the problem.

The people I'd planned Utopia with were also mortgage owners—and liking it. Half the neighbors were comrades, New Commitment types from the old Maquis coffeehouse, now senior lecturers, media pundits, urban planners, "consultants," and academics, plus one big TV star I'd known as a weedy little Polytechnic Trot, now a talk show host, a sort of anarcho–Johnny Carson, with the faded eyes and High Church manner of an electronic prelate. (Of course, like so many successful media types, he was a discreet member of Vanessa Redgrave's Workers Revolutionary Party.) The others in the terrace seemed vaguely connected to a sort of Pink Front of Labour barristers, heads of Social Units (what they?), and researchers into what for whom I never quite learned. Also a sprinkling of "Hampstead widows," divorced women with enough settlement cash to buy in less fashionable postal codes of South London what they could not afford in the posh northern hills around the Heath, NW 3. What about de woikuhs? I asked Helen. Her smile—she was already in love with our House—faded. "It's a fact of life, Gus—we're helping to push them out, just as the rich forced us out of Covent Garden." The square's former tenants, she reported, had died or sold up, leaving behind a small pocket of old-timers who kept themselves to themselves. Helen refused to be sentimental about the dear departed. "It's not exactly like the Enclosures," she reminded me. "We'll be paying them for the rest of our lives." She looked at me dubiously. "And we *will* try to be good neighbors, right, Gus?"

Honestly, I tried.

But it was no good. Even the local Labour Party, crammed with student Trotskyists who loathed Labour's leadership far more than the supposed Conservative enemy, threw me out of my first meeting because I didn't think abortion on demand was the highest priority for organizing in a community with so many Catholic churches. It didn't take a genius, just a pair of eyes, to see that our lovely little gentrified streets were encircled by huge public housing estates full of poor Irish Catholics or Caribbean Pentacostals and armies of unemployed teenage girls eager to jump the housing queue by getting pregnant. "Perhaps the comrade," the chairladyperson gaveled, "would be happier in another Labour ward?" Proposed, seconded, and unanimous: I was out before I was in.

Helen, who'd had her own battles with feminist Trots, was hanging curtains when I came back to report I'd spoiled things for us with the local activists. She sounded almost apologetic. "It's probably my fault, Gus. What have I got us both into?"

Into a lovely old Victorian house on a pretty street in a newly desirable London neighborhood.

I could not stand it.

What was the big deal? Most coal miners owned their own houses nowadays. Hemingway had La Finca. Even Rose had a large monster in Highgate, all Charles Addams gables and dark staircases. Successful writers needed a house, I told myself. But did they?

Helen, scared she'd done the wrong thing, at first was apologetic and defensive about The House. She only wanted me happy which made me feel guilty which made me try to make it up to her by telling myself we had a great setup which only made me more depressed which got me angrier and guiltier which ... So I redoubled my efforts to integrate with the local folks.

Next stop, the Mason's Arms, the pub at the far end of the terrace where the working-class holdouts drank.

Joe Hill had advised, "Don't mourn—organize." Helen agreed. "You've organized miners and auto workers. Why not try it on your own doorstep?"

Nobody could give me lessons in how to talk to English workers, oh no, I swaggered into the Mason's: I knew the drill, just stand about with a mild and bitter in your hand and, however long it took, wait for somebody to break the ice. So a day, a week, passed. Nothing happened. These guys hated us "incomers." Finally, pushing it, I offered to buy one of them a drink. "You a poofta, then?" he growled. "No," I blurted, "just an asshole like you." After the fight, I got thrown out of the Mason's Arms.

Helen, taping up my bruises, was philosophical. "Well, that takes care of the proles. Maybe we ought to try drinking with our own." "Our own" was the poshed-up pub at the near end of the square, the Glorious Nelson, patronized by Saatchi & Saatchi ad executives in one corner and Labour Party strategists in the other, neither speaking to each other or to Helen and me. Where's this mythical English pub with jolly proprietor and faithful Rover in front of a blazing fire? I demanded. So Helen and I retreated to our fortress home, wondering how to do this domestic adventure right. Helen, a natural gardener, got along with other women on the street just by chatting about the pros and cons of store-bought mulch; I was the problem.

One more time.

When in doubt, call a meeting. Uranium was the issue, death by gamma ray the spark. Flatbed railroad cars bearing flasks of spent nuclear waste passed our backyards almost every night on their way from the Windscale processing plant in Cumbria to Dover port and from there to some godforsaken Third World country bribed to accept this genetic dynamite. Denials by British Rail and British Nuclear Fuels Ltd. that there was no, repeat no, contamination risk in case of derailment made us all very skeptical. The U.K. nuclear industry, like its American counterpart, lies by habit and choice.

It felt really good to be organizing again. Helen helped me write a leaflet inviting the neighbors to "protest and resist," and to my surprise almost fifty showed up. All shades (of white), from rabble-rousing WRP-SWP-IS-militant to staunch Tory. While Helen played wife serving biscuits and tea, I outlined my brilliant plan to send a delegation to the Department of Environment while briefing our local Member of Parliament with questions aimed at embarrassing the government.

At the back, near the paint ladders and tarps that still cluttered our ground floor, a local Trot I recognized from the meeting that had thrown me out stood up. "Who appointed you Prime Minister of Southwark?" he demanded. A Tory woman said we needed a nuclear deterrent. A Social Democrat refused to work with the Trotskyist. A woman with an Irish accent asked where we stood on Troops out of Ulster. A man with a Kensington accent accused her of fomenting strife by calling Northern Ireland by its imperialist label. Older, calmer Labour Party types made constructive but boring suggestions. Dick Slocum, our across-the-street neighbor, a plump property developer who chaired a key committee on the local council, wondered why we had to operate "anarchistically" outside the established political structure. (Dick, an old pal from New Commitment, was married to a feminist who had created a tabloid sensation by suckling her infant at a Westminster Abbey investiture.) A local youth who announced he was a real anarchist suggested a small nuclear accident might be "jolly good publicity" for the cause.

And of course, a middle-aged man, dressed differently from us, in a formal fifties-style suit with starched collar, called for the floor. Aha, a worker. He dropped a bombshell by reading a resolution from the local branch of the National Union of Railwaymen denouncing us for planning to sit down in front of oncoming trains, thereby causing undue stress, perhaps death by accident, to "me and my colleagues, who, may I remind you, are the ones who actually do the manual labor of shifting the nation's goods." Total, intimidated silence for a moment.

Tactfully, I noted the NUR delegate's resolution and tried to pass on to the next item. Whereupon one of the Labour Trots snarled, "Why are you patronizing the comrade worker?" The Social Democrat took issue with the Trot, which gave Dick Slocum a chance to slag off the Social Democrat, whose whimpering was interrupted by one of the Greens calling Dick "fatso," which horrified the Tory lady and caused Dick to stomp out with some of his friends, which more or less collapsed the meeting since the Trots, hastily caucusing, also decided that my methods were "hypocritical bourgeois democracy." Suddenly, the house emptied. Helen and I stood at the door, urging everyone to come back next week, but knew they wouldn't. O Polly, you'd be ashamed of your son.

When they'd gone Helen made us both gin and bitters, and we sat in our bare front room on the couch staring out at the night-strewn street. "I'm sorry," I said, "I tried, I really did." We touched glasses and drank. She gestured out there. "This," she said, "isn't quite your scene, is it, Gus?" She turned her large blue eyes on me seriously. "So then, what is?"

The 1970s was no time for a Marxshire marriage. We didn't yet know it, but the social contract was being not rewritten but torn up. We Marxshiremen continued to live as if the gentlemen's agreement by which most West European governments survived, with a mildly socialist state agreeably supervising a mildly restrained capitalism, would last forever. Since we knew Marxshire folk flourished no matter who was in power, we had no reason to assess the real strength of the "forces of reaction" that, hating our guts, had been quietly planning revenge since 1945. From a great height, we laughed at Mrs. Thatcher's beehive hairdo and splendidly bad dresses, even—God help us— her lower-middle-class origins. If "she" was the best our deadly enemies could throw against us, we were safe. So why not mortgage ourselves to a system that might, perhaps, require a bit of tinkering here or there but had proven, over the years, that it was blessed with an inbuilt self-correcting mechanism?

Marxshire prospered exactly as had Pompeii.

"Cheap shot," said Helen, especially upset when I kidded her about the presence of the "good names" who seemed to set a certain moneyed tone in our movement dedicated to the poor and downtrodden. For some reason, the collateral branches of the same families that ran Britain from the top appeared on the letterheads of organizations that defended the bottom. Plus we were also talking about her best friend, Emma Gore-Templeton.

Helen was Emma's shadow, or vice versa. Maybe spirit-ghost is a better word. The fact of Helen freed Emma to go beyond Helen, so consumed by self-doubt and second guesses. Every step my Helen—so outwardly bold and self-confident—took was slowed by the torture of self-negation. Emma, used to blotting up—exploiting?—other people's wayward energies, easily appropriated Helen's dark, doubting electricity. Creatively speaking, they were twins.

Curious, this. Rose, too, had had a shadow Rose to fuel her career. She kept me away from her second half, Kate Lewisohn, who owned an antique shop and was consumed by literary ambition but had no talent. Several times a week Rose and Kate met for tea, and spoke daily by phone, long confidences from which I was strictly excluded. Rose told me this was because she feared I would run off with Kate, but the real reason was that Kate was her most private property.

Slowly I saw that Kate was Rose's money in the bank, someone who had, at all costs, to be kept in the shadows if Rose was to survive creatively. Kate, stumpy legs firmly stuck in the earth, always head to head with her customers and suppliers, had several functions, not least as an extra pair of eyes and conduit for gossip, and a double-check on the reality Rose was always afraid she might lose hold of. Is it possible to keep a Siamese twin in the closet?

Helen was fairly clear-eyed about Emma but also fiercely, tenaciously loyal. Only in private did we joke about Marxshire's class divisions, the predominance of those good names, and the curious fact that money, and its social station, spoke with thunderous authority among us, too.

Especially when backed by a feminist analysis.

Emma, one of the reigning princesses of the Old New Left, had moved into women's liberation to do what she'd been prevented from doing by us male New Comers, take charge. It was her birthright.

The Gore-Templetons had been supplying England's elite since Henry VIII rewarded his henchmen with huge landholdings stolen from anti-Reformation Catholics. Lord Ranulph, who had entertained Billie Stoutheart and me at his Northamptonshire estate, the size of Rhode Island, was Emma's uncle. Another Gee-Tee was currently the Queen's equerry, yet another the Conservative whip in the House of Lords. But Emma refused the guilt that made most top-drawer Marxshiremen and women cringe when reminded of their advantages. Not for her the tormented shame of other rich feminists. "I am not," she said briskly, "going to waste my time blubbing over something I couldn't prevent: namely, being born into the exploiting class. The thing is to *do* something about it, no?"

As naturally as cream rising to the top, Emma had ascended to her rightful place at the head table with other British feminist stars like Germaine Greer and Juliet Mitchell. There, by hard work and much writing, she'd carved out a niche as an "explicator" (her word) of radical feminist doctrine; unlike Greer, Emma didn't flirt with her audiences while condemning the ideology of flirtation. She was direct, ham-handed, honest. She wrote with an instinctive, almost superhuman badness, combining the worst of angry Marxism and clumsy academese, and lectured so opaquely that her reputation as a thinker was unassailable. A "psychohistorian" committed to reclaiming "lost women"—female doctors, scientists, writers, even wives and mistresses whose achievements were forgotten or ignored by male-oriented scholarship—she fought, as an Inner London Authority education governor, to feed her views into the under-sixteen school system. She was in the great British bluestocking tradition, and I'd loathed her on sight.

Emma "spoke for" my own generation of New Commitment women whom she claimed we guys had made invisible and second-class. Thus, she was out to even the score and repair a historical crime against gender. But revenge, even historical reclamation, can have unintended effects; Emma was in danger of becoming one of the "men" of feminism, heavy and unforgiving. Nobody is more male-oriented than a woman who feels misused by men.

Emma's grating voice, confident bearing, and argumentative style were softened by a brilliant, all-receiving smile and a dress sense that made even Rose O'Malley look like a Dior model, endearingly awful hippie beads-and-fringe ankle-length dresses rotated with cavernously baggy overalls. But of course I never commented on Emma's getups; with her broad shoulders and strong arms she'd have laid me out flat.

Helen hated my making fun of Emma, with whom she'd roomed at Cambridge in the early sixties. At college, Helen recalled, "we screamed at each other for the whole three years. It wasn't that she felt superior to me, only she wouldn't let me feel inferior to her. I'll always be grateful to her for that. She's my other half—it will take a lifetime to work out if it's the better or worse half."

When Emma, who missed my Helen and did her strenuous best to be fond of me, moved into bachelor digs in Southwark to be near her soul sister, I redoubled my efforts to find something to like about her, if only to please Helen. With application it wasn't too hard, partly because there was so much of myself in Emma. "You don't fancy her, do you?" Helen asked nervously, exactly as Rose had grilled me about Kate Lewisohn.

I laughed. What a question. But didn't think to notice Helen and I were coming apart at the seams.

The high fever had crested, the radical tide was ebbing. Without the support of hectic all-night meetings and the nourishing stress of overcommitment, without the external violence of police charges at demos, we were getting stranded on our own private island.

Neither of us was aware of it at the time. Emma, bless 'er 'eart, smarter than mine in this case, tried to warn me. "The movement is losing strength, Gus. I can feel it in my bones. There's a backlash starting out there. Perhaps the younger women can take it on full strength, but Helen and I are getting of an age, as they say. We may

soon have to start thinking of ourselves as women as well as feminists."

What did that mean? I should have paid more attention,
because when Emma abruptly got married, to a stuffy, bowler-
hatted barrister, and announced she was pregnant, it came as a
shattering blow to Helen. "Come on," I said, "we were the first to
settle down, Emma is just playing copycat." But Helen knew better.

Looking around, Helen saw how many of her women friends,
including several who'd been radical feminists and lesbians, were
enthusiastically tying the knot ... to men. Emma simply was part of
a wholesale charge into marital domesticity of an intensity that left
Helen and me far behind. Helen began to feel isolated in a range of
feminist feelings that her sisters were fast abandoning in practice.
"Look," I said to my wife, "I've been there before." It had happened
to me in the fifties, when many of my American friends sidestepped
McCarthyism by embracing marriage as a secular religion. Helen,
bridling at my Wise Old Man pose, complained, "Everything I ever
do you've done before. If I gave birth, you'd lecture me about your
labor pains."

Babies.

They were starting to sprout like mushrooms all over the Movement, almost as a political statement. Emma and I even joked about
it. "I'm preggers," Emma admitted, "for the same reason Israeli
peace workers volunteer for combat. It helps my credibility."

"You of all people don't need that," I pointed out.

"Can't you see?" Emma said. "The struggle is entering a new
stage. Longer, more difficult and complex. This"—she complacently
patted her enlarged tummy—"is my foxhole."

But Helen and I had no foxhole.

BOOK 4

SOFT MONEY

A *Channel-blown wind snipes rain at the window where I stand,*
emperor of La Finca sin Sol. Not only a room of my own but a whole
floor-through, courtesy of Helen's insistence that I not feel claustro-
phobic in my own home. What was Hemingway's prospect? My views,
back and front, command a city I have presumably conquered. It's all
here. Another novel in my still-portable Corona typewriter. A file cabi-
net full of BBC payment vouchers. A pile of books to review. Revolu-
tionary posters on the wall, mementos of battles last fought at
Grosvenor Square, Red Lion Square, Ridley Road, the Embankment
(a real trap, they hammered us underneath the arches). My knee hurts
when it rains, I'd left part of a shinbone on the sidewalk outside St
Pancras Town Hall. A rent strike, was it? I'd climbed to the top of the
town hall spire and raised a red flag—even the police were afraid to
chase me that high. What a glorious view, the whole of London spread
out at my feet on a sunny day. The melee from above, just like now. All
I need to complete the picture of Retired Radical Writer is leather
patched elbows and a pipe. Is this the end of Rico?

Life went on at 23 Vicarage Terrace. The House, after its repairs and
"doing up" and dreadful first experiences with the neighbors, settled down like an animal in slumber. Helen got in a few pieces of
genuine firsthand furniture, we installed central heating (hooray!),
and through a Disability Grant (my broken shinbone) from the
local "loony leftie" council, we made improvements including a real
bathroom. I began to feel like, well, an Owner. Daytimes, leaning

over my front garden fence, I waited for the postman (Henry Travers in *It's a Wonderful Life*) for a good chinwag, waited for the local bobby (Jack Warner in *The Blue Lamp*) to stroll by with a cheery "Mornin', all," waited above all for a new, solid Gus Black to take over from the old restless neurotic. Waited and waited.

In Los Angeles there is a major industry that is hardly ever mentioned in the same breath as movies and aerospace but may account for even more of the GNP: education. With its many layers of schools and colleges, California is one big education factory, egalitarian and business-oriented at the same time. In contrast to Britain, even the poor, if they can pony up a couple hundred dollars, can go on to some form of higher education.

UCLA, USC, Pepperdine, Loyola Marymount, Pomona and Claremont and UC Irvine and Riverside and all the other local private and public educorporations collect and spend billions of dollars, employ thousands of staff, embark on ambitious building programs—and are hardly ever perceived as part of the "power elite." Yet it didn't take a Marxist with a cracked shinbone to see, for example, that a large number of L.A.-based managers, bosses, top lawyers, editors in chief, CEOs, TV station owners, and investment gurus either had gone to these schools or felt, for reasons of sentiment or civic rectitude or self-interest, a close connection to the proximate campuses. Collectively, the universities—my Marxshire mind rummaged around its dusty vocabulary—function hegemonically to perpetuate a prevailing ideology that almost never challenges, and is usually in strong support of, a capitalist consensus.

Then there are places like San Andreas State.

"I agree," crackled the transatlantic voice on my telephone at 23 Vicarage Terrace, "that San Andreas State sounds more like a nervous breakdown than a proper university. Indeed, our students refer to us as High Anxiety U or some such, either because of our perilous proximity to the fault line or the way we manage their academic affairs. Your reputation for taking risks precedes you. May I tempt you to join us as a Visiting Distinguished Teacher for a few weeks?"

The siren song was sung by the improbably named Luther Luck, chairman of the Cinema Studies Department of SAS, as he called San Andreas State. Professor Luck claimed to be a fan of my writing and wanted to have lunch with me. Wasn't it an expensive way of meeting authors he liked? I asked. "Oh no," Luther Luck responded, "we have all this soft money, you see."

"Soft money," Luck explained, was cash, not built into the budget, that could be spent at his discretion.

My instincts told me (a) that Luck was an operator, and (b) to keep away from academia.

"I'm sorry, Dr. Luck, but I tried teaching once and nearly got my brains blown out." Dear Mildred in Detroit. Too dangerous.

"Yes, I heard that you didn't exactly distinguish yourself," Luck said. "On the other hand, San Andreas State is not a very distinguished school. But I am authorized to pay you ten thousand dollars for three weeks' presence on our beautiful hillside campus—what would that be in terms of a declining English pound? Plus, this is my best offer, something most Angelenos would kill for: a parking pass."

This guy was diabolical. He had two-thousand-mile-long ears—just how much had he heard about Detroit?—and he must know that the BBC and *Vogue* combined paid me a fraction of what he was offering.

"And," he threw in, "it would mean your returning to Los Angeles—the place that nearly killed you twenty years ago. Be warned: it may still be a Venus flytrap for those it missed the first time."

How did Luther Luck know a Rocket never refuses a dare?

"What do they want you to teach?" asked Helen, legs tucked under her on the couch. Her smile was tense.

"I forgot to ask," I said.

"Americans!" She tried to make a joke. Then she cocked her head her head a little defiantly. "Go ahead, Gus. You might even enjoy it. And we could use the money."

"Why are you trying to get rid of me?" I said.

"I'm not," Helen said and pulled me down to kiss me. "I'm trying to save our marriage."

In his office, whose enormous picture window overlooked a step-tiered campus that appeared to be made of plaster of paris and Astroturf, my temporary boss Luther Luck shrugged when I asked what I would be teaching. "You'll think of something," he smiled. He was wrong.

My first SAS class reminded me of my first BBC live broadcast. To ease my nerves, I'd stayed up all night and arrived at the Portland Place studio with a clumsy sheaf of notes, and just after the green light flashed, Clive James barked, "And here is Gus Black to read us through the night with, if I am not mistaken, Marcel Proust's *Remembrance of Things Past*, or is that *War and Peace* you're about to launch into, Gus Black?" Mortified, I threw my notes to the floor and said the first thing that came into my head: "You're a right superior Ozzie bastard, Clive James." (The BBC is a stickler for both names.) And my reputation was made because, as the assistant director general noted to his subordinate who passed it on to Third Programme which talked to Talks-Features which dropped a word with Arts (Live) which relayed it to me, "We *expect* Americans to behave like that. Use him again."

At least Clive James and I spoke the same language: Beebish. The SAS students and I shared apparently nothing. One look at their fresh, open, less than inquiring faces and I froze. But, as she often did, Polly Black came to my rescue. In mining camps, textile mills, on sidewalk picket lines and in smoked-up meeting halls, I'd never, ever, seen Mom at a loss for words in public. Nothing surprised her or put her off her stride, not even sudden violence. (Once I'd seen her put her body between a striker and a scab wielding a large pair of shears. "Weren't you afraid, Ma?" "What's to be afraid? The scab knows I know her address.")

I knew, or thought I knew, my students' address.

They were a strange student body. Because of their opaque language, which consisted of coded words like "peer group" and "lifestyle," "comedic" and "self-esteem," and my total ignorance of their minds, I had to follow them, sometimes literally, to their homes to get a handle on who I was dealing with. Overseas students aside, most SAS enrollees came from a Los Angeles I hadn't a clue to: Simi valley, Santa Clarita, Alhambra, Pomona, Flintridge–La Canada, the featureless plains beyond San Fernando, San Gabriel, and Orange County, concentric rings of de-urbs hemming in Los Angeles County. There was a there there and they lived there but I wasn't there.

Something had changed. The vast postwar sprawl had become even more detached from recognizable reality. Ten-thousand-dollar tract homes on a GI mortgage were one thing. The winding strips of red-tiled "developments" that now threatened to strangle L.A.—all those Grecian temple Aztec altar French chateau Tara Swiss chalet English country home three-bedroom three-bathroom six hundred thou and up (let's say a million) pet cemeteries—had to be, well, what? They talk about black illiteracy, do they know about suburban illiteracy? How could a white middle-class kid from the outer suburbs connect with anything short of a science-fiction novel?

Now, for the first time, I understood why most of my students related only to sci-fi. Asimov, Bradbury, and Arthur Clarke were our first de-urb writers. All honor to them.

And, catch this, it was no longer the bohemians and pretend poets who took screenwriting and Film and Film Politics (my course) but the Dekes and Kappa Sigs and Zeebeetees and Sigmanus—the frat boys. In L.A. terms, a Cinema Studies degree was better than an M.B.A.

What had I got myself into?

"Your future?" Luther said.

Because more than half my students were female, Luther pushed an inch-thick departmental memo into my hands. "Sexual harassment policy. Read it—it will self-destruct in ten seconds. Try not to go up in flames with it," said Luther, an old *Mission Impossible* addict.

I saw no real problem. Women students did not come on to you if you didn't to them. But what should a new teacher do about the charge of electricity that flew around the classroom and seemed a natural function of the business of infiltrating, and being infiltrated by, young minds?

"Nothing. Do nothing about it," commanded Luther.

Easy for him. He had a gorgeous new wife in Marina Del Rey.

But there was a feminist problem here too. By the time I arrived at SAS, the first radical women's liberation wave had receded. As in England, a lot of cutting-edge feminists were tired and exhausted. Their "daughters" might have been born on Krypton, so little did many of them know about the struggles of the recent past. Yet, invigorated by a legacy of whose source they were ignorant, my women students took up the old battle in ways never intended or predicted, more narrowly focused on personal ambition.

Part of the legacy was anger, a quasipolitical edginess at "patriarchy," at the inevitable putdowns and sexism—and sexiness—encountered on dates, in the workplace, in the family. A small number of my women students went out of their way to provoke male behavior that they then had a wonderful time condemning. My boy students were wary, confused, alternately macho and "sensitive."

More than one came into my office to ask plaintively, "What do they want?" I told them Freud had asked the same question, and they asked what films he had directed.

Is this like saying that women who dress well provoke rape? No. Did these young, attractive women emit subtle messages to men they knew were not terribly educated to feminism but on whom they depended to rise to the bait with a pass, a word, a suggestion? You betcha.

I was a hit. No Mildreds this time. So many students signed up for my course that Luther Luck asked me to stay on for another, full semester. Forget it, I said, I was no Mr. Chips. Luther said, "No danger. Your student evaluations leave much to be desired. Even so, SAS is a 'revenue-generating, profit-driven institution'—I quote from its fund-raising brochure—and students find you a soft option. How does forty thousand dollars sound?"

Gulp. For three months' work I was getting a year's worth of British salary. I rang Helen, who was cool but not discouraging.

"Stay if you're enjoying yourself. I'll fly out to visit you. How's that?"

Good Helen.

And good Luther Luck.

Luther's office, with its spectacular view of the 405 freeway as it crested between Beverly Hills and the San Fernando valley—SAS's joke name was Mount Saint Mulholland—became my second home in L.A. He hadn't been kidding about taking on odds and bods he wanted to have lunch with. The half of the department he had been responsible for hiring was as eccentric and inexperienced as I was; the others were Ph.D.'s whom Luther simply chose to ignore. "Film courses are by their nature oxymoronic. How can you intellectually justify going to the movies? It's nonsense. But a pleasant way of earning one's keep, don't you agree?"

I didn't get Luther. A small, tidy, balding man in a Brooks Brothers suit and conservative bow tie, he glowed with a sort of cheerful despair. Normally I was a quick study on people, but by the time I departed SAS I'd learned little more about him aside from his taste in books—his shelves were lined with biographies of film directors he admired, and he had written half a dozen of them himself—and his relaxed comments about England, where he periodically took digs near the British Museum to do research. He liked to talk, eat, and drink, yet there were fences. Made of iron, I was to learn.

By inference, and a few hints discreetly dropped in our modest drinking sessions, I learned that he had been to Vietnam. As near as I could deduce, he had been wounded on patrol, returned to make a documentary about his old platoon, then "retired" to academia to write books. He became almost angry if I pressed him further.

What sort of American was this?

Once, slightly in my cups, I asked him.

He just stared at me. "An American who stayed," was all he said.

Jews "return" to the Promised Land. General MacArthur said, "I shall return" to the Philippines, and did. War veterans go back to old battlefields. But the age of discount air fares has discounted the romance of exile. All you have to do is pay a few hundred dollars at a Piccadilly bucket shop, land at LAX a day later, rent a car, and you're an American again. No ghosts, bands, or flowers, no Penelope embracing Ulysses. Yet.

Hadn't anybody noticed I'd been away?

I blame gays for what happened next. Somebody has to bear the guilt.

Engels or somebody once said, "Being determines consciousness." So do sweaters.

Most of the year in England you freeze and shiver under layers of wool, which is the only way to survive Anglo-Saxon winters, or even the so-called summers. Under L.A.'s blazing sun, near-heatstroke forced me to shed my

corduroy jacket
viyella shirt
thermal underwear including longjohns
cavalry twill trousers
long wool socks
Yorkshire fell walking shoes

and go native, stripping to a pair of Hawaiian shorts, T-shirt, and huaraches. Suddenly I had to cope with the lusts of an unburdened torso. My flesh was on fire with freedom.

From my dirty louvered windows at the Alhambra Gardens, a fifties-style Spanish courtyard-with-swimming-pool in West Hollywood, I had a panoramic view of my past and present. Over there, beyond Trumps and Morton's, was my last American apartment, where the FBI tails Mutt and Jeff had camped out waiting for me to "come in, they all do sooner or later." And up on Sunset Boulevard, shadows of an older, more raffish Hollywood, the Benedict Talent Agency, Ciro's, Scandia, Mocambo, Garden of Allah (or rather, the parking lots and Big Mac that had replaced them).

Best of all, F. Scott Fitzgerald's apartment on North Laurel was one street over, a reminder of who I was in my best self. Ben Hecht, Thomas Mann, Raymond Chandler, Theodore Dreiser, Dorothy Parker, John O'Hara, and Faulkner all had lived around here at one time or another. And they say L.A. isn't a literary town. So they'd come to grab the money and run. Was I any different?

Sociologically, West Hollyood is a sliver of L.A. County lying inside the body of Los Angeles like an overactive spleen. Once an enclave cleverly zoned for nightclubs and brothels, today it's an independent little city at the epicenter of a line drawn from Paramount Pictures to the Polo Lounge, Aldous Huxley's Hollywood Hills home to the much-diminished 20th Century-Fox back lot. Instead of hoodlums and whorehouse madams, West Hollywood's leaders are politically aware gays (forty percent) and old geezers, or "seniors."

Gays and the power of suggestion.

Down on Santa Monica Boulevard, on Melrose, on the Strip and down by Fairfax, up by San Vicente and all through the woman-named streets of East Beverly Hills, I could see, actually see, grown men kissing, necking, hugging, embracing, sucking, and bellyfuck-ing … each other. Ku-ryst. But there it was, undeniable fingerlickin' Kentucky Fried chicken homosapiens assholeboring flagrant brazen right out in the open making out. You can't, you just can't, see all this stuff going on around you without some little coiled spring in you springing erect with a blaaaang! Monkey sees, mon-key does.

Time: Early 1980s. *Scene:* Venice, California. The stone jetty at the foot of Rose Avenue. A smog-red November sun bleeds into the waterline, a purple haze off the Santa Monica mountains snuffs out last light. As usual a straggle of regular sunset-watchers on the beach commune with the dying sun god.

Hands rammed deep in my last remaining wool lumberjacket (it's what passes for winter in L.A.), I notice a girl bundled up in a tufted sweat outfit and hood. At a distance I've seen her before, but now she's standing almost next to me on the high-tide mark, looking out to sea from behind enormous shades.

Uh-*huh.* I exhaled an audible sigh. "Makes you think twice about being an atheist, doesn't it?"

She kept gazing at the exact point where the blood-drenched sun sank under the surf. It had been my best shot. I was out of practice; I was a husband.

Then she turned slowly, took off her dark glasses, deliberately folded them into an inside pocket of her gray parka. She'd been so hidden by clothes and reflecting shades I'd expected a classic California beach blonde. She was black.

She cocked her head exactly like Gloria Grahame does at Humphrey Bogart in *In a Lonely Place.* "Frankly," she breathed, "I thought you'd never ask."

Holy moley, she was one of my students.

Biology couples most men to women. History drives me into their arms. Marci Washington, behind the looming shades on Venice beach, was the last in a long line of attempts to hook up with the people who often hated me the most.

Be careful, said my heart. All over America female students were suing their teachers. Until now, I'd felt insulated because I (a) was a passing stranger, and (b) instantly detumesced on reading their essays.

Luther Luck had warned me to keep a professional distance between myself and the gorgeous young blondes in my lecture classes. But he hadn't mentioned dark beauties who were single-parent mothers of twenty-year-old sons and had "attitude."

At thirty-nine, Marci was fiercely focused on breaking into Hollywood as a writer-director-producer. Anything, *anything,* that got in her way was contemptible, including me at times. She hated my showing *Birth of a Nation* as an example of white racism in the history of film. "You just don't understand these California pecker-heads, Teach," she warned me on our first date. "They see that shit and think it's great art." "Well, it is," I said. "Do you know how many Nee-groes"—she curled her lip at the word—"got lynched as a result of the race riots after the premiere of Griffith's atrocity, you fool?" she almost spat. As a matter of fact I did. "Then you're not only dumb"—she stood up—"you're a fucking asshole." And swept out of the beachside cafe, followed by the stares of patrons marveling, as I did, at this light brown explosion of loveliness.

I hadn't felt this way toward a woman since Helen slapped me on our first date.

It really began, as many good things do, with an apology. She slipped into my office a few afternoons later to say, "I take it back—you're not an asshole."

"Just dumb?" I said.

"Look." She slumped into a seat near my desk. "You don't know what it's like to be an overage black woman student on scholarship in a classroom with kids half my age—my son's age—who drive Porsche Carreras and treat me like some dusky belle out of *Gone With the Wind*."

"Hold on," I said. "There are a few other black students on campus, and none of them has reported any racial harassment or insults."

"You don't get it, do you?" she said.

"Well," I said, biting my own hook, "why don't you teach me?"

Marci Washington—high school dropout, former actress, agent's secretary, and catering assistant—was my first black woman. Billie Stoutheart, the London model who finally married a baron ("My brither had his heart set on a duke, but this bloke's estate is closer to Lunnon, was I raght?"), did not quite count since she could not have cared less about color. Marci Washington was old enough to have gone south as a SNCC volunteer in the sixties, and had a broken right arm set at a slightly askew angle, courtesy an Alabama deputy's baton, to prove it. She held that arm like a shield of honor.

In a way, Marci reminded me of Rose O'Malley—the fierce inner heat, the indignation, and (as luck would have it) no problems about taking me into parts of this new country most other writers couldn't reach.

"Watts? No big deal," she said. "I was born in that armpit."

Scene: Nickerson Gardens, a black Beirut in South Central L.A., the ghetto, or "the community." Nickerson is a housing project notorious for violence and gang killings. My guide, Marci, raised here, slowly drives me through the low-rise estate while I take notes for one of the BBC Alastair Cooke–style *Letters from L.A.* I record weekly in the KABC radio studio. The boiling sun makes Nickerson a pressure cooker. I'm in my academic disguise, horn-rim glasses and Harris tweed jacket. (Luther Luck likes me looking "English.") Marci is in an off-shoulder embroidered blouse, thin rayon skirt, and sandals. She has the compact build and easy grace of a club dancer, which she once was. We're in my rented T-bird, air conditioning on full blast.

Marci looked over her shoulder. "I'm antsy, Teach."

Still scribbling, I didn't look up. "How come? This is your turf, you said."

Marci said, "Was. Back then nobody could afford armament."

Noticing a group of lounging black boys up ahead, I put away my notebook.

The black youths moved into the street, blocking our way. Marci slowed the shiny black T-bird to a crawl. "Oh shit," she said.

We were surrounded. Marci muttered, "Whatever you do, don't roll down the window." Her knuckles were almost white on the wheel.

One of the boys leaned down and knocked on Marci's window, gesturing her to open it. Two others, wearing Michael Jackson jackets and red bandannas and cornrows, stood in front of the car, admiring it. In fact, they were all wearing something red: Bloods territory. Were whites considered Crips?

Marci, softly: "Brace yourself, Pops. This is gonna be hit-and-run."

Alarmed, I said that was vehicular manslaughter.

She said, "Them or us, old man." Her controlled, mature-student front had dropped. Even her accent changed.

One of the boys climbed onto the long hood and pointed his finger at us like a gun. Stealthily, Marci shifted into lower gear for a rubber-burning getaway.

"That's one dead nigger in a second," Marci murmured.

"No, don't!"

Marci turned a look of pure contempt on me. With deadly force she said, "You crazy white cocksucker—they're gonna waste us."

And then, of course, the overheated Thunderbird stalled.

The boys' leader leaned down, one hand on the door handle, and said through the closed window, "Anything we c'n help with, you li'l golden peach?"

Marci put on a bright smile and rolled down the window a small inch. "Ah'm Marzi, Miz Washington's gul. Over on Imperial."

The lean, silk-shirted leader, with the most elaborate cornrow hairdo of all, said easily, "Can't say I know th' lady." He tried to open our car door.

Marci spoke quickly. "Mama died. Nobody in house. Jes' takin' this john there. You dig?"

The boy jiggled the locked door handle a bit, then decided:

"Whyn't you say so?" He called out to his pals, "She jes' fuckin' his ass for bread." To Marci: "But we need some too, Golden Peach."

Marci, pure sex now: "Later, man. Ah'm sure we come to a private arrangement."

The boy leader laughed. He bent down, wet his finger, reached in through the window crack, and let her kiss it. "Y'all come back real soon now," he mimicked, lazily withdrawing his hand as she rolled up the window again.

Smiling coolly, he backed off. The others reluctantly climbed off the car, their eyes still on us as prey.

I hissed, "Start the fucking car."

Marci, in control now: "Shut your mouth."

After a couple of tries, she sparked the ignition and nodded pleasantly to the boys, who stepped back just a little to let us pass within inches of their bodies, contemptuous toreadors.

As we turned the corner, I said with total relief, "Good thinking, Marci. You get an A for the day."

Marci let the car pick up a little speed as she looked for a quick exit. Then she glanced over at me. "I just saved your shivering li'l ass, Teach. You gonna do a lot better than that."

I did, too.

A true story: Kimberly was twenty-one and "functionally illiterate" despite a high SAT score. She'd hung around me after class all semester, talking about a subject common to a number of my students, her dad's cruel abandonment of her (i.e., his recent divorce and remarriage), and the "Wicked Witch of the West" (her stepmother).

When I kept giving Kimberly low marks for poor work, she protested by resubmitting, uncorrected, her last essay about one of the films I'd shown, Paul Jarrico's strike classic *Salt of the Earth*. I had asked all the students to "compare and contrast" a film of their choice with its present-day real-life analogue. For her term topic, to see if sweatshop conditions still existed, Kimberly had gone downtown to the Cooper Building, a fashion mart, and after shopping all day reported that she had seen only happy employees.

"Did you speak to anyone, even a salesperson, about job conditions or wages?" I asked. "No, but I could tell," Kimberly said. "Kim," I joked, "have you ever heard of the class struggle?" "What's that?" this cinema studies/sociology fourth-year double major asked. "Are you kidding?" I said. Next day she filed with the dean of students a charge of "verbal sexual harassment" against me.

When I told this tale to Marci Washington she nearly fell out of bed laughing. "Oh, man, will you never learn? These middle-class white chicks don't want a Socratic dialogue with you. And they don't really want your body either. They just like to see how far they can push you."

The problem, I complained to Marci, was that the women students weren't liberated enough. If they had a feminist critique, it would establish, for me, an intimidating ethical norm that would regulate, even censor, any careless needling I was inclined to aim at both men and women students but that women were predisposed to resent more.

"Oh, that's easy," Marci assured me. "Just tell your students that their final grade depends on how emancipated they get. In no time at all you'll have a classroom full of little Betty Friedans—and then you'll *really* have problems."

L.A. was amazing. You could order miracles, like a phone within twenty-four hours when it took up to twelve months in parts of central London. The beach was half an hour's drive, and there was a heated swimming pool downstairs. And Marci. Too much. Only Helen could rescue me.

But she couldn't come right away. The government department for which she worked was being heavily Thatcherized by the new woman Prime Minister, and Helen had to stay to fight for her job as a senior economist. About my L.A. euphoria, an exultance-hysteria of almost medical proportions, she was as usual calmly understanding. "Come home when you like, Gus. Don't stay in America for the money. It's not worth it. If you're unhappy, get on a plane, and you know I'll be there to meet you. Aren't I always?"

She didn't get it.

Just then Luther, my American father and Mephistopheles, offered me another three months at SAS. Given the state of Britain's economy, I really could not afford to say no, could I?

This time he wanted something in return. "Just once, come to a faculty meeting. You have faced fascist bayonets. This will be a piece of cake."

After the meeting, Luther found me dazed in the men's bathroom staring at my face in a mirror. He stood at the next mirror enjoying my predicament. "What's this?" he asked, cheerily adjusting his bow tie. "Speechless and unsure of yourself? You should try us again on a day when we're not trying so hard to be collegial."

Then he pulled a corker. "You know, I'm not very political, which you must find slightly dull. Why don't I arrange a lunch between you and SAS's best-known other socialist?"

I grunted assent, and the next day I was at a Faculty Lounge table with America's most famous left-wing renegade, Webster Wallach.

All over Western Europe, I'd encountered leftists who had fled the fold for New Philosophy, Nouvelle Politique, Nuovo Pensiero— "schools" of disillusioned fish swimming through a Marxist net now so full of raggedy holes a whale the size of Mount Everest could wriggle through. Curiously, Britain saw less of this, since the English (as opposed to Scots, Irish, and Welsh) are genetically indisposed to theory, and because the Labour Party, rickety as it was, had not lost all credibility. What particularized many of these New Thought intellectuals was a bile against old comrades and, by implication, their own previous lives. Long ago I realized I'd never make a pukka intellectual, when I left the Communist Party and found it impossible to give up my Stalinist friends. They are as much a part of my life as all the errors, crimes, and mistakes I have committed.

Webster Wallach was a lesson to me in rigorously principled behavior.

By a certain age, we are responsible for our faces, it's said. If so, life had played a cruel joke on Webster Wallach, SAS's dean of the Communications School. Potbellied, goateed, with wet lips and Coke bottle eyes, Webster looked like John Belushi's idea of an East European Communist apparatchik, a power-mad wimp with a ruthlessly macho intellect. "Come on, Gus," Webster protested mildly, "I've fathered four children from three wives. Who's got the balls, you or me?"

Webster was the U.S. radical movement's favorite turncoat. Mention his name (as I had) to the ordinary sixties survivor, even those no longer active, and the response was dramatic and instant: "That rodent!" or at best, "Fucking Benedict Arnold!" Once a fanatic revolutionary, notorious for his platform screaming manner and affinity for the most obscure Marxist sects, he had turned on his former comrades with joyous venom. Currently his chief hobby was pursuing the left in the media, "left" being anyone who disagreed with his born-again Republicanism.

"You disappoint me, Gus, you really do. It's so banal for you left-ists to keep accusing me of being the same narrow-minded doctri-naire I admittedly was as a radical. The struggle to free my mind of its Marxist chains also liberated me from the necessity of being a hangman. I guarantee: once we cleanse the press, television, and the arts of their liberal subversives, you'll be surprised at how laid back I'll be."

Webster, who had switched sides but not temperaments, was a Whittaker Chambers who had not quite found his Alger Hiss, I told him over the Faculty Lounge's chicken tostada, otherwise known as "Salmonella Special."

"Ah, so they've got to you too, have they?" he smiled almost blissfully.

Webster was a hater. Life without grudge was unthinkable; it provided the fuel cells of his considerable brain. He was one of the least neurotic people I'd ever met. Hatred was his balance wheel. Literally, he loved hating. With reason. Like many of us on the left who have personal cause for disillusionment, Webster had an iron-clad case. In the sixties he and his sister had harbored some Weath-erpeople who persuaded the sister to collaborate in a bank robbery during which she was shot to death by FBI agents who had set it up as a sting. Webster's best friend, it turned out, was a police informer, and when Webster denounced him, the left denounced Webster. Not only denounced him but turned him in to the authori-ties in one of those classic New York factions-within-factions betrayals. Instead of going crazy, Webster patiently constructed, over a period of time, a coherent politics of disillusionment. The questions he asked—had the anti-Vietnam protest movement caused unnecessary deaths in Cambodia? did the left romanticize pure thuggery disguised as revolutionary violence (Panthers, SLA, etc.)? was Ronald Reagan, the recently elected U.S. president, quite the idiot he seemed? even, was the Russian Revolution really "nec-essary"?—were worth asking. In this sense, Webster was the ghost in my own closet, acting out my own doubts and persisting trau-mas. Webster's great virtue was that he had jumped the ideological fence so cleanly that his "position" was never marred by a single doubt. It was a relief once again being with a true believer.

Luther Luck, who professed political indifference but could hardly contain his loathing of Webster, was horrified by my regular lunches with him, which struck Luther as arrant disloyalty to my younger self. Luther underestimated Webster's fascination for me: I'd never known anybody quite so physically repellent who gloried in his ugliness.

"My most recent wife says we shouldn't have a kid because he might look like me and have her brains." He grinned with real pleasure. In private, Webster smiled a lot, if only from the delight he took in his present life. Aside from an academic paycheck, he made a bundle lecturing right-wing groups about the "liberal menace," accepting American Heritage or American Enterprise Institute grants to purge this PBS station or that public theater of its Red taint.

Of course, Webster's nonacademic books described, in Pentacostal detail, his evil past life: "I was an ideology abuser the way some men abuse drugs," he smirked. (Webster was a great smirker.) He was expert at forgiving himself, if not others. "You peaceniks and protestors," he murmured—Webster rarely raised his voice except in a paid lecture—"are responsible for the deaths of millions, no, tens of millions, of innocent people, from the gulags to the killing fields of Phnom Penh. Gus, their blood is on your hands." All said with a sweet, wet, comradely smile of real friendship.

Lunching with Webster, I basked in his aura of certainty and self-approval. Yet even as we spoke he was hunting down my friends. "Look"—he was rabbiting on a gorgonzola-and-walnut salad, "I'm not trying to recruit you to anything, so relax. In speaking with me so publicly, you're defying leftist death squads of the future. Gus, you at least still retain an awareness of the necessity of human relationships."

Webster's martyred eloquence stopped me cold. I looked, really looked, at him. This guy, I thought, is saving me lots of time. He says out loud what I sometimes think. But if he is the logical outcome of "further thoughts," I don't want any part it. Suddenly it struck me that much of my politics was neither ideological nor even at times logical but the result of what I wanted my face to look like. Was it true, as Luther Luck kept insisting, that in the end politics came down to who you enjoyed having lunch with?

"Webster," I said, "we're going to have to stop meeting like this. You're bad for my digestion."

He looked up from his salad. "So they *did* get to you, Gus?"

His gargoyle face relaxed. I had made Webster Wallach's day.

In March 1981 a lovesick Colorado psychotic named John Hinckley pumped several bullets into Ronald Reagan and his press secretary,

James Brady. Most of my San Andreas State students seemed more affected by the assassination a few months before of John Lennon, but I was oddly moved by Reagan's grace and humor under fire. Was I becoming a Republican?

"Probably not," judged Luther Luck, "but you're certainly not an American liberal either."

Then who was I?

Half my brain was Marxshire-made, the other half frozen in the 1950s with Doris Day's "Que Sera Sera" and fintail Caddies. Either way, I was brainless in Gaza, and the Iran hostage crisis didn't help.

SAS had a large foreign intake, including a number of Iranians. Until the Shah toppled, they'd sat in class docilely, the women particularly. Comes the revolution and more than half my Iranian students start wearing chadors and shouting at me. Hey, what did I do? But they weren't interested in arguments, just my head on a plate.

Marisa, an expatriate jeweler's daughter who had been the gentlest and least forthcoming in my class, now wore a chador and a deadly grim expression that could only mean trouble. When she could bear it no longer, she burst into my office and, cradling an imaginary machine gun in her arms, made barking sounds. Her whole body shook with the rattle of an Uzi, or was it an AK-47? That's right, sweetheart, I thought, act it out, don't do it.

"What's the problem?" I asked after she ran out of ammo.

"You condemn the Ayatollah Khomeini, who leads our people out of prison to a brighter dawn." I winced. At her age, did I too say things like "brighter dawn"? I tried to placate her. "Your American hostages are our freedom!" Marisa shouted. Then she leaned across my desk. "I have just shot you, Dr. Black. You cannot lie to us anymore because you are dead." The lady was serious.

"Marisa," I said, "I'm not a Ph.D. Don't call me 'Dr.'"

"There, that proves you are lying to us." She flounced out.

Luther could hardly contain his amusement. "So," he said with immense satisfaction, "your Third World students believe that you're an imperialist flunky, do they? Karmic justice for an old undergrad radical, don't you think?"

I retired in disarray to the Alhambra Gardens, and Marci Washington.

"Who do my students think I am anyway?" I complained to her.

She turned a magnificent smile on me. "A racist dog like most white males," she said, as if explaining the laws of gravity.

Was I guilty about Marci? No. Did I feel bad about betraying Helen? No. Was I getting tired of Marci's racial anger? Yup. Were there compensations? Is the Pope Catholic?

Because Marci was a chili freak, we often had a cheap dinner in Barney's Beanery, a blaringly loud diner just down from the Strip that had pool tables and so much macho it refused, in this heart of gaydom, to serve gays.

Tonight, surrounded by pseudo-rednecks playing Tammy Wynette on the jukebox, we sat contentedly over Coors and chili burgers, oblivious of the Dukes of Hazzard clones (probably lawyers by day) who slouched in manly poses around the bar.

Then a red-bearded Hells Angels wannabe with tattooed arms materialized at our table. He stared at Marci, stunning tonight in a virgin white cotton dress that brilliantly set off her ebony skin.

I'd had nightmares about what I'd do if a racist insulted Marci.

"Can we buy the little lady a drink?"

Oh God, he had a partner, John Carradine's unclaimed son, hanging his gaunt, broken-toothed face over the bench partition of our booth and breathing toxic beer fumes over us. He grinned at Marci.

"These guys are right out of *Deliverance*," I whispered.

"*Texas Chainsaw Massacre*, I'd say." She spooned more chili with salsa.

Barney's crawled with such characters. Nobody took them seriously except sometimes themselves.

Redbeard moved closer to Marci. "Young woman," he introduced himself, "whatcha doin' with this four-eyed wimp?" Even his accent was phony, Alabama by way of Ma Maison.

Carradine Jr. blocked Marci as she was sliding out of the booth. He also reached over and pushed me down when I got up. "Hey—" They shut me up with hard stares. Marci looked like she was about to cry.

Instead she said, "Fuck off, you turds. Before I blow your balls away."

Redbeard, Carradine, and I stared at her petite .22 pearl-handled, or was it a .25? She cocked it, pulling back the hammer à la Doc Holliday. Redbeard promptly retreated—"You certainly aren't in the mood for happy hour, are you?"—his voice now pure California interior decorator.

For reply she ate another spoonful of chili one-handed, without lowering her gun.

After Redbeard and Carradine faded away, she replaced the little automatic in her canvas shoulder bag. In shock, I asked if it was real or toy.

"Man" —she shook her head—"won't you ever grow up?" And got up to pay the check. I followed her out. Next time we'd try Hugo's down the street for sure.

We walked along the noisy boulevard in silence, then turned up my street. Finally I begged, "Say something, will you."

I tried to take her arm, but she shook me off. She must be mad at me for not protecting her. Twice now, counting Nickerson Gardens.

Suddenly she stopped to look at me in a friendly way. "Then you don't think," she asked, almost like a little girl, "it's unfeminine for me to pack a piece?"

"Hell no," I assured her, an instant convert to No Gun Control. "You saved us grief."

Genuinely relieved, she explained she'd bought the gun because so many of her SAS classes were at night.

I asked Marci if she was sore at me for not pulling a Rambo back there.

Marci wrapped a brown arm around my neck in an affectionate bear hug. "Who, you, Teach? You my drinkin' buddy."

And, arms around each other, we climbed the ticky-tacky steps of the Alhambra Gardens together, singing in unison.

> "Oh, lay that pistol down, babe
> Lay that pistol down
> Pistol packin' mama—
> Lay that pistol down."

You can't cheat on your wife without blaming her. Helen, in abandoning me to lawless L.A., had to share the guilt. It was largely her fault. Why had she let me go so easily? Anyway, what I did to educate myself to the new realities of America—e.g., Marci Washington—would be approved by Helen, who meant only the best for me.

Great.

Marci and I had begun half living together, not a brilliant solution to either of our dilemmas.

Fiercely eager to graduate, Marci hit the books hard, sometimes in my small apartment at the Alhambra Gardens because it was air-conditioned. I liked her in my place, she looked fine in the blue terrycloth robe she wore while studying.

Today she was tired of swotting. Outside was a blistering summer day, and the air conditioner competed with us arguing over her favorite topic, the System, which seemed to bite harder the closer she got to graduation.

"Requirements, units, class loads, grades. Goddammit, I wanted an education," she moaned.

Grading papers, I only half heard. "Then what," I said absentmindedly, "are you doing in college at your age?"

Marci put down her econ text. "I want to prove that an old affirmative action bitch like me can make it. All my aunts and uncles keep wondering if I'll do it. Even my son"—cared for by a grandmother in Las Vegas—"doesn't take me seriously."

Why not just count your blessings and get on with it? "Taking yourself seriously is all that matters, Marci."

"You're so goddamn smug, Teach."

"Stop sounding like Sidney Poitier in *The Blackboard Jungle*."

"How about Dorothy Dandridge or Lena Horne?" she said acidly.

"Them too."

"White liberals, ha!"

"Black radicals, mau-mau!"

"Man, if you heard yourself talking, you'd run a mile from that liberal honky bullshit college."

"Honky yes, liberal no," I replied. "Why'd you choose a campus like mine anyway? It's even more right-wing than USC or Pepperdine," two of L.A.'s conservative colleges.

"There, see?" She got up, agitated. "'Campus like mine.' You identify with all that establishment crap."

"They pay my wage. And you still haven't answered why you're at SAS."

"Man, you've totally forgotten what it's like to be a poor student. No, you never were. That GI bill was just the whites' form of affirmative action. I'm at 'my campus' because they paid me to come. Anyway, how come a 'socialist' like you took a job there?"

It was a living, I said uncomfortably.

"Is that all it is?" she said. "Like they put a gun to your head and said, 'Go ahead, eat the monthly paycheck or I'll off you.' What a hypocrite."

Where did she come off so self-righteous? It went, she said, with having to put up with stupid white men who controlled her academic destiny.

"Oh, stop your whining. If blacks put half as much energy into positive achievement as complaining, they'd—"

"Watch it," she said. The temperature was rising fast. "You wonder why we've got attitude or don't make grades or drop out? Because I'm a street nigger. Everything I know about life is contradicted by you white faculty guys."

"We've got black teachers. Go and find one. Anyway, you're no street nigger. And probably never were."

For some reason, my remark about black teachers struck home. She took a moment to recover.

"Your Nee-gro faculty are all Uncle Toms," she retorted. "Oreos. Total sellouts."

"As opposed to partial sellouts like me?"

She seemed on the verge of real tears. "You haven't heard a word I've said. Not one fucking word."

That drove me wild. Helen's words exactly when we quarreled. I reached across the dinette table and grabbed Marci to me, knocking aside her pile of textbooks. She resisted, pulling away.

"I want to study, man."

I yanked her to her feet and kissed her hard. "Like hell you do, you little ..."

"Aw, man, not this, not now."

I stopped in mid-rape, then stalked into the small living room. All I could hear was the air conditioner's loud hum and the ever-present L.A. police helicopter overhead. Shaken, I stared out the louvered window at the swimming pool.

Marci came in. Softly: "You okay, Gus?"

I didn't dare look at her.

Up to now, I'd thought sexual aggression laced with race hate was other men's property. And mumbled an apology to this effect.

She smiled, for the first time today relaxed. She went over and slipped a hand in mine.

"What are you always telling me? You're never too old to learn."

It was only a matter of time before Marci, or I, flipped under the strain of her being an angry black woman in a predominantly white, affluent university, of being too old in her own eyes to break into the movie business on her own terms, and of sleeping with a Jew. I wish I had Spago dinners for the many times we argued over (a) Israeli oppression of the West Bank Arabs, and (b) who "really" ran the drugs destroying her community in South Central L.A. "Look at the equation, man!" she yelled at me. "Who gets the profit, who gets the pain? While we swallow the misery, all those rich white Beverly Hills west side liberals make"—here she rubbed the fingers and thumb of one hand together like Shylock—"make the gelt." She was terrific at not so veiled allusions. "Beverly Hills" was Jews. "Rich whites" was Jews. "West side liberals" was Jews. The anti-Semitism was hard to take; calculated betrayals even more so.

Because we lived within (as she pointedly said) pistol range of each other—her little pad was over on Melrose—there was a strict rule, no surprise visits without a phone call first. One day I remembered to forget.

She came to the door at six-thirty a.m. in her electric blue robe.

Why hadn't she answered my calls last night?

Sleepily, she ran her hands through her close-cropped Afro, making my heart skip a beat. "Oh, man," she yawned, "don't be so dumb."

We argued on her doorstep. She said, "I don't want to hear how unhappy I've made you. Don't you have any self-respect?"

Too much like Rose O'Malley.

Wild-eyed, I barged past her through the open door and headed straight for the tiny bedroom. She dove for her Barnes & Noble canvas book bag on the couch and produced the ever-trusty gun. I was too mad to be scared.

Crashing into the bedroom, I almost fell on top of a naked man sprawled on the sheet-crinkled bed. "Wilfred!" I gasped.

I turned to Marci, who came in aiming her pearl-handle. "Wilfred?" I was incredulous.

Wilfred St. Regis was another cinema studies teacher at San Andreas State. And black.

I pointed at her lover. "Can't you do better than that?"

Wilfred, a terminally mediocre teacher, got even worse student evaluations than mine.

He sat up. "Outta here, you white piece of crap, before I—" Yale-educated Wilfred deepened his voice and rapped like a Crip whenever he lost an argument at departmental meetings, which at Luther's behest I was still attending.

I smiled down at Wilfred. "You stupid jerk. She can sue us *both* for sexual harassment. Or haven't you read that hero sandwich of a memo they circulated to all faculty?"

Still Superfly, Wilfred tried again: "Push off, whitey."

I sat on the edge of their bed, smiling to myself.

Marci's gun hand went limp. "Wilf, knock this guy on his ass."

I turned to Wilfred, who'd slunk back till the sheet covered him again. "Don't do it, Wilf lad. You're a married man with kids and a wife smart enough to know about California community property. Even if it's hard for you—think, man."

Wilf considered his position. Almost seven a.m. in a strange apartment with a female student holding a .22 on a demented white colleague.

"Marci," Wilf pleaded, "I don't want any police around here."

Gun in hand, she leaned against the wall in despair. "Wilf ..."

Satisfied I'd messed up their night of love, but heartsick, I went to the bedroom door. "I was crazy about you," I told Marci.

"You gave me no peace of mind. None," she said.

"We had something going," I insisted.

She shook her head. "You invented it. Invented me."

I lifted her chin. She was deathly pale, a kind of grim bluish color that clashed with her robe.

"We invented each other," I said. "And there's no patent on love."

I kissed her tight, cold lips and walked out. On impulse she came after me.

"Can we still be friends?" she asked plaintively.

"You want a friend," I said, "buy a dog."

At last I got in a real Robert Mitchum line.

Helen chose this moment, finally, to show up—a new, more self-confident Helen. Baby, take me away from all this. "Not until I see Grauman's Chinese and Marilyn's grave. Are Joe DiMaggio's roses still delivered every day? I didn't come six thousand miles just to rescue you from blue skies and gorgeous blondes—you idiot"—and fell into my arms. It was all right. Yes?

Marci forgotten—see how easy it is?—I guided Helen around L.A., which she knew only from books and movies. So far, from the distance of art, she had adored the U.S.A.; indeed, her pro-Americanness made her a rarity on the London left. Yet on this her first trip, my cosmopolitan, sophisticated, movie-literate Helen was turning out to be inerasably English. Seen up close, most Americans were a shade offputting, she confessed. Helen found especially hard to take our ongoing military crusades dressed up as social reform ("All these wars, on poverty, crime, whatnot"), our fondness for overblown rhetoric, overstated enthusiasms, and overrated dilemmas. And those grating American voices. "The women especially," Helen said. "Feminist or not, they still have this whining hysteria I'd hoped we'd left behind. What *is* it that goes on here?"

Luther Luck was an exemption to Helen's prejudices. They liked each other on first meeting. What did she see in him?

"He obviously likes you, so we share that," Helen said. "And Luther and I are snobs. In fact, Luther and I probably have more in common than you and I do. I'd make a good corporate wife if I could stand Americans in the mass."

They were also linked by a more ambiguous emotion: a gradually growing disapproval of the object of affection, me.

Helen had changed during our separation. She was bolder, a bit more sure of herself. "Part of it," she said, "is I'm getting used to your absences. Which is a good thing for both of us, I guess. And"— here her voice dropped a little—"I'm ... involved again."

My heart sank. But thank God, it was only the Movement.

Despite the risk to her government job, she'd hit the streets to protest Mrs. Thatcher's Falklands war and had begun writing about economics from a feminist angle. "You'd be proud of me, Gus—I titled my first article 'Statistics Can Be Sexy.' How's that for gutter journalism?" She added, "Of course, I'm not a novelist like you or Rose ..." Suddenly she looked timid. "Is that all right?"

"Then"—again as if introducing the subject of a new lover— "there's also Greenham."

Greenham Common, Middlesex, a few miles outside London on the perimeter of a U.S. Air Force field, was the site of a now permanent encampment of women protesting the Cruise missiles inside the base. This wasn't my Helen's style, she'd always steered clear of tight little self-referential women's groups. "Oh no," Helen spoke up, "it's not that at all." Her eyes sparkled as she described how a straggly march of a few Cardiff housewives had almost overnight mushroomed into a movement of forty thousand women from all over Britain. "It's inclusive, Gus, not exclusive, otherwise I wouldn't go. The strength is coming back to us. The only problem is, I've still got to dress badly to be accepted, but it's a small price to pay for sisterhood, don't you agree?"

There was a new, or rather old, glint in her eyes. She was even thinking of becoming a candidate for the local council. "At least I can read a profit and loss sheet, which is more than I can say of most of the comrades." People in the district waved hello to her now, she reported, and she knew the compost problems of almost all the gardeners in Vicarage Terrace. She had even won entry to the proles' pub, the Mason's Arms. How? "Silly, I made friends with the barmaid. You certainly have gotten rusty."

Greenham—living in windswept homemade tents on stolen weekends, huddled over a wet portable stove with Emma Gee-Tee and a few of her old women's group—had rekindled Helen's fire. "If only you could be there, Gus," she enthused, "but of course they voted to exclude men. Still, you can make a lunch for me whenever you like."

"You're not going to turn into one of those career protesters?" I wondered.

She blinked. "When I first met you, you wouldn't have asked that."

□ □ □

Not only Helen had changed; England too. The country Helen brought me back to had, for the first time since Winston Churchill, a Boss. Much to everyone's surprise but the Prime Minister's, Mrs. Thatcher was firmly in control by dint of a nice little war in the Falklands that raised her sixty points in the opinion polls. None of this womanly nonsense either; she had ordered the deliberate torpedoing of an Argentine cruiser, the *Belgrano*, as it sped away from the war zone. Boadicea in S/M leather: my unscientific vox pop revealed an undercurrent of feeling in the country that we deserved a jolly good whipping from Nanny Thatcher, how painfully nice, because we had been such ba-a-a-d children until she came along and firmly put the nursery in order. England had never had a woman leader of the House, and nobody, including the men in her own party, knew how to deal with it except by regression.

On the left, there was almost a sense of relief that somebody was finally in charge. The 1979 "winter of discontent," when the work force revolted after four years of voluntary pay restraint, had traumatized the nation. Dustmen, railwaymen, and public service employees embarked on an irksome, exhausting series of go-slows and shutdowns that caused widespread suffering and displeasure with the unions. Labour, in tenuous power, had thoroughly mismanaged the annual misery of strikes, stoppages, and industrial action. That particular long cold dark winter had changed me from a partisan who would walk anybody's picket line to a consumer-victim. Why had I not noticed before that strikes cause pain to people other than the strikers? Being a householder makes you see things differently. My garbage wasn't collected, my phone didn't work, railways and Tube were erratic—it was like a General Strike without the aims of one. Even to many of my lib-rad neighbors in Somewhere Southwark, it seemed as if the country was out of control.

The new Labour Prime Minister, Jim Callaghan, who replaced Wilson, had chosen that moment to fly off to Guadeloupe in the Caribbean, returning (with a tan) to complain to the waiting TV cameras, "Crisis? What crisis?"

Those three words gave the next election to Mrs. T and her Tories.

I began to understand why so many ordinary working-class voters stamped their ballots in favor of the class enemy. God help us, we needed what Mrs. Thatcher promised, a release.

Me, too.

And then, just when I was getting used to the fact that a blue-rinsed battle-ax, a grocer's daughter without a shred of "style," was giving birth to a monstrosity named "Thatcherism," Luther Luck called again. This time he had hard money.

I became an official part of the Brain Drain.

Helen and I did not talk much about the deal Luther was offering, a regular six-month commute to SAS. It seemed a lot of money for a little work. We both knew that while she had a real job in the Department of Trade and Industry, I was freelance in a shrinking market where a fresh generation of young and hungry Fleet Streeters was willing to work for half my fee or none just for the chance; things were tight. The sixties and seventies really were over; we were going back to the thirties minus the solidarity.

"What'll I do, honey?" I asked Helen.

"You know, so why ask me?" she said.

* * *

On the first night back of what was to prove my regular London-to-L.A. richochet, Luther and I broke open a bottle in his office. Just before dawn, as I put my jacket over Luther, who was dozing on his foldaway futon (he did not drive when drinking), he opened one bleary eye.

"I'm curious—what would the young radical Gus have thought of Professor Gustavus Black?"

What a bastard.

I kissed my fingertip and anointed his forehead. "Gus was a Marxist, Luther. They understand about survival."

"Ah yes, survival," Luther sighed. "Well, I certainly hope you survive this survival." And was instantly asleep.

I almost didn't.

Luther's question nagged. What *would* younger Gus have thought about escaping America as a dissident and crawling back as a minor foreman in its educational factory? He would probably be a little disappointed in myself. But then, he was in good company: so were my blood brothers and sisters on the Los Angeles left.

Take Ted Gollan, a blind Prometheus who had paid his dues over and over because that's what John Wayne would have done if he had been a socialist.

Ted, a burly, raw-throated Texan from a *Last Picture Show* small town in the Panhandle, a street organizer in the sixties, had been clobbered by a policeman during the '68 Democratic Convention. He could hardly see anymore but liked being seen: hence our meeting in the Beverly Hills Polo Lounge. He wore extra-thick lenses to signal his legal blindness, held no grudges, never whined; and he was also not sure he wanted to see me back in America.

"Man," he demanded, "what the fuck are you doing here? People of my generation—okay, a sprinkling of us—idolized you because you stayed away. Air mileage lent enchantment. It was like you had the integrity we lacked. You can't let us down; we need icons on the left."

I tried to see behind Ted's bottle glasses, but he refused to crack a smile. "You are kidding?" I asked.

"Sure I am," Ted replied. "Pity the movement that needs heroes, to paraphrase Brecht or Tommy Lasorda. But shit, man, we don't need you hanging over our shoulders like Banquo's ghost telling us, Nevermore nevermore. Or was that Poe's raven?"

Originally, I'd met Ted when he was a young New Leftist at Studies on the Left at the University of Wisconsin, and had kept fitfully in touch since. Now an active player on the Los Angeles liberal scene, he was a "media consultant."

"What *is* a media consultant?" I said.

"Gus, that's why we loved you." He finally laughed. "You always asked questions that had no answers."

Ted complained that because of his surprising income, he was upper-class and felt uncomfortable about it. "But then," he reminded me, "social guilt is an indispensable part of our west side L.A. lifestyle. We never leave home without it."

I told Ted I was almost one of them now and was even thinking of buying, not renting, a car.

He misunderstood. "Why are you putting me down, man?" he said angrily. "Anyway, where were you during the civil rights sit-ins and sit-downs and Freedom Rides and New Mobe? I don't hold it against you that you split. But having deserted the front line, it ill behooves you to turn around and take shots at the real combat soldiers."

Couldn't gainsay that; the lead pipe illegally wielded by that Chicago cop with number-concealing tape over his badge had left a crease across Ted's skull that was clearly visible through his thinning hair. Ted and Marci Washington had real war wounds. My own, including the Code Blue panics every time I sat down to a typewriter, couldn't compare. But front line? They existed anywhere in the world you chose to dig in, I told Ted.

"Crap," he said. "The British economy that's kept you going till now is what we Americans let it be. You bought that English exile on American dollars, kiddo. You can't escape us that easily—not that you didn't try."

Ted took off his heavy glasses and folded them in his hands, staring almost sightlessly at me. "And goddammit, show me more respect," he commanded. "I'm going to Washington to be in Gary Hart's cabinet when he wins the Democratic nomination." Ted was part of a loose network of brainy backroom boys, mainly anti-Vietnam protest veterans and SDS honchos, who staffed the thinking echelons of policy studies institutes that were the left's answer to Rand and Brookings.

Despite his proven courage, Ted, like Tom Hayden and other sixties militants, now called himself an "economic democrat" in order to disguise his socialist leanings. I told Ted that the old Communist Party had tried such dissembling and look where it got them. Sure, we were part of something increasingly, and rightly, discredited. But we couldn't spend the rest of eternity disavowing our past, nor repeating endlessly, "But real socialism has never been tried," when who cared? The coming collapse of com-soc state capitalism was the best thing that could happen to us, a gift from heaven. We could be reborn without the bullshit, and if it turned out we were nothing but bullshit, well, it had happened to better people than us.

Ted kept blowing nervously on his lenses as if that would help him see better. "I thought I was the blind sonofabitch." He shook his head. "Don't you understand anything? Let me tell you the real difference between your generation and mine, because you seem to have run altogether out of the brains to know it for yourself. Back when your generation was on the barricades protesting mass unemployment, fascism, war, discrimination, whatever, you personally got the product of your own struggle. Those wages you struck for went right into your own, Gus Black's, pocket. Those fascists you wanted to stop were out to kill Gus Black himself. You were fighting for your lives. Literally, man. Not us, not my age group. Despite ourselves, we're getting fat off Reaganism the way so many right-wing and not so right-wing liberals—remember how we hated them?—fed off, at a discreet distance of course, the Vietnam War. Today my bunch are alienated even from the fruits of our rare victories. You fucking Neanderthal Marxist sumbitch, don't you see? The system we hate likes us. So do us something!"

Ted's wife, Eva, who drove him everywhere, was at another Polo Lounge table studying for a prelaw exam. When he signaled her she came by and we steered Ted outside to his shiny new low-slung red Ferrari.

"Say," I told Ted and Eva, "I'm looking for a car. What's this hog cost?"

The left was my game, and I knew how to play by its rules. But it was hard to get used to all this consumer choice in America. Where did I fit into Democratic Socialists, Venceremos!, El Rescate, Justice for Janitors, Slo-Growth, Medical Aid to Vietnam, Peace Now, not to mention whole constellations of double-barreled political groups linked to a Hollywood scene that the college film studies department was plugged into?

"It breaks my heart to watch an addict get ready for his next fix," said Archie Boylan, bringing me back to street reality. In the dim light of Molly Malone's, an Irish bar in West Hollywood near the Alhambra Gardens, he loomed reassuringly large. Whenever I lost touch with what politics really is about—the underclass and its con men, hustlers, thieves, pimps, and bunco artists—Archie could be counted on to try to mess up my life along with his. No, not this time.

"Relax," he said, "I'm more or less legit these days. All the warrants out on me are civilian paper. No big deal."

Nearly a decade after the Vietnam truce, Archie still hovered in GI limbo as a military deserter who had never bothered to collect his amnesty papers from Fort Benjamin Harrison, Indiana. We had known each other since the '68 Tet offensive when, dumped on a Vietnam-bound levy, he'd split from a Louisiana army camp to continue a lifelong career on the run. One police sheet I'd seen on Archie listed grand theft auto, robbery ("It was only a drunk American Legionnaire I rolled, and you know what I think of those old farts"), prison escapes, and scams without end. Plus his military crimes: enlistment under age at sixteen, dishonorable discharge for insubordination, reenlistment under a false name, numberless AWOLs.

From 1969 to 1972, I had been stationmaster of the London branch of a worldwide underground railway that smuggled Vietnam-era deserters in and out of Britain to safer countries like Sweden and Canada. On one of my inspection tours, I'd found Archie slowly freezing to death in a Stockholm snowdrift and carried him back to London with me like contraband. A drugged-up, boozed-out nineteen-year-old Boston "Eastie" raised in reformatories and orphanages, Archie had taught me in return the tricks of my new trade. In a nutshell: "Most deserters like me at the time they do it don't know why they do it, it's the most serious thing a guy can do is spit on the flag and be a traitor, and it's gonna take as long as I live to figure out why and how I had the guts, you don't have a spare fifty bucks lying around the house, do ya?"

Archie insisted that like him, I was a born deserter, "always running, always will be." He should get together with Ted Gollan.

"How's the little woman, then?" He let me buy him a Wild Turkey.

As third-best best man at my wedding, he had helped start the riot in Helen's flat. "That was when I was still in shape," he coughed, a bulb-nosed, paunchy, sweating, overweight thirty-one-year-old hulk going downhill. "All this extra weight," he wheezed, "is a better disguise than plastic surgery."

I told him about The House.

Archie raised his glass and laughed in my face. "Here's to marriage—and all other social diseases."

I also told him about my search for the New Politics.

"Good luck, pal," Archie said. "I would of thought the Old Politics was enough to last you a while. Didn't you get tired cramming that shit down our throats?"

I resented that, because as stationmaster I had strictly enforced a rule that all "conductors"—unpaid volunteers who "babysat" AWOLs—refrain from imposing their views on the vulnerable youths in their charge.

"Okay, okay," Archie relented, belting his Wild Turkey, "you weren't as bad as some, I'll give ya that."

"Thanks for nothing," I said.

Archie said, "All you Commie Yids are the same. You'd rather have an ideology than get laid. Relax, Gus. The war is over."

That was rich coming from a man who had not been able to rest in one place since Tet. "Look who's talking," I said.

"I'm gonna settle down any minute now—when I find a broad who can keep her mouth zipped except for blowjobs. Lemme tell you, Gus, next to black snatch there's nothin', I mean nothin', like babes named Rebecca Rabinowitz from ACLU."

"I knew one day you'd revert to type, you beer-bellied, sexist, Irish Catholic Know-Nothing reactionary fuck."

He was unperturbed. "Did I hear someone call my name? But look on the positive side. I ain't a car thief or dope dealer anymore. I got a job as a bus driver."

"Courtesy of who, you ungrateful prick?"

Archie smiled innocently. "The Movement. Who else? Don't you think I know that? I milked you guys for what?—thousands of dollars. Suckers."

"Guys nothing," I reminded him. His specialty was conning Movement women out of folding money. I mimicked his hustle. "'I deserted from Fire Base Phoenix 'cause I felt so guilty mowing down all those poor helpless Asian peasants with a fifty-caliber from the open door of my Huey gunship....' The closest you ever got to combat was a military stockade at Tan San Hut."

Archie was insult-proof. "How come you never blew the whistle on me?"

"Because you moved too fast. Or you lied so badly I kept thinking God was sure to hit you between the eyes with a bolt of blue lightning."

"Yeah," agreed Archie, "that makes two of us."

I stared morosely into my glass and told Archie that I was having trouble getting a handle on this new America. Why couldn't I just accept it?

Archie thumped my back. "Cheer up. There ain't nothin' to know. Just do. That's knowin'. Didn't Sartre say that—or was it Johnny Carson? Me, I drive a school bus and screw college girls who like to do their slummin' in bed. But you know lots about that, don't ya? Preach to their souls but keep your eyes on their tits."

"I never," I said primly, "touched any of those AWOL groupies you brought around." They had been half my age: Holden would not have approved. But one had tempted me.

Archie waggled his finger under my nose. "That bimbo Bonnie blindsided you. Admit it."

"Redneck bitch."

"There ya go. Scratch a socialist and there's always a priest jackin' off underneath the cassock."

I pursued my own thoughts. "It's depressing. I've been making the rounds of the L.A. left. Most of them are Jewish, just like in my generation. When are we ever going to reach the goys?"

"Never, I hope. What would us Irish Catholic reactionaries do if it stopped bein' a Jew-kike-Commie conspiracy?" Archie gave me a little shake. "When are you gonna get the message, Gus? Heartland types like me are pro-God, pro-property, and pro-lific. We give you socialists the surplus value—see, I do remember your boring sermons—that lets you preach against the surplus value system, if you get me. Give it up, man, and join the orgy."

Lower and lower still. "Didn't being a deserter teach you anything, Archie?"

He thought hard. "Sure. When you're in trouble find a middle-class liberal to buy you out of it. And, oh yeah. Next time a judge gives me the choice of enlistin' in the military or doin' jail time, I'll take the stripes you wear on your back, not on your sleeve." He put his arm around me affectionately. "And what, dear ol' pal, did bein' a deserter babysitter teach you?"

I sighed. "Power belongs to the people—if you can ever find the sonsabitches."

* * *

If you're looking for sonsabitches, start with yourself.

Jack Kerouac and Neil Cassady had hit the road searching for asphalt nirvana, but Archie Boylan and I had a more modest goal. During my first spring break, he and I, in his rusty old Nash Rambler station wagon with purple and yellow surplus carpet upholstery, scouted the interstate highways for deserters we knew west of the Rockies.

The U.S. Army had been good to me, for luck I even carried my Fourth Division green ivy patch in my wallet. But on joining the anti-Vietnam resistance, I had gravitated to the low end of the Movement, its dregs. Deserters, unlike "resisters" or draft dodgers, were mainly poor city or farm kids who had enlisted rather than waiting to be drafted; that is, they had volunteered, then split. It had taken me a while to figure out where in antiwar activism I belonged, but once I met types like Archie there was no question. Unlike many deserters, who flipped over after going AWOL if only to justify an act that horrified most of them, I was not a Charlie lover. Ho Chi Minh had killed too many peasants, including my socialist comrades, on his road to power, and I was not about to succumb to the Movement's slushy view of "Uncle" Ho. This did not endear me to the various American Deserter Committees I had to work with.

"Yeah, you always were a right-wing opportunist," said Bonnie. We'd picked her up in Monterey, where, after spells as a barmaid and construction worker ("I quit after those proletarian pigs sexually harassed me practically right off a girder one day"), she'd become a psychiatric caseworker at the Veterans Administration. "Listening to vets bullshit was the only thing I had any real experience at, if you recall," Bonnie said.

"You just can't keep your hands off us," Archie yelled over his shoulder to Bonnie in the backseat, packed with empty beer cans and whole crates of motor oil to feed his failing Rambler engine.

"Still a schmuck," was all Bonnie said.

Throughout the Vietnam War, Bonnie, a tall, leggy blonde with a Missouri twang and fanatic loyalty to Movement men, fucked, cherished, nursed, and supported U.S. deserters from Vancouver to Uppsala, anywhere they had sanctuary. More Blaze Starr than Florence Nightingale, as a rebellious teenager she'd run off from a Chillicothe farm to Haight-Ashbury at the height of dope-rock, which burned her out, turned her on, politicized her fury at most (male) adults. By the time I met Bonnie in London she was hard-core revolutionary, full of disdain for Marxshire Methuselahs like me. She kept her balance by overidentifying with AWOLs and constantly accusing backsliders of selling out. But trust nurses, they're the ones closest to patients. Bonnie was a major asset to someone like me who needed reliable conductors on the underground railway. Over time we cobbled together a working relationship except on one point: sex. She delighted in provoking my fear of sleeping with teenagers, starting with herself. "What's your problem, old man? Afraid to admit the worst? You're like my grandpa—full of shit and wet dreams about young pussy. What's wrong, Gus, am I too old for you?" Bonnie was nineteen.

Since the Vietnam cease-fire, she'd cooled off to work for an awesome range of revolutionary groups—Communist Party, Socialist Workers Party, Revolutionary Communist Party—searching for an elusive purity where cadres were as heroic as their speeches. Finally choking on the bureaucratic routine of small airless offices, she had gone to graduate school—and become a radical lesbian, she announced to Archie and me. Male sexism on the left had "turned her," she said, staring hard at me.

"Hey," I said, "it wasn't my fault."

"There, that's what I mean," she said. "Being gay isn't a fault."

"That's not what I meant," I said.

"That's what you guys always say," she said.

"Since when I am I 'you guys'?" I said.

"Since you became one of them," she said.

Archie, watching us in the rearview mirror, grinned. "Just like the old days. You two are still in love."

Not exactly like the old days. This time I didn't have to sleep in the bottom couchette of a North Sea ferry on its way to Sweden or Denmark or France while Bonnie and Archie, helping me babysit a "package" (loose AWOL), flailed madly groaning at each other inches from my cotton-stuffed ears. Now, chastely, we stayed in the same motel rooms on I-30. For Holiday Innkeepers our story was that I was their father, and Bonnie said I looked the part these days, what had happened to me? and I said what's wrong with the way I look? and she said if you don't know I don't want to be the one to tell you. I thought she was joking but soon found out otherwise.

My first real look at the American provinces was through the eyes of their deserters.

Although the war was over, many deserters were still fixed in a war mode. On the run, dead, even underground when everybody else was overground and taking subscriptions to *Rolling Stone*. The legal reality was that if you were willing to go in and apologize, you won amnesty. The military no longer actively pursued AWOL fugitives; even during the war the Pentagon hated admitting that whole divisions of men—seventy-two thousand in one year—had split. Technically, eight years later, nothing worse than "bad paper," some form of less than honorable discharge, hung over most deserters' heads. But that made little difference to some of their worn-out psyches. In two weeks' hard driving, mainly through the Southwest and Rocky Mountains, we checked it out, comparing our fevers to theirs.

"Yeah, I'm glad to be back. Served some stockade time wasn't all that bad except for the lifer guards slapping you around. All I want to be is an American again. Not that easy anymore, if you want the truth.

Can't say why. When I tell people I was in Sweden during Vietnam they just give me this funny look and ask if it was anything like *Sound of Music*. Sweden and Switzerland sound alike around here. Things are normal, I guess. I run Dad's farm—he's sick now—and even vote Republican like my family does. The past, that's all long gone, isn't it to you, Gus?"
—DAVE, 32, *WORKING ON A TRACTOR IN A FIELD OUTSIDE*
VISALIA, CALIFORNIA

"H'lo, Archie, hello, Bonnie. You still on the run, haw haw. Gus, haven't you found anything honest to do yet? I like this bar 'cause it's so dark, I meet all the ADC guys here so we can't see how much older we're getting. That deserter trip turned me around for sure. I'm a member of the Proletarian Vanguard Fraction now. Live in a commune, no, can't tell you where. My life's dedicated to the revolution. Like to make a little contribution, seriously?"

—RICK, 34, *OAKLAND, CALIFORNIA*

"No, I don't wanna see you or hear from you or even know you."

—"MULE," 33, *CEDAR CITY, UTAH*

"No, I ain't sorry. Took no guts for me to enlist, any damn fool coulda done that. But sure took balls to take off like I did. And stay out as long as I did. I sure do thank you, Gus—an' all the other folks who helped me. Come on in and meet th' family."

—SAM, EX–TANK DRIVER, BOZEMAN, MONTANA

"Well, who we got here if it isn't Gus? Went AWOL from jolly old England, I see. Just joking. Archie, they told me you were dead, now that I can see you I believe it. Did you and Bonnie get married? Don't look at me like that, girl. I'm putting in full time on the amnesty campaign, there are still a lot of lost souls out there who don't even know their rights. We have an office downtown. Yeah, I got involved after all. How would you like to come to the my party convention, International Socialists? I'm on the National Exec. Not bad for a seminarian, eh?"

—ANTHONY, LATE 30S, SEATTLE, WASHINGTON

"Don't tell me you're still riding that old dead horse, Gus. You kept saying being a deserter would politicize me, and boy were you wrong. All it taught me was stay away from Sweden in the winter. Next war why don't you find some safe houses in a warmer place. Hey, you like my wall? I've collected every *Playboy* cover since it first got published.

Playboy, not Karl Marx, saved my life those long winter nights. I'm back in the mill, they didn't care what kind of discharge I have. I do, so long as it isn't thick and yellow, get it? Hey, Bonnie, you used to be able to take a joke."

—JACK, 35, ROSEBURG, OREGON

"I can't stop running. My brother got killed at Hue. We went in at the same time and took this R and R together in Honolulu. Greg went back to Nam to finish his tour, it sure finished him. I did some surfing at Waikiki, then took off for Canada. Greg wrote and said I had to do what I had to do, that's the last letter I got from him. After he got killed Mom came to visit me in Canada. My dad called me a traitor and even tried turning me in until Mom said she'd leave him. Mom said we had to be a stronger family now with Greg gone. I tried going home but couldn't hack all the family tension and arguments. Dad wasn't even in a war, so where's he get off? I'd like them to meet my wife, who's a Canuck, and the two kids. But I sure don't want him yelling at them too."

—*Paul, 34, schoolteacher, Vancouver, Canada*

"I got this deserter thing all talked out of my system years ago. I never bring it up if nobody else does. It's like it never happened. I'll bet the Vietnamese wish they could say the same."

—*George, 38, Phoenix, Arizona*

On the way back to L.A., the car broke down outside a dry little railroad town called Barstow. Archie just left the Rambler wreck by a siding, and we split up to go our separate ways by Greyhound. (Naturally, Archie had to borrow fare back east.) Reluctant to part, we dawdled over drinks in a bar near the tiny bus depot.

Bonnie said, "Some of those guys are in worse shape than us."

"Yeah," Archie said, "but some are doing okay, better than us. When are *we* ever gonna grow up?"

"I was grown up once," Bonnie said, "and I didn't like it."

"When was that?" I asked.

"And you"—she leveled those big-gun eyes on me—"you were closer to achieving something than a lot of us fuckups. You had a *duty* to live better, Gus."

Archie cut in. "Nah, duty is for lifers. And ossifers. Don't listen to her, Gus. You're a real deserter too. Born to betray."

"You can't be a deserter forever," Bonnie argued.

I told her the locomotive of history had sped past my stop.

She looked at us. "God, will we ever stop running?"

"I hope not," said Archie."

"I want to," said Bonnie, trying to mean it.

"Don't look at me," I said. "I don't even know where to apply for amnesty."

Instead, amnesty applied for me.

□ □ □

Hello madness my old friend.

The London-L.A. commute was in my blood. Bliss of forever escaping life at thirty thousand feet. SAS final exams over, pack bags fly to Heathrow, check in with BenGy, who kept my desk next to his unoccupied, prowl a few Liverpool streets, make some broadcasts, kiss Helen at Terminal 3, land at Alhambra Gardens, say hello to Luther, set up typewriter, furiously work the phones for half a dozen Fleet Street papers, teach, go to any political meeting that will have me, pack bags, grab plane, taxi to Broadcasting House, bop around town press flesh keep smiling so editors won't forget your name, I'm for hire, pack bags ...

It got a little confusing then. London's skyline broiled in a Hollywood smog, Bermondsey women wore Zuma beach bikinis, a Malibu sun shone on Vauxhall Bridge, my feet trod Santa Monica sand in Regent Street. I was a Master of Time and Space aboard 747s that kept me moored in mid-Atlantic, Captain Kirk deluding himself he's in command, Mr. Spock hypercertain of his self-control. "Ho-ho-ho," chuckled Marek the Interplanetary Space Villain, "I knew you'd break under the strain. Now let a real man take over...."

"What is your full name, sir? What kind of medical insurance do you carry? Are you on Medicare? Do you know where you are? Are you allergic to—"

"Are you in pain?"

What was she talking about? All I felt was this tiny prickle of sweat at the back of my neck. My right jaw ached a little but—

Then, Jee-zus, it hurt.

There is a golden city beyond the first fears of childhood which, like an open orphanage, accepts any small child who has lost his way.

Who was this tall, gorgeous redhead who looked vaguely familiar sitting alertly at my bedside, her swellelegant legs tucked under her, waiting for me to die in Intensive Care? Bit of aw righ' tha'. Can't beat Beverly Hills Memorial for service—this smashing new nurse, or was she a social worker? Dr. Levitt, my cardio, looked strangely at me and canceled my intravenous Demerol. Nobody told me who the nice redhead was until the cleaning lady leaned over my bed to whisper, "If you don't want them to think you're crazy, Mr. Black, better say hello to your wife."

Oh, Helen.

Later I learned she'd flown in as soon as Luther Luck phoned about my heart attack suffered during a class lecture. Without luggage or even handbag, she'd improvised a nest for herself at my bedside. So why did I start yelling at her?

Some men, I've heard, get mellower after their myocardial infarctions, if only to keep their arteries open. Me, I kicked ass, at first metaphorically, then literally. A cold, tight anger drove me back to life from the forest of translucent tubes and wires that had settled on me like camouflage netting. Nobody seemed to get the point, least of all my doctors or Helen. I wanted to die.

In a towering fit of rage, I almost physically pushed Helen into her taxi for LAX after our first few recuperative days alone at the Alhambra Gardens. I had to be by myself now.

"But you're always alone," Helen sobbed as the driver piled in the bags we'd bought her in L.A., "even in our marriage."

"Then divorce me!" I roared, the vein in my head pulsing with a thrombosis in waiting.

Well done, Black.

Who was this old man in the mirror? Only thirty days into my heart attack, I looked like my pop on a losing pinochle streak at four a.m. In their worst nightmares not even blind John Garfield or Brando in his wheelchair looked this way. No matter from what angle, I was Walter Brennan complete with stooped shamble, palsy, crushed-in toothless face. Wuz you ever bit by a dead bee?

Well, at least I didn't look like Webster Wallach.

With Helen gone, I didn't join a rehab group or Battered Hearts Anonymous but sweated it out alone, day after day, first lying then sitting then slouching upright on a folding beach chair at the edge of the Alhambra Gardens pool, thinking (at last), reading Svevo or R. Crumb, eating and sleeping when I pleased, feeling sorry for myself in my own depleted body. I had no choice but to change the film in the projector. One morning, when I couldn't stand it anymore, I rang up the corner video store and, for a delivery charge of ten bucks, rented a whole new sheaf of films for my VCR starring a special breed of actor.

Out my apartment window flew in classic formation the heroes on whom I'd patterned my life up to now: Spencer Tracy quenching oil fires, Cagney muscling bartenders, Coop loping into a town full of bad hats; in flew a whole new batch of icons to live by, handsome gray foxes bristling with sex appeal: John Wayne in *The Shootist,*

Paul Newman in *Absence of Malice,* most of all Burt Lancaster as the aging petty hood in *Atlantic City* laughing lustfully as he shoots the thugs picking on his young girlfriend. There was life after Tab Hunter.

But I still needed a woman to care for me even if he was a man.

In the Year of Her Reign Four—Orwell's 1984—I flew my wrecked body back to Thatcher's Britain in time for a national coal strike. Wait, reader! Would you register it better if I said I returned to the front line of the climactic battle between Western social democracy and European Reaganism? Probably not. Coal miners are not sexy copy. They still use heavy muscle to dig our fuel out of the earth in what is perceived as an outmoded, "dirty" industry. But industries are made up of people who often create a work culture that becomes more vital than the work itself. British mining villages had been, until now, the nation's first line of resistance to sterile modernism. Although such resistance took a political-industrial form, at heart it was a fierce defense of traditional values that the entire country would have applauded had the dissidents not been wearing a miner's loincloth and headlamp.

But in British middle-class culture, miners are not only (occasionally) admired but also despised. In truth they drink, screw, fight, work—collectively. They are feared because they come from "down there" and show it by their solidarity and on their actual bodies. Even today, among younger miners, it's hard to find one who does not bear physical scars of the trade. The machines that were supposed to liberate the mines kick up as much, sometimes more, lung-burning dust as the old pick and shovel. You don't feel sorry for these men; they jeer at self-pity. But you also don't deliberately and systematically destroy them, their villages, and their workplaces. That is, unless you are Mrs. T.

A funny thing about the small-town lower bourgeoisie, into which Margaret Roberts Thatcher was born the obedient daughter of a Grantham, Lincolnshire, shopkeeper, is that their deepest psychic terror is not death but bankruptcy—or worse, falling a notch on the social ladder into the manual working class. In a private corner of their minds they keep a cartoon image of this nauseating void, which in sick dreams on bad nights is occupied by a monster suspiciously resembling the stalwart British miner with his brawny arms wide open to receive them—a dark family secret because so many respectable Britons have, or had, relatives who worked in the mines. Jock or Llewelyn aye hard-drinking lads knock their wives about a bit too Bolshie if you ask me still he brings in a wage. Indisputably, there is something about digging coal, it's so bloody group-minded, that inhibits the entrepreneurial spirit. So the miner has to be wiped out if society as seen by its best capitalist minds is to free itself of old bonds (tradition) and restraints (values). And his village culture must be erased if only because it bears the social memory of resistance. Even today, the 1926 General Strike spearheaded by the miners remains a persisting, vaguely unlocatable trauma for company chairmen and Prime Ministers not even born then.

This loathing of a particular section of the working class is dressed up as "new industrial thinking" or "efficiency" or "the nation must break the union stranglehold." Yet the mining business the Tory government chose to assault frontally is an industry that in many ways was a model of manager-employee cooperation and union acquiescence in, even encouragement of, technical innovation, including union collaboration in closing down unprofitable pits. Fat lot of good it did the miners when Mrs. T came to power. Politics, more than economics, demanded an all-out attack on coal.

To set her nation free, Mrs. T aimed to do to the British miners what Ronald Reagan had done to the U.S. air controllers' union in 1981: destroy them.

This time Maggie and her Conservatives hit lucky, because the miners were led by Arthur Scargill, a "charismatic" president whose ego was almost a match for Hers (we'd gotten used to the royal feminine personal pronoun) but who, unlike her, lived in the past. The past, which is the miners' real treasure, in this instance became their cross.

Any fool could see, I grumbled, twitching with angina in front of my TV set at 23 Vicarage Terrace, that the miners' strike was another glorious defeat like Gallipoli or the Charge of the Light Brigade. The tactics were all wrong, I ranted like a retired old general to his forbearing wife, all wrong, an idiot could see that—

"Gus," Helen interrupted, "either go see for yourself or die in your chair of another heart attack. I can't stand to see you burst a blood vessel this way."

I looked up from the nine o'clock news. She was crying. "What's wrong, baby?" She shook her head almost bitterly. I did not understand.

She came and sat next to me on our brand-new Habitat couch. "You're killing yourself trying to be so careful with your heart. Have the guts to get out of the house."

Poor Helen. Poor Helen nothing, she hadn't even been waiting by our Queen Anne pewter firescreen when, just in from L.A. unannounced, I'd barged through our Sandersons-gloss black front door with its shiny brass knocker only to find The House empty and had to be told by Dick Slocum, the slithery worm with the knowing smile from across the street, that Helen was away, again, camping with the Greenham Peace Women in Berkshire. "She's been unusually active, you know," Slimy Slocum added. What was he hinting? It was public knowledge that many of the Greenham women were gay....

That first weekend home, alone and unwifed, I caught up with the thick file of newsclips Helen kept for me during my now routine absences. Arthur Koestler had killed himself and his wife in a double suicide in Hampstead. (Hmmm, now there's an idea.) Mrs. T's political protégé Cecil Parkinson, a.k.a. Mr. Brilliantine, the Conservative Party chairman, had abandoned a Tory woman candidate he had got with child, so much for Conservative family values. And the Iron Lady herself had barely survived a massive IRA bomb attack on her Brighton hotel. That I could sympathize with. Only last year Helen and I had been at a Sunday concert in Regents Park when the military band was blown to pieces by IRA shrapnel, and a few weeks later a flying chunk of iron from a Piccadilly postbox with an IRA letter bomb inside had almost decapitated me.

If the Provos got her, I'd miss Mrs. T, whom I'd come almost to depend on to define my socialism. Until She came along, we were nowhere, groping blindly, improvising, madly evading a sense that what seemed a good idea in 1945 simply no longer worked. We're a funny race, we socialists, we're terrified that watering the milk also poisons it.

Can a myocardial infarction change your political sex? Just as the 1981 assassination attempt had softened me on the old liar Reagan, so I began, reading Helen's accumulated newsclips, to feel vaguely uncomfortable with the tone of Marxshire's attacks on Mrs. T. There's no snob like an egalitarian snob. Margaret Thatcher's sin seemed to be Her gender and class. In the *Listener*, a woman academic carped at Thatcher's "not vulgar but low" looks and the way she embodied "the worst of the lower middle class." In the *Times*, a theatrical producer blasted "her odious suburban gentility and sentimental saccharine patriotism." Mrs. T's hairdo, dress sense, and speech mannerisms were criticized more than her actions. When even striking miners and their wives placarded London with signs screaming DITCH THE BITCH, I knew they were heading for the big plunge.

But if the miners were going down I wanted to be with them.

There is a curious peace that comes to men in a losing battle. I'd joined the 1984–85 miners' strike at its most historic moment, when almost all the pickets knew they'd lost but felt a sort of existential necessity, if such a thing exists, to go down fighting.

"Watch it, boyo," cracked Hywel Morgan, "we've got enough on our hands without all that unreadable French shit. You've lived in Paris, so tell me: how come a bloody ugly twit like Sartre pulls in all these lovely birds?"

I chose South Wales over Yorkshire because Thurcroft was now hostile Scargill country, the home bunker of the union leader, the strike's General Haig. And Len Doherty didn't live in Thurcroft any-more, having hanged himself in a Sheffield garage. Why does any-body commit suicide? I don't believe in suicide "explanations" because nobody ever knows, not really. But after months of digging, ringing up his friends, an enterprise to control my anger at what he'd done, I learned the basics. He was a hero at last done in by his heroism. Get this. Len wore a neck brace and was in constant pain as a result of having thrown himself at a PLO terrorist hand grenade hurled into his airport bus during the '72 Munich Olympics, which he was covering for his newspaper; his city room colleagues told me that he never got over his guilt because the bomb he kicked away, saving many lives, killed a small child. "Tha daft Jew!" Len had roared at me in the Miners Hall. But in the end he had become the Jew.

I went up to Thurcroft during the strike. But the fact of Scargillism—follow me, boys, into death and beyond—and the hos-tile indifference of those few Thurcrofters who admitted knowing Len meant the village was lost to me.

Scargillism. Male muscle, class loyalty, personalized combat. (Be it said, our "Arfa" attended Len's funeral along with most of his exec board.) Fatally, the National Union of Mineworkers leader had cho-sen to make the strike a test of personal strength, mano a mano, with Mrs. Thatcher, even though she had the big battalions: police, troops, media, timing, and huge stocks of coal to tide the country over.

"It's crazy," I told Hywel as I manned a bank of phones in strike HQ in Pontypridd, South Glamorganshire.

"So," drily replied Hywel, "was the Somme. The bloody bitch is beating us to our knees, and we'd rather die than surrender. Very stupid, if you ask me. But we have to pass *something* on to our sons—little and all since the jobs are gone. It's legends we're creating, all very Homeric. And I wish you'd go home to your nice new house in London, because we don't have time to nurse an anorexic cardiac case who looks the way we feel."

But Hywel tolerated me in Ponty, if only as comic relief, or because he sensed I would rather die on an NUM picket line than wheeze out my life in Vicarage Terrace. "It's not more pickets we need, you foolish lump. We need better brains to figure out how to avert total devastation. Between Mrs. Thatcher and our own exec, we're in a fine mess. But from what I hear, you're in as big a shit-hole as the rest of us." The retired miners who worked the phone bank with me joined in Hywel's laughter. How did they know Helen and I were in trouble?

"You really knew Richard's wife Elizabeth?" these elderly miners at the phone bank grilled me. They were asking about family, Liz Burton, our Dai's woman. South Wales produces not only coal but also large human dramas like Richard Burton, Dylan Thomas, and, king of Pontypridd, whose city center is roped off whenever he alights from his splendid white Rolls-Royce convertible, Tom Jones. No, I wasn't having this, not sitting out the strike spinning tall Hollywood tales to a bunch of miners no longer fit for action on the line.

"It's straight class war," Hywel warned me when I insisted he take me with him on flying picket duty. "They play rough and so do we."

"Good," I said.

"It's your funeral," he said. "Please make me a liar."

With South Wales itself tight for the strike, Welsh miners were free for guerrilla actions elsewhere, so for two weeks I oscillated around England's waist in Hywel's ancient Humber with him, Gwyn, and Arvon, from pits marked for death by Thatcher, attempting to pinpoint vulnerable power stations and Channel coal ports. Easy, this, since no place in England is more than seventy miles from the sea. We—I was now a we again—were reduced by heavy police checkpoints on main and side roads to desperate acts, even train robbery. We'd hide along railway embankments on slow curves, then scramble up to flip open the hatchways of passing coal cars, quickly scooping the contents into burlap bags and melting into the darkness like anthracite Robin Hoods to bring the coal to hard-up miners and their needy families or to sell it on the "alternative" market. If pressed, the Welsh are creative thieves; Hywel had entirely rebuilt his stunningly beautiful mountainside brick home mainly from materials expropriated from nearby building sites.

It really was hopeless, yet riding around with Hywel and the boys was a tonic because I was part of it again. I'd flown high with the miners and their union, and though I was a natural deserter, I had to be with them at the finish. It was a bloody finish, too. I had a black eye and a split lip from a police baton charge at the tiny coal port of Winterton-on-Sea, when the lads, who'd grown up on rugby football, met the enemy head on and in the melee I was flung in the air like a balsawood man. How humiliating. I, once so expert at riots, tossed aside by a single swipe from one mere fuzz. On the road back to Ponty I was inconsolable.

"Gus here," Hywel announced, "thinks he's still Rambo. Bloody intellectuals never know their place."

A collection of black eyes, broken fingers, mauled clothes, we dispersed in Ponty, and Hywel took me home with him to Cwybran in the Merthyr valley near Ebbw Vale. Hywel's pit, too, was one of the many on Mrs. T's hit list. If it went, the village died. "But you know," Hywel said in the small parlor, surrounded by his four young sons and a beaming, concerned wife, his feet up by the fire burning from coal we'd stolen, "it's not the Tories or Herself we're fighting but our own stupidity and inability to learn from history. Coal, as we've known it, has had it. Without a coordinated energy policy we might as well kiss these valleys goodbye." Then he shooed the boys out, and he and Bronwen casually lit a joint. *How Green Was My Valley* with a counterculture cast.

"Phrases like 'coordinated energy policy' are a bit thin-blooded compared to 'massed ranks of revolutionary working-class soldiers striding into a socialist sunrise,' aren't they?" I asked.

"Oh, that ancient stuff"—Hywel waved it away—"is just old-fashioned male politics." Even Bronwen looked surprised.

"It's a terrible confession for a Welshman to make," Hywel said, "but the traditional way of thinking based on pure muscle power simply does not work anymore. The women may be thinking more intelligently than us."

Bron said, "The valleys will never change, Gus. Here he is

inventing a new non-male politics, and he hasn't ever discussed it with me. You are horrible." She leaned over and kissed him.

When it became only too obvious that I was delaying the inevitable in Cwybran, Hywel forced the issue. One night after pub closing, he walked me over the hills near his house and put his arm around me. "You're always welcome here, you know. We're very short of the readies and can use your contribution. And you do your share of cooking and cleaning—Bron's quite impressed. You'd make somebody a great wife. Why not try Helen?"

The bastard was sending me back, exactly as had Len Doherty (RIP) twenty-five years before, to face the marital music.

Don't press your luck when things are iffy between you and the Mrs. I should have phoned ahead.

"Hey, Helen, I'm back!" I swept into The House. She was home, because her Greenham gear, wellies and raincoat and open knapsack, was all over the front room. But when I went upstairs the bedroom door wouldn't open. Then, slowly, a key turned from the inside, and Helen appeared in a red fuchsia dragon-dyed silk robe that (I noted sourly) didn't go with her coloring. She stepped into our hallway to shut the door behind her. Christ, I'd already played this scene in L.A. with Marci.

Helen evaded my angry, righteous stare. Then, quietly, "What did you expect, you fool?"

I stepped past her into the bedroom. Wilfred St. Regis would have been preferable, maybe even one of the Greenham women. It was Dick bloody Slocum the bloody Labour Party bloody politician-cum-developer from across the bloody road. I whirled on Helen.

"You couldn't do better than *that?*"

Helen shrugged. "He's here, you never are."

The fat lump in the bed—what a paunch!—spluttered, "My fault, Comrade."

"Comrade!" I screamed. How could Helen? This, this ... bloated toad with his Flapper Age lounge-lizard pencil mustache and gummy slicked-back hair and corpse-white skin and tiny slit eyes and blubbery lips and no neck ...

I turned to my wife. "I'm sorry, baby."

That's when we tumbled down a flight of stairs clawing and screaming at each other.

BOOK 5

THE LONELY BOMBARDIER OF PRIMROSE HILL

*F*ade-in: View of Primrose Hill, London NW 1, through powerful binoculars, slightly off focus. Binocular shot travels along horizon, taking in wide panorama from Hackney marshes to tall chimney stacks of Hammersmith power station. Focus more sharply on St. Paul's, phallic Post Office Tower (shut for IRA bomb repairs), finally swiveling back to Primrose Hill. Whoever is behind glasses adjusts focus for full impact of view etched sharply against late afternoon sky. It's a stagy effect. Silhouettes of people strolling along pathways, joggers, a kid flying a kite. Even the trees look prop. If it's possible for nature to appear artificial, Primrose Hill is the summit of the landscaper's cunning art.

On a search-and-destroy mission, binoculars zoom in on young woman yuppie with briefcase, striding purposefully up hill, then move to housewife toting plastic shopping bag, carry on to blonde Valkyrie in aerobic togs doing her thing, fix on her lovely butt, then almost regretfully move away to woman resting on one of hill's benches. Study her a moment. Fifty-something, a fuller-bodied Marlene Dietrich, stunning in a tight-fitting shiny black raincoat.

GUS BLACK'S VOICE (*behind binoculars*): Bombs away! *Fade-out.*

You never stop being married. You just act single.

Would Rose O'Malley's curse never lift? "Where is your self-respect, your dignity?"

Fade-in: Ext. Primrose Hill summit. Day. 1985. Dietrich lookalike on bench is still immersed in a London literally at her feet. Abruptly her vista is blocked by a man.

189

GUS: Say, that's some view.

VERA (*amused by him, enticingly foreign*): You would make a terrible spy. Your field glasses reflect sunlight, I could see you all the way from here. In the wartime Czech underground you wouldn't have lasted five seconds.

GUS (*even more interested, sits beside her*): Tell me about it. *Fade-out.*

Vera, too, was recovering from a heart attack. A widow, she had also been wondering if there was life after separation and was sex worth it anymore.

She was not, I discovered, in a hurry to find out. But I was.

A weight of love was off my shoulders. And best of all I'd been through a major industrial strike and a domestic trauma without a heart attack, emerging with just enough angina to prove I was alive.

Helen had neither starved nor frustrated me. There was no "reason" to break up. It was just my faithless body choosing again.

Even the style of our splitting up had been as Conran/Habitat as moving into this pretty little gentrified street. Helen's terror-stricken cries brought anxious neighbors and Pink Front friends running, plus a newly and vastly pregnant Emma Gore-Templeton carrying a tiny elephant in her belly, to witness my brutality. Would nobody intervene before I killed this witch wife who lent me so much freedom and love? By midnight our living room was crawling with the strangest people I'd ever seen: our friends.

Be just. They had done magnificently in a difficult situation. Their sort of efficiency I usually saw only in the aftermath of street accidents that in the best districts immediately drew an informal nursing corps with blankets and comfort for the aggrieved hit-and-run. Nobody can beat the English middle class at disasters. *My* middle class.

Or, as Emma said, "You loved each other. Maybe still do. You just can't stand each other anymore. Now bugger off, Gus, and let the blood dry on the walls."

I'd been reborn in the plague time.

A renter again, I scoured the leafy corner of Marxshire called Hampstead for a new roof over my head. Pinch-faced landlords, delighted to meet a BBC "name," didn't scruple to murder me with their extortionate rents for "Lovely view, don't you think?"

Arabella was my fifth landlady today.

She immediately apologized for wasting my time. Her ad in the local paper was wrong, she'd changed her mind, something about a homeless cousin (probably invented) to whom she had promised the two back rooms. "But do please have some tea—I know how ghastly flat hunting is."

Ari, a fellow journalist and broadcaster, was back from a Beirut hospital after being blown up by a car bomb. Though disfigured, in a dark light—the only kind in her basement flat—she could be Katharine Hepburn less twenty years.

Burt Lancaster and Kate sat on the couch with their tea. Then I reached across and took the cup from her hand. She rose to my embrace.

"You don't mind my face? The scars?"

We kissed hotly. I began to unbutton her blouse. She helped me. I bent to kiss her breasts, one arm curled around her arched waist, the other excitedly pulling down her brown wool skirt. Moaning and grabbing my hair, she started unbuckling my belt. My breathing was hoarse as my free hand played with her partly undressed body. Unable to wait, she unzipped my fly.

"Use it," said Ari breathlessly.

"I'm trying." I wriggled.

"No, I mean a condom."

"I didn't bring one."

"You brought business references but no protection?"

"Landladies aren't usually this nice."

"How stupid and irresponsible of you. I didn't come out of a year in hospital to go back in with AIDS."

"I'll run down to the corner chemist."

"No, I have some here. In the bathroom, under the sink."

In one clumsy move I lurched in the direction Ari pointed while trying to step out of my shoes and take off my socks and trousers at the same time. In the bathroom I found a box of Durex rubbers. Removed a small, slightly oily silver-foil package, ripped it open, tremblingly dropped contents on floor, pulled out another, couldn't tear it open, more I tried more it resisted. Suddenly it gave and condom slithered out as if jet-propelled, arcing into open toilet. Breathing hard, I dug out last condom, slowed myself enough to bite off edge of foil, made a face as I tasted lubricant, very carefully removed condom, stared at it—I hadn't seen one this close since VE

Day 1945—put my finger in it to see which way it rolled, couldn't figure it out, sighed in frustration, and started to place it on my (to my eyes) gigantic penis, which promptly shrunk.

Defeated, I hobbled back and slumped at Ari's feet. "Sorry. It's like trying to figure out a Rubik cube."

Naked on her couch, Ari seethed. "You blundering, blithering idiot—you were going to be my first lover since the accident. This was important to me." Then, looking more closely at me, she giggled. "On the other hand, you've given me my best laugh for a long time. Did anyone ever tell you you are a bloody ridiculous man?"

All too many, dear Ari.

Rose O'Malley for one. Within twenty-four hours of my taking a bachelor flat in Primrose Hill, Rose came round with a homemade fruitcake and an "Oh well ...," her eyes burning with triumphant curiosity.

Burt Lancaster, back on the singles scene, gazed steadily at Deborah Kerr thirty years after they made love on a Waikiki beach. Dana Andrews, long retired from the NYPD, stared at Laura Hunt back from the rainy dead. Rekindle my fire, Rose, I thought, but only said, "Lemon or milk?"

She smiled and adjusted the sari she was still in the ghastly habit of wearing. Let's see, if I got rid of that dumb Grandma Moses bun, ripped off the sack and put her into, hmmm, not Zandra Rhodes, still less Laura Ashley, how about Dior or maybe smartly tailored Chanel separates, whisked her to a diet farm, and—

Rose, as always, knew what I was thinking. "I *like* this dress," she said firmly. Ah well.

Then she said, "Things haven't gone too badly for me, you know. Not badly at all."

Ha, as if I didn't know. In the last royal Honours List, she'd been named a Dame Commander of the British Empire, rare honor for a writer. The last literary dame, I reminded Rose, had been Rebecca West, "also"—I waggled my finger at her—"a staunch anti-Communist."

Rose, a picture of greedy, sedate fame, cocked her head at me almost coquettishly. "Now, now, old friend," she warned. Meaning: no politics, no Aly, no sex.

I pushed it. Had Rose actually met Brenda, *Private Eye*'s name for the Queen?

She stiffened. "She's a *very* intelligent woman. Like me, but unlike you, not university-trained." Then she unbent. "I hear you're an American professor now. That's your punishment for all those lectures you used to give me—"

"—in bed," I cheerfully noted.

Rose winced.

"What *do* you do for it now, Rose?" I asked, curiosity getting the better of manners. I genuinely wanted to know if it stopped at our age.

Teeth slightly bared: "You bastard." Then, "I gave that up a long time ago. What's the point?"

"Rose," I said, "there never was a point. We just do it."

"If that is the best we can do—'just do it'—I am unpersuaded."

I really couldn't help laughing, she sounded so like Alice's Red Queen. But then a shadow of the old guilt fell between us: I had not, after all, been able to rescue Rose.

"I've been badly treated by men, Gus—so very badly," she had told me in our first encounter almost thirty years before. And the details! Secretly I had been impressed not only by the shenanigans the polite English got up to but by the caliber of names Rose listed as lovers. Mandarins all, poets and parliamentarians, Labour leaders and world-celebrated journalists, Communist theoreticians, influential editors, West End playwrights, and famous single "confirmed bachelors," then as now a euphemism for homosexual. On her shabby couch that day I had privately resolved that if I couldn't outwrite them I'd ... Out loud I said, "The dirty bastards." "No, don't misunderstand." Rose had smiled bravely, wearily, tolerantly. "It's not their fault, don't you see?" She launched into another gripping tale of how many of her English lovers were whip men or boot men or exhibited other symptoms of an expensive private education. "But Rose," I'd sputtered, "some of these guys are my heroes!" "Keep a sense of proportion, man. It doesn't stop them being decent social democrats. Wanting to beat a woman, shit and piss on her, doesn't mean they hate her personally. At least it shows some ... originality." When she'd turn them down cold, they'd leave her without a thank you. Her main gripe, as I recalled, was gentlemen friends who asked her to pretend she was a nurse or policewoman. Rose hated uniforms and steadfastly refused.

"So after all that, dear Gus," she repeated, "what is the point?"

I leaned across her on the couch and covered her hand with mine. "This," I leered.

She didn't remove her hand. Instead she said, "You're inviting another Hiroshima, you know."

Come again?

Unbelievably, she was still preaching at me. Something about the futility of antinuclear activism, imminent Apocalypse, ruined civilizations, global suicide, the tragic limits of human intelligence. Whatever we did, preferably nothing on the streets anymore, all was lost, and a jolly good thing it was, too, since it was nothing more than what we the human race deserved. Clearly, Rose's stray into the Other Zone had been more profound than mine. After Dr. Last and schizophrenia, I'd just slunk off with a godawful headache and a great desire to sleep it off before I resumed normal transmission. Rose was of sterner stuff. She had looked into the face of the Great Beast and pronounced him—It—us. In a word, hopeless. Except, perhaps, if we stooped to the indignity of playing for time. The Swiss, their style of civil defense, deep-dug bunkers against the inevitable firestorm, might teach us something about real survival ...

Finally Rose had found the perfect turnoff.

"Aw, Rose ... we used to be Communists."

"Smart Communists keep the bomb," she said. "Look at Russia and China."

This was definitely not the way to go.

I told Rose I'd bought some groceries "just in case." Feel like cooking?

She fixed me with a regal, not unfriendly glare. "You are perfectly amazing, Gus Black."

Well, how about it?

Her hand under mine turned into a fist. She pulled it away. "I tire easily. Another time."

That got to me. I wilted early too. Still, at sixty-eight, Rose was a wonder: two bad knees, a lame ankle, arthritis, yet fuller of life than two of me. I'd bet she still made a juice-oozing meatloaf. The memory, almost an odor wafting across the years, moved me closer to her. But she leaped to her feet, rising on tiptoe to offer, as usual, her cheek. I wrapped my arms around her and drew her to me.

"Mmm," I said, breathing in, "that's a new perfume."

I kissed her full on the lips, which instinctively she returned, and just as instinctively my hand reached up to fumble with her sari. Why didn't these goddamn things have buttons?

She drew back. "Do you know," she said, "I think you would, too."

"What's the harm?"

"You're incorrigible."

"I'm also single again."

She looked at me. "Not for long. I know you. Bee to honey. Some socialist."

"I'm a soldier, Rose. Of the revolution. That includes the sexual revolution."

She smiled and pushed me away. "My old Gus. Still in the trenches after the action has passed him by."

"Better trenches than fallout shelters."

Alas, she was at the door, saying goodbye. I dutifully kissed her cheek and let her go. Just before leaving, she patted my arm maternally.

"My little Red Peter Pan," she said.

Rose had waited thirty years to deliver that zinger.

Astride the wild white buffalo of lust, I surveyed the plains of London from Primrose Hill through my Zeiss binoculars, General Custer about to attack his doom. Plenty of fresh meat out there, enough for an army, enough to make any sane man happy, but never sufficient to satisfy a longing for, God help me, Helen. But look at all those serious accidents out there waiting to happen! Gallop, scramble, get there fast: Susan, Amanda, two Carolines, Lydia, Vanessa, Penelope, athletic and amiable, postfeminist, a quick generation junior to Helen, dimly aware of Rose's writing (unlike Helen's group, which knew her by heart), compacted with ambition, razor-sharp to slights but dulled to the recent history of their gender, they were smooth as torn silk and open to everything but the fiery lessons of collective action. They talked like and sometimes were stockbrokers, and screwed like angels, and made me feel, for the first time, the pain.

Jack the Ripper Black even placed an ad in a magazine and signed up with a marital agency. After meeting a dozen or so of the hundred replies, I was utterly baffled. What *do* women want? "Hunks with brains, poets with investment portfolios, our fathers before they met our mothers," said the last of my dates, a brunette Australian beauty who glanced at her Rolex two minutes after we shook hands at the Rossetti pub and lied about a prior dinner engagement. Did I look that bad? I asked her. "Try Hampstead," was all she said.

I went back to the binoculars.

But Hampstead proved inescapable.

"You don't like us women very much, do you?" demanded

Anthea, a scrawny Brunhild in full Nazi regalia, soon after we started going steady. Wehrmacht helmet, shiny black boots, SS-style belt. I hardly noticed anymore.

"You NW 3 types are too rich for my blood," I yawned. NW 3 was Hampstead/Marxshire's postal code.

Anthea bent down over me, letting the leather suction cups on her nipples brush my bare chest. I tried to get excited.

"Nonsense," she rapped, "Hampstead has always nourished great writers—Byron, Evelyn Waugh, Sylvia Plath. You don't need slums to create *Kultur*."

Tactfully I didn't point out that her bedroom had dim red lights, velvet hangings, and even a tiger skin.

A naked Himmler, she sat up contemplating me. "I know what will cheer you up," she said brightly. Propelling her thin, bony, sensuous frame off the huge playpen of a bed, she dragged a canvas bag out of the closet and began picking through it matter-of-factly. "Hmmm. Thongs. Pliers. Bullwhip. Manila rope. Handcuffs. Leather mask. Ah yes, there it is."

My heart sank. Oh God, something new.

She reached in and pulled out a Luger pistol. I sat bolt upright.

"Don't worry," she soothed, "it's only a toy replica. I got it at a knockdown price."

"Where, Berlin?"

"Camden Town."

Again I protested: "But I'm Jewish."

"So what? I am too."

This surprised me. I told Anthea there was something wrong with two Jews pretending to be Nazis in love.

"Don't be a bore, you've liked it up to now. Just because I'm Jewish doesn't change things." She brought the Luger into bed and played with it and herself at the same time.

I watched briefly, then took the gun away. There were limits. "I thought you were a feminist, Anthea. This stuff really turn you on?"

She gave me the sort of withering look I'd seen her hurl at prosecution witnesses at the Old Bailey. Small, wiry, large-eyed, Anthea was a civil liberties barrister as well as a contentious television personality who gave freely of her time to Amnesty International, especially on torture cases. On Primrose Hill my Zeiss had instantly spotted her walking her Borzoi, but our affair, though only a few weeks old, had already exhausted me. ("Affair? How quaint," she smiled. "Nobody has affairs anymore except adulterers.") A true sexual gymnast, she didn't so much fuck as tear out my eyes, chew my nipples, bite my flanks, suck my mouth till it bled. Impersonally, clinically, passion by the numbers. And now the Nazi bit.

From somewhere Anthea produced another pair of Storm Trooper boots, which I tiredly put on. They made me feel silly.

Too late. Anthea's eyes glittered. She'd been wanting me to dress up from the start. Her voice thickened as she tried to keep control.

"You look tremendous. A real man," she said with emotion.

I turned the boots this way and that, then stood up in bed. Anthea handed me her SS belt and buckle, which I silently donned. She trembled slightly in her Wehrmacht helmet as I towered over her. My cock rose.

"This stuff," I marveled, "really works, doesn't it?"

Anthea said, "Mein Führer, I am yours."

I stared down at her. "Hey, hold on," I cautioned. "I don't mind beating hell out of you now and then. But this is a no-no."

She hissed Teutonically, "Yesss. Yesss."

She began licking my boots. I recoiled, but she wouldn't let go. She grabbed my legs, rubbing the boots against her small breasts, so alarmingly erect they practically tore through her leather thongs.

My cock stood up like a Nazi salute. "Dammit, Anthea, stop that. You'll be wanting me to sing the Horst Wessel song next."

In an ecstasy of anticipation: "Would you? Would you, Mein Führer?"

Instantly my member drooped. Anthea blinked at it. In shame and embarrassment she took off her steel helmet and placed it discreetly over my private part.

What happened?

She looked up at me, full of sad tenderness. "Auschwitz. Your flag is at half-mast for the six million murdered Jews. I understand."

Slowly I unburdened myself of the SS regalia, sitting on the bed to pull off the boots.

"Anthea," I said, "you really had me worried for a minute there."

She watched me turn into Gus Black again, the aging bombardier of Primrose Hill.

"Men are such cowards," she sighed.

So right.

Of course this one-sided sketch of Anthea is a travesty of the liberal conscience. Physical torture—graphic accounts of beatings, bayonetings, castrations, electrode-shocked nipples, gory vivisection of pregnant peasant women and butchered nuns—wasn't invented to give Amnesty activists like her a sick sidelong pleasure at the recital. Many governments now habitually use torture as an instrument of political suasion. The instinct to expose and eliminate this barbaric practice is just and proper. Anthea has it both ways.

I wanted to be a man. Not Anthea's idea of him, a Calvin Klein Nuremberg rally Ken doll, but genuinely "caring, gentle, compassionate, sensitive, nurturing, committed"—all the buzzwords floating across the Atlantic to infect a venerable English vocabulary with American aggro disguised as tenderness. But how reconcile my feminism with the street macho that had formed me? Damn Helen for forcing me to think about it all over again.

☐ ☐ ☐

"Enough already about your wife," Lori protested. "Let's watch another golden oldie." Lori's idea of an oldie was last year's Madonna video.

She was twenty-two, and a Valley Girl. We were in my king-size bed at the Alhambra Gardens.

The London-L.A.-London commute had again become the fixed point, almost the only equity, in my life. And Lori did not mind my getting up at all hours to stick my head into a tiny shortwave radio to listen to BBC World Service news. "Anything about Princess Di?" she'd sleepily call. Lady Di had made a huge hit with Lori by dancing with John Travolta on a recent White House visit. "I knew," Lori breathed, "I just knew John couldn't be gay." Ah, I responded, but what if Lady Di was? Lori pouted. Like Rose, she did not find my jokes very funny.

Lori was helping me explore Reagan's America from a teenager's viewpoint. No, unfair. Lori was okay, just saw herself slightly over the hill because she had tried but failed to be a Los Angeles basketball "Lakers girl." Life seemed to be over for this aerobically agile, perfectly formed, compulsive shopper "since before junior high, that's how bad I am, Glendale Galleria, Sherman Oaks Galleria, Topanga Mall, Fox Hills, you name it, I lost my credit card virginity there," distantly Jewish with those WASP good looks common among girls whose first names end in a vowel. I "validated" her "identity" as a "nondysfunctional human being," she said. (Lori was a fan of afternoon radio doctors.) I was her Big Daddy, she was my idea of safety, neither an SAS student nor a feminist nor political, cute as hell, small, bouncy, with a magnificent tan and tiny even teeth, a walking ad for Melrose Avenue's latest. Her current favorite outfit was a tight pastel half T-shirt ending just above her bellybutton, baggy designer jeans with a heavy studded belt to highlight her petite waist, and hand-tooled cowboy boots. Atop her small head was the latest craze, a kitchen-mop haircut that cost her a hundred bucks and made her look (she hoped) "like more serious, like an agent or woman producer, you know, or Glenn Close in *The Big Chill*, did you see it? It's about all these old people who used to be in the same fraternity or something," Lori told me when I picked her up during happy hour in a Santa Monica bar. She wanted to be taken seriously, so used big words she got from the Phil Donahue show. My approach had been, as usual, unoriginal. As she sat with a girlfriend watching reruns of *Classic L.A. Laker Games* on the bar TV, I'd saluted with my margarita. "Oh, I say, I'm from England, what is a slam dunk?"

Like so many white middle-class Southern California women, Lori was a professional student, having ended up at UCLA as a fine arts minor and Alpha Epsilon Phi major. What now? Real estate, of course. Meantime, she sat on my bed filing her nails while moodily watching yet another showing on my VCR of Nick Ray's *In a Lonely Place*, with Bogart as Dixon Steele, the homicidal screenwriter, and Gloria Grahame as Holly, the girl next door. Lori and I were naked and apart. She was deeply disappointed in me.

"Did I tell you," I remarked, "that I used to know the director? He's dead now."

"Don't you know anybody alive?" Lori yawned, inspecting her miniature feet, then gave a friendly, open smile. She would have smiled at Charles Manson.

Watching Dixon Steele place his arm around Holly, whether to strangle or kiss her we didn't yet know, I put on my thin-lipped Bogie smile. "Sorry, kid. I keep forgetting death doesn't exist for you."

She pouted some more. "It's just the way you harp on it. All those funerals you seem to go to these days."

"At my age funerals can be almost as entertaining as Laker games."

She frowned. At first she'd liked being with a "mature" man, but now it depressed her. She tried convincing herself. "You're not old ... not very."

I bared my teeth in a Bogart laugh. "Say it a little louder, sweetheart, and we both might believe it."

Lori kissed my chest automatically. "Oh, Gus, you've got a fine body. Honest."

When I didn't register, Lori jumped from the bed and switched off the VCR. With Steele in my voice, I told her to turn it back on. Petulantly she switched on the TV instead but got bad luck: Cary Grant and Ingrid Bergman in *Notorious*. Lori looked at the screen and sighed listlessly. "Who're they?" Her idea of an aging star was Tom Hanks.

My eyes were glued to the climax, where Grant carries a sick Bergman down the long staircase past Claude Rains and his Nazi mother. I said, "You know, kid, the only time I ever really feel unfaithful to Helen is when you and I watch old movies together. It's worse than adultery."

"Maybe," she said, swiping viciously at her nails, "you two should have made out more and gone to the movies less."

Sadly, *Notorious* reminded me of the times Helen and I sat entwined in each other's arms in front of any Hitchcock we could find. "She turned me on to John Frankenheimer," I reminisced, "and I made her see why John Ford was more than just a reactionary sexist."

Lori, brightly: "I loved him in *Star Wars*."

Who?

"John Ford. Luke Skywalker."

That was Harrison Ford, I corrected.

Lori shrugged, her lovely nude shoulders practically meeting her ears in a girlish gesture. "Oh well, one Ford looks like another to me. Anyway, you like me being a dumb Valley Girl, don't you?"

"You do the part so well," I said in brittle-hard Cary Grant Cockney.

Lori put down her emery board. "You really know where to stick the knife, don't you?"

I hadn't meant to insult her.

She studied me. "We're breaking up, aren't we?"

I put *Notorious* on mute. I knew the dialogue by heart anyway. Still Cary Grant, I said, "You can do a lot better than me, Lori.

You're young, pretty, and into real estate. That should be an irresistible combination to L.A. men."

"But not to you?"

I turned to look at her. Lordy, lordy, young bodies. "No," I said, "not to me. Not now. Not at sixty."

"I could study up on old movies. Honest, I could."

She was feeling bad because I'd said it first. We needed a graceful exit.

"Listen, kid," I said, going from Grant back to Bogart, "where I'm going you can't follow," and the whole end-of-*Casablanca* speech.

Lori, her small, alert eyes moistening, stared fixedly at me throughout. "Oh, Gus," she said, "that's beautiful." Then she looked slyly at me. "What's it from?"

I smiled, proud as a father at his daughter's graduation. "See, you're learning."

As breakups go, ours was easy. When Lori hesitated, all I had to do was let her, for the first time, see my nightly going-to-bed routine. Naked as usual, she leaned against the bathroom door, fascinated by the procedure.

"You sure you want to watch this?" I asked.

She nodded.

"Okay, it's your lookout," I said.

First, in the mirror, I scrutinized my hair for dandruff, then removed the cumbersome British National Health hearing aid, then took off my close-up reading glasses—one of three pairs, each with a different function—and blew on them, cleaning them before placing them in a soft case. Stripping to my shorts, I took a pill for indigestion, then a blood pressure pill, followed by a beta blocker for my clogged artery, followed by an anti-inflammatory for arthritis and a pill for my high cholesterol. I put a Band-Aid around a fingernail bitten to the bleeding quick. Removed my back brace, an ugly pale pink corset with two steel rods sewn into the fabric, and draped it over the bathtub. Took heat rash ointment and applied it to my crotch. Then unwound a permanent bandage from my knee, damaged in a long-ago riot. Finally I lifted my leg up to the sink and carefully inspected an ingrown toenail, using tiny scissors to pare here and there, and dabbing in antifungoid tincture. At last I was ready to brush my teeth. I removed my partial bridge, four teeth knocked out at Trafalgar Square '68, brushed it, and placed it in a Lofthouse's Original Fisherman's Friend lozenge tin.

Lori hadn't batted an eye. Tough babe. Until I began the final step.

"Gus!"

Grinning evilly: "Yeah?"

Lori, really shocked: "Dental floss?"

Suddenly I saw her seeing me as I was: an elderly man without a shred of the style she thought she'd admired in me.

She said, "It's so ... icky."

Sadistically, I reached for the tin holding my false teeth and rattled it in front of her eyes.

"You're right, sweetheart," Bogie-Black said. "Would you care to watch while I unscrew my wooden leg?"

I thought she'd faint. Instead, she ran into the living room and with obvious relief began to pack her overnight bag. Bye-bye, Valley Girl, you were adorable to the max.

Accept it. It was better teaching young women than fucking them. When I confessed this to Luther Luck, he echoed my remark to Lori: "See, you're learning."

Even with Luther's help, it was hard to be back again. I was more used than I realized to gray clammy days, strong Typhoo tea, and a sense of being enclosed by limits, hedges, fences: tradition. Americans made fun of my "English" accent. And I was too hooked on the main English art form, failure, to be a good American. More and more, I missed the English agnostic attitude toward whether or not one succeeded—in the U.K. it was not a theological but a survival issue only. Fear of a certain type of success had originally driven me across the Atlantic to a culture where disaster was enshrined as victory. (*See* Gallipoli, Dunkirk, Arnhem, etc.) Screwing up was a form of civic virtue. It had (laugh track here) liberated me as man and writer.

But in L.A. the fine craft of muddling through was universally perceived as losing it, man.

Is there anything worse than a loser?

Yep. A socialist who doubts his own motives.

When in doubt, lean on the left. I gave it another shot.

This time New Directions–UAW, CISPES, Save the Rain Forest, Tikkun, Farm Workers Support Group, Santa Monicans for Rent

Control, Southern Leadership Christian Council, Friends of the National Lawyers Guild, Fifth International, Socialist Workers Party, even Gus Hall's old (my) Communist Party U.S.A. In my long absence, of course, things had changed. The left was balkanized into often contradictory, even antagonistic "identity politics." There was an ecology wing, a feminist wing, a New Age wing, an All Men Are Poets If They But Knew It wing, etc. As a good Marxshireman, I knew that the ecology-things-of-the-spirit-more-than-gross-matter part of the left—could it even be called left?—would probably take over from the old rigid vanguardists with whom I had most in common. But deep in my heart, I couldn't, in this as so much else, make the jump to modernity, realism, a future politics of greater spirituality. I was a hardass, and therein lay the problem.

Rose's shadow hung heavily over these meetings. "Still at it, old friend? You'll do anything to avoid the writing desk. Why waste your energy on puerile activism? Grow up!" I wished I could. But making agendas seemed as natural as breathing; worse, I needed it to organize, as well as shield me from, American realities. Okay, especially after Winterton-on-Sea brought me so painfully to earth, I couldn't make do with fists alone anymore. But stuffing envelopes and canvassing were not too dishonorable, were they?

Who was I kidding? It was over. My career on the left. Had nothing to do with ideology, philosophy, principle. The real reason was more brutal: my body. My aching, scarred back and infarcted heart simply couldn't stand more than sixty minutes of bullshit in any one day, and what left meeting takes less than four hours in a draughty/overheated room/hall that would test the stamina, lungs, and metabolism of a trained athlete? Sure, at these meetings I saw heroic, elderly, frail, and infirm comrades, often in wheelchairs and sometimes gasping through oxygen tanks—inspirations, no doubt. Like hell. My sore buttocks had written me out of the U.S. left.

Who would take care of me now?

"Poor baby, you don't seem to manage very well without a woman or a group. Reality just isn't your bag, is it?" said Frances Dellinger.

At San Andreas State I now shared an office with one of America's most distinguished feminists, Betty Friedan's collaborator and Gloria Steinem's mentor. "Distinguished? That means long-winded and boring, doesn't it?" Frances inquired. Luther's prankishness had led him to recruit Frances to teach Women Transparent and Invisible in the American Film, and to house us together.

Frances gave no quarter and asked none. She knew all about me, or thought she did, from Rose's novel *Loose Leaves from a Random Life*. "I've got to hand it to you, kid." She swiveled around in her chair to stab a Camel unfiltered at me. Like Rose herself, Frances was permanently half hidden in a swirl of blue smoke. ("If you're one of these health Nazis who can't stand a little honest combustion in the air, you can just fuck off and find another office.") Her tolerance of me was tinged with malice. "You've got the guts of a bank robber returning to the scene of the crime. Or did the likes of Rose O'Malley chase you out of England?"

Rose's book, I'd learned, had bestowed on me a mild notoriety among the sort of literary feminists Rose herself could not stand. "But don't you try getting any mileage out of that," Frances warned the first day we met. "If you're anything remotely like O'Malley's portrait of you, oh boy, kid, are we going to have fun together!" she chortled.

Frances could not resist ganging up on me. "And why not?" she demanded, looking up from grading her Feminism: The Next Stage student essays. "If you want a wet nurse, go to a gentler soul like Friedan. Me, I'm the Lizzie Borden of women's liberation. Har-har!"

How could I resist her?

Frances, trimly sexy but defiantly unmadeup, soon embarked on a perpetual Saturday Nite date with me, hanging loose, even beach partying. Her only rule was no serious talk after five p.m., and if I ever tried it, she simply said, "Give me a break, kid, I'm tired from the office."

I was her male bimbo.

When I protested that she wasn't taking me seriously enough, Frances smiled grimly. "Revenge is sweet."

"Come on," I said, "I'm on your side. Basically. Sort of."

"Yeah." She appraised me. "That's probably what you told O'Malley too. Pure gold-plated b.s." Had Frances seen too many Thelma Ritter movies?

We were strolling along Santa Monica beach just under her palatial Palisades house. "My husband, bless his chauvinist heart, died early and rich." She jerked a nicotine-stained finger at the hillside mansion. "Actually I was in love with the s.o.b. I grew up in his arms."

I complained that she was being unfair to me. Everyone was entitled to a fresh start in America.

"You're breaking my heart." She accepted my hand to clamber

over the seaside rocks, then relented. "Okay, I'll let up. But you go easy on us too. A lot has changed since you notched up your scores on our hearts. Back in the fifties women were merely neurotic. Now we're your worst nightmare come true." She threw her head back, laughed at me as heartily as Malcolm X once had, and said the same thing. "Oh, Gus, if you could just see your face!"

Hey, come on, we're just two people, a man and a woman and a great view.

She turned to me. "You amaze me, you really do. With your record, I should eat you alive. You're lucky I like men."

"I'm not sure I like women anymore," I confessed.

"I like that 'anymore.' Or are you trying to be honest? Don't. We're awfully tired of 'honest' men hiding their sexism. But who knows? Maybe if you of all people can learn, it's not hopeless. Younger women tell me there's a new breed of man coming up the road. Not feminist exactly, but ..." She cut herself short. "But hell, you don't even know what I'm talking about, do you?"

"You preach too much," I said.

"Look who's talking."

"Goddammit, Rose—"

"What did you call me? Well, in a perverse way it's a compliment, I suppose. Poor O'Malley. What did she do to deserve a guy like you?"

"She just got lucky," I said.

Marci Washington had put me in Reeboks, Ralph Lauren chinos, Clacton & Frinton shirts, Armani linen jackets, and a slight chignon, which was how successful movie men dressed, she insisted. I drew the line only at the rabbinical Steven Spielberg scraggly beard with add-on turned-around baseball cap, the badge of drop-dead Hollywood male success. I hadn't lived this long, and come this far from Chicago's west side, to look like a Lawndale loser, a yeshiva bocher.

Melissa said, "It's a good look, except that dumb Chinese pigtail in back. Do you mind?" And she reached behind me with a pair of nail scissors and deftly rendered me human again.

Melissa was my price of admission to the Mouse Pack.

Like me, none of them could "sustain a relationship" ... "make a commitment" ... "find their vulnerability" ... or any of the other cant phrases that passed for discourse in the hustling, Hollywood-centered middle classes of Los Angeles that were my new social base, like it or not. The Mouse Pack combined, in exquisite balance, the two subcultures my body had impelled me into: heart attack and divorce. You need never be lonely in L.A. if you split up with your wife after an m.i. I had a lot of male bonding to catch up on.

It was all part of my search for something more enduring than left politics: that thin trace of contrariness that surfaces in American life when the male stomach finally turns. Nowadays I was obscenely grateful to anyone who spoke plain English or Old American, expressed a cranky opinion in unadorned prose, or swam upstream against the authoritarian torrents of family-oriented, child-centered "love" that seemed to be drowning everybody in molten pink plastic. In recent American history it has usually been untenable men, depressed and saddled with unfashionable prejudices, terminally blundering with women—I speak of H. L. Mencken, Edmund Wilson, and their main heir, Lenny Bruce—who bore the culture of active, uncategorized dissent.

"Hey, wait a minute," called Bull Buell from Kelly Klein's patio, which had a clear view of the HOLLYWOOD sign. "I know a woman in Brentwood who fits all that to a tee. My ex-wife was one depressed bitch who thought I was the biggest sellout in the world. Don't she qualify?"

Then, around Kelly's massive Stickley oak poker table in his steel-stilted Beachwood Canyon house, we set to arguing over whether there were any women writers or artists who could possibly compete with America's Great Cranks, it being understood that this was merely a tired variant of the old chestnut, Why no female Michelangelos?

"If she exists," said Kelly, helping Bull turn the swordfish steaks on the barbecue, "she's probably a TV comedy star. You have to watch television to see anything subversive these days." Kelly, being a hugely successful TV producer-writer of a long-running sitcom, had an axe to grind.

The Mouse Pack was my new gang.

And Kelly was my latest blood brother, a direct descendant of Len Doherty, BenGy Tyler, and Hywel Morgan.

Kelly would have liked the comparison. He was a serious man in an unserious business, a prince of Hollywood with the imagination of a boxing promoter and the infighting skills of a hungry young middleweight. A displaced scholar with a Yale Ph.D. (thesis topic: James Joyce) and ten long years as a Borscht circuit standup comic, he had hit the gong with a TV comedy called *Dad & Me*, a nostalgic look at his Cleveland childhood and a blue-collar father who, unlike Archie Bunker, hated racists and bigotry. When the money poured in, Kelly built himself a top-of-the-canyon house copied almost slat for slat from one of his favorite movies, *North by Northwest*. Shrewd devious, honest, candid, blasé, generous, paranoid, and open, he was not the world's best judge of character—he liked me—and he flourished in the company of fractured men, as I did.

Like the professor he almost became, Kelly patiently gave me lessons in how to convert my London literary talents into Hollywood money "without selling yourself out, because if that's your plan you'll end up even poorer and a bigger schmuck than you are." First rule: "Low-key is a loser in L.A., pal. So get rid of all that Bloomsbury self-deprecation shit. Here it registers as uncertainty. And let's start dressing like a winner, okay?" Meaning (a) polyester was out, and (b) whatever was "in" had to make me look healthy. "You never know," advised Kelly, "when the Beverly Hills health police might knock on your door at two a.m. Maybe last year a bunch of us would be lazing around the pool doing coke, but today, if you notice, our fingers are compulsively at our carotids while we furiously jog in the afternoon smog that'll kill us quicker that dope, but since John Belushi died it's no longer an option. This town can't stand another scandal like that."

So, under Kelly's guidance, I now breakfasted at the Polo Lounge or Farmers Market, where I lolled at the screenwriters' table (actually several), pretending. My rented T-bird convertible was barely passable; Hollywood Jews preferred BMWs or Mercedes, anything German, forget Japanese, Rommel wasn't a Samurai. And Kelly started taking me to Laker games—the L.A. version of Ascot's Royal Enclosure—to be seen at courtside. Hey, yeah, this felt okay. "You like it, don't you?" Kelly smiled evilly the first time he took me to Spago. "Sure," I agreed, "everything but the food. You call this a pizza?" (It had squab on it.) He sighed and punched me in the arm. "I'm usually good with people with learning disabilities. Maybe you'll be the big exception."

A True Story: I go to an all-male gym now, mainly Beverly Hills agents and others in the business. In the sauna several guys lounge naked or with towels demurely circling their waists. As usual, a strained silence in the steam.

A small, potbellied, middle-aged man breaks the tension. "Hey, what's wrong with us here? A 'hello' won't kill us. What are we afraid of?" he asks nobody in particular. Harrumphing, rustling of newspapers, no response. Uneasily, our eyes glance off nearly naked bodies. The little man persists.

"Look," he says, "a little friendship doesn't mean you're asking for family secrets. Why are men such cowards?" More silence. In exasperation, he points to a young Adonis. "For instance, you there, what's your name? My name is Larry."

Young Adonis, built like a Rams linebacker, clears throat. "Er, I'm Greg."

"See?" exclaims the paunchy little man. "You lose nothing by expressing a little friendship."

Greg untenses a bit. Man asks, "And what is it you do, Greg?" Young Adonis says he is a prop man at Paramount.

"Oh, that's swell," says little man, "and what do you do to relax?"

Greg broods, then says, "Uh, let's see, I ski, wind-sail, weight-train, backpack, jog, wrestle, and some triathlon."

Little man absorbs this in awe. Then exclaims, "Gee, I'd like to fuck you!"

Divorce, breakup, guilt, infidelity, impotence, rage, "loss of self-esteem" (feeling rotten), exhaustion due to nonstop emotional bargaining, sexual boredom—welcome to the wonderful world of L.A. men.

They, now we, were a loose Hollywood circle of divorced, separated, split-off, or unhappily spliced men spinning in sexual space, all looking, finding, losing, hoping, turned off and on again.... sandra she's different so warm vivacious the bitch on the first date gets into my classic camaro and says this isn't the statement you want to make is it followed by is your bmw in the shop i don't know what diane wants but then i don't know what i want do you know what i want what the fug am i asking you for i'm paying alimony and child support to two women my shrink says the money's a potency symbol maybe but it sure hasn't helped my sack life i save maybe half a dozen lives every week at beverly hills memorial and can't save my own how's them little apples what do you mean i'll never find a warm stable committed relationship as long as i use clichés like that who the fuck are you to talk your books sell in the tens sure i love my wife and kid just hate the architect-designed contractor-supplied nanny-assisted gardener-trimmed package it's wrapped up in okay so i'm not being honest i married her on the second rebound and the kid is her blackmail so do me something they haven't already i'm past forty and can't afford the luxury of youthful self-destruction but oh god sometimes i miss them days susan thinks i'm at the gym when i hang out in topless bars do you believe all that stuff about hetero aids i read in the new england journal of medicine back me up on this gabe that guys can give it but not get it what are you guys bitchin' about none of ya 'cept gus a born loser if i ever saw one makes less than two hundred k a year look at kelly with his nielsen top ten sitcom his bathroom costs mor'n my whole house y'all wouldn't be seen dead in a four-wheel-drive blazer like mine sure i keep a .30-.30 in the gun rack i seen easy rider just like you ladies ...

Successful men, not a coal miner or check forger among them. Gabe Levitt, my cardiologist, had introduced me to this Circle of Six, now Seven, exactly like the Rockets A.C., which met for Friday prayer sessions, a.k.a. poker, in Kelly's Hitchcockian pad with its panoramic views of the San Gabriel Mountains. Gabe said, "I'm not sure what our link is except messing up with women and a vague Jewish guilt—even the guys who aren't Jewish, maybe it's contagious around here—about making too much money from what we're good at." Gabe lacerated himself because he was so much richer than his slum-doctor father and had a wife who was so insanely busy on the disease-of-the-month charity circuit "that whenever I say hey, honey, can we spend a little time together, she gives me a look like I've just withheld treatment from a crippled child." Danny Gold, a top-of-the-line film editor, was collaborating with his gay daughter on a script about a gay daughter co-scripting a screenplay with her father.... "Sure it's incestuous, but I've got half a million bucks in child psychotherapy wrapped up in that kid, and it's payback time. This script is a solid sale." Mort Blumenthal, an "independent producer" ("I have so many development deals going I feel more like a real estate promoter than a filmmaker—hey, is God telling me something?"), was glumly married to a superrich toothpaste heiress who demonstrated elegant contempt for his hustle while backing "socially relevant" projects that actually paid off and gave her both the money and status Mort didn't earn off his Chuck Norris Meets Karate Kid subepics. Mort was still being pursued by his ex-wife, a former Weatherperson who demanded co-credit and half the profits from every idea and script that originated during their marriage. Baxter Johns, a big-feature director who made one mill a picture ("plus a percentage of the gross not net, what kind of idiot do you take me for?"), kept marrying women who blamed him for abducting them from their "creativity"; his present wife, whose hobby was running a homeless hostel in Santa Monica, demanded that Baxter race home early from the set and do his share of the housework and nannying to give her some "quality time." ("I'm the only thousand-dollar-an-hour maid in Bel Air.") The group's other non-Jew was a stage Southerner, William-Bill "Bull" Buell, a retired TV news anchor who had accidentally become a hugely popular character actor (Wilfred Brimley without the twinkle), and who relaxed by abusing us. "I'm not Joosh like mosta you guys"—he'd switch on a fake-authentic accent that millions mistook for rural wisdom—"an' I ain't got a analyst, and I'd ruthuh die drunk than go to anuthah AA holy roller meeting, so I can say out loud what you wimps don't dare. It ain't about 'relationships' or 'lack of communication' or 'failure to commit' or any of that Dr. Ruth shit, it's about pussy pure and simple, but just like the Rams you guys are in trouble because you forget the fundamentals." Bull's thing, like mine, was rash sex dares. "My last girlfriend's husband kept calling me on his car phone to say he was coming right over to shoot me in the head, so my lawyer takes me to the D.A., who says, "Don't bother us, buy a gun," so I bought two more, what do you mean what kind, the most expensive of course." On general principle, Bull kept a Walther PPK strapped to his ankle even when taking a shower.

I was the group's "woman"—that is, I was not "in development" or writing screenplays or taking meetings or putting together a package. I was therefore weightless, transparent, invisible, like the women Frances Dellinger taught about in her film course, in a city where words that didn't move twenty-four frames per second through sprocket holes didn't count.

Men with a private agenda, we were somehow the victims of feminism, with a drive to lose our inner freedom by imprisoning ourselves in the woman's alleged need to hold us captive. Male backlash ran through our chatter. Oh yes, we'd been bruised, hurt, damaged by women aware of their independent energies. But now our revanchist, rampant egos, collectively reinforced on Friday nights, were back in the saddle, because once again it was respectable for men to speak openly of their fear of "powerful women" and their preference for female "junior partners." "I always did think Lolita got a bad rap," Mort said. "Amen," seconded Danny, folding.

I was appalled, outraged, excited, and confirmed by being back with "the guys." Yes, yes, this too had happened to me. I loved these men for not making me feel cretinous about screwing up over women.

Junior partner sounded okay to me. But not to Melissa.

She wasn't my type. Too glam. Her on my arm I'd have to fight guys off. I didn't have it anymore. Look at that, will you? Just when I'd kicked the movie-fantasy habit, along comes Jane Greer in a pageboy platinum-blonde cut, freckles like Mom's, except Polly never wore anything like that simple white Palm Beach off-the-shoulder number with gold sandals. Golly.

I shut my eyes, hoping she'd go away. Nope, bold as life, with a couple of other women invading my final resting place, Molly Malone's near the La Brea tar pits on Fairfax, sagging seats and Irish tricolors and wailing Gaelic folk singers that sent me home cursing flatted fifths. The blasting sun from the suddenly open doorway hurt my eyes, so I hadn't got a clear shot at her, but when the darkness set in again she emerged like everything I ever wanted.

I sat paralyzed. Besides, it was an unstated rule at Molly's, a hangout for Irish nationalists and NORAID collectors, "Danny Boy" and "Up the Provos," that you never came on to women who filtered in from the aerobics gym next door. But when her friends left, I sidled up to the bar and pretended to watch the Dodgers game on TV.

Up close, her glamour was pleasantly mick, broad freckled forehead, open, not sultry face, and an unwavering gaze that was a little unsettling. I looked around.

"Excuse me," I said, "can I borrow your tortilla chips?" Openers have never been my thing.

The bartender, Sean, came along to give me a bowl of my own, the bastard.

Well, do it or don't. Outside, on the burning streets, I was getting awfully tired of dating, L.A.'s version of the rack and screws. Most of the women I met these days were working mothers, but they sure weren't like my mum, Polly Black. My dates were professional women earning big salaries while being full-time-and-a-half parents who "nurtured" their children and sure didn't want any advice from me. But honey, I'd say, let's get a babysitter. And soon learned better. Instead of coming home exhausted from the office and telling Cinnamon or Jason to fuck off with the neighborhood kids for a while, I'm just too tired to play with you, my dates Jessica and Tracy and Amy and Deborah insisted on starting their day all over again at seven p.m. and treated their children almost as if they had been abused all day because Mom had not been with them. The kids looked fine to me, but they'd caught on to what was expected of them: whining. Indeed, mother and child had set up a caterwauling whose message was unmistakable: *Do* something, *be* something, more for me. Mom's gritted, martyred smile only seemed to exasperate the kid, whose demands underscored Mom's guilt and drove her harder to ruinous perfection. (This syndrome also made the Mouse Pack crazy. The three guys still married worked incredibly hard to make huge livings for their families, only to come home and meet yet more demands to be Superfather from wives who had dropped their careers to be Real Women.) I learned to keep my trap shut the night I told Sherri that maybe kids shouldn't be weighed down by too much adult participation, sometimes they should be let alone, when I was a kid the police would have been called if anyone over sixteen had been seen hanging around a baseball diamond full of children, so much for Little League. Biff, she slapped my face. "Only a man who hates children and should never have them would say that!" She was right, what did I know?

But it left me going to the movies alone, which was worse than sleeping by myself. Maybe I should place another ad in the *New York Review of Books:* "SWJPMNGLWNSVFLSSW seeks ..." ("Single white Jewish professional man nongay left-wing nonsmoker vivacious fun-loving spontaneous sensual writer ...")

Loneliness was driving me nuts. Make your move or forget it, chum.

"Sean." I called the bartender over. "Would you tell that woman over there that normally I sit here in depressed silence and never, well, hardly ever, approach the opposite sex but am about to make an exception in her case? Will you do that for me like a good fella?"

I am a good tipper. Sean went over and leaned into the blonde's ear. She turned her head. And smiled dazzlingly. Thank you, God, one last time.

It turned out—God's judgment is never simple—that she was an IRA militant.

I should have walked out the moment I mentioned Ulster and

she corrected me. "Don't you mean the Six Counties? Ulster is the British imperialist name for what they divided and rule." Just my luck, an American Marxshirewoman.

I had stopped being "progressive" on Ireland the night of that IRA letter bomb in Piccadilly, preceded by dynamiting half an army band in Regents Park, almost taking parts of Helen and me along with the imperialist-occupier clarinet player. Nothing personal, mind, any innocent passerby would have done, since indiscriminate slaughter is the IRA thing. For every planned target like Lord Mountbatten, blown to pieces on his private boat, the Provos had massacred hundreds of ordinary Irish of both faiths, by mistake or a botched phone warning or on vague "suspicion of collaborating with the security forces," or fur th' hail of it. Living with the IRA in Britain had forced me, from ground up, to reconsider the implicit totalitarianism of modern revolutionary political thought. Who got it in the neck when you liberated the oppressed? The rights and wrongs of a particular issue—Ulster, Palestine, Namibia—were less important to me than the fact that my side sometimes was trying to kill me.

Big change, that. My politics now really were personal.

It turned out Melissa Shannon had better credentials in her movement than I in mine. A fourth generation Irish Catholic patriot, Black and Tans executed Great-grandpa in Easter Rising, Grandpa jailed by the Brits for dynamiting a mainland post office, Dad a U.S.A-born honcho for NORAID, the Provisional Irish Republican Army's front for dipping into wide American pockets to smuggle guns to Ulster disguised as welfare for families often disemboweled by the same Provo bombs NORAID paid for.

"A small price to pay for regaining our land and liberty stolen by Protestant fifth columnists imported after the Battle of the Boyne to implement Cromwell's genocide against the Irish peasantry," intoned Melissa after her third margarita.

Don't push it, Black. Nod agreeably. Say anything. Don't mention those London nail bombs.

But the human spirit can take only so much. I decided to ruin my evening. "What," I interrupted her spiel, "are you going to do about Northern Ireland's permanent majority of working-class Protestants who would rather cut their throats, or preferably those of the Catholic minority, before agreeing to a 'united socialist Eire'?"

She looked me right in the eye. "We'll just breed them into submission. Would you like coffee at my place?"

But keep Melissa off Eire and she was a treat.

"Look," she told me at her little frame house just down from Sunset, "I'm thirty-five. No husband. No kids. No steady job, except like everyone else in west L.A. I've got a screenplay 'in development.' And I stopped going to confession the day Janis Joplin died. Do you have any idea what that does to my dad, who hasn't missed Sunday early mass since he was an altar boy?"

Melissa was from Southern California's "inland empire," a vast subregion of Los Angeles crammed up against the San Bernardino mountains and the Mojave desert. In an explosively expanding L.A., once distant outposts like the San Gabriel and Pomona valleys were now practically inner city (with gangs to match). Melissa, who had grown up in Irwindale, a single-industry town of commercial gravel where her dad was a retired foreman, had gone to a local community college, then to University of Southern California—San Andreas State's main rival for private students' money—to major in drama. "I wasn't a bad actress," she confided, "just scared. Absolutely intimidated by the De Niro and Jodie Foster clones in acting class who had this drive to succeed even if they had to kill for it. I just didn't have that kind of confidence in myself." Her classmates' competitiveness, and her own fears, drove her out of college to "real" work: flight attendant, rookie cop ("I failed the cowardice test"), nurse trainee, model, and now part-time caterer. Today her life revolved around her aerobics class and the script she was writing with another woman. "We'd win an Academy Award in the Almost category. We've almost sold ourselves as a team almost a dozen times, almost. Gus, you're a writer—isn't there a better way of making two hundred thousand dollars?"

She was asking the right person.

Screenwriting for Angelenos, I saw, was what novel writing had been for me, a socially acceptable way to delay adulthood. "You talk like my dad," Melissa smiled, "but then, you're almost the same age. Of course," she added quickly, "you don't look it."

America was aging me like cured ham. Until now I'd avoided the age thing in England, where the climate keeps you looking young and feeling old. Like James Hilton's Shangri-La. Coming back to the States meant reinserting myself into a "normal" age cycle, normal for Americans. My body looked younger, thanks to fanatic workouts at the gym, while my face got more creased and lined. The effect was disconcerting even to me.

Age made L.A. people uneasy. "To be ignorant of what happened before you were born is to be forever a child," said Cicero. He would not have been so pejorative if he'd lived in Beverly Hills. Talking and thinking about the past, my second-favorite activity, had to be accomplished like Raffles breaking into a safe, discreetly. Angelenos did not object to age because it was ugly; it was the implied history they didn't like. Having a real past was a minor social disgrace. "You're always talking about the dead," Lori had complained. "The dead" was anyone not currently in *People* magazine.

Hollywood friends seriously advised me to keep quiet about my age and never, on pain of social excommunication, mention any film made before John Landis. Who? I said. Forget it, they said. But I teach old films, I said. Keep it in the classroom, they said, quickly changing the subject.

You could lose your job, or your wife, if you cited your age—this is the men I'm talking about, God knows how the women hung on. Okay, it wasn't like being a secret Jew in Nazi Germany, but the reflex was the same. One sixtyish agent I knew had trained himself with the help of his therapist to deny flatly in the office that he had ever seen any film made before *Easy Rider.* ("They start calling you a golden oldie to your face if you remember *Citizen Kane* or *Best Years of Our Lives.*") Another pal, who had lopped twenty years off his age, made me promise never to divulge in front of his new wife exactly when I'd known him.

Even the Mouse Packers, tummeling in a business where the competition might be nineteen years old, forced me into a gerontological niche. When Kelly Klein once too often introduced me at Trumps as "This is Gus Black, he was around when they were still making *I Love Lucy,*" I remonstrated, "Hey, go easy on the Grandpa Kettle stuff." "But we love you being as old you are," Kelly insisted. "You're a living link to ... er, well, I'll think of it in a minute." "Very funny," I said. "Next time show your love some other way." "Just so you don't get a face lift," Kelly said.

What's wrong with a face lift? I said.

There had to be a way for a man of age to behave both appropriately and sexually.

"Look at it this way, Melissa," I told her. "Dating the oldest living man in captivity is like plastic surgery—it's got to make you look younger." She glanced sourly at me; it was okay for her talk about my age but not all right for me. Otherwise we got along, seeing each other every night: movies, the beach, the Dodgers, whose third baseman, Pedro Guerrero, she had a crush on.

"If you interview him and let me go along, I'll ... I'll give you the best gift a California woman can give a man," she breathed.

"Your chastity?" I asked.

"No. A guest session at my gym."

God knows I was happy with Melissa, who didn't make me feel young, just better. A glimpse, maybe, of okayness, the ordinariness I'd chased all my life. Or were we using each other to excuse ourselves from the sex game? Was I her Freudian fath—

"Oh, for Jesus' sake," Melissa groaned, "stop taking responsibility for the whole world. My dad's always saying, 'Accept what God offers you and then a little more.' I should introduce you two—but not in my lifetime."

That hurt. I really wanted to be part of somebody's American family, sit down with the old man in his den, explain my intentions, all that. It was part of what I'd missed by escaping to England. The White Rock Girl on barbershop calendars, the Green Hornet, hotdogs and play ball!

Melissa yawned. "Come to bed, honey. The Dodgers aren't in Brooklyn, Marilyn Monroe is dead, and nobody does windows anymore. There's only one thing that hasn't changed. Come find out what it is."

But "it" wasn't working. Technically, fine, but afterwards, as if nothing had happened. Melissa told me not to be silly, I was imagining things, but I trusted my neurosis. I wasn't sure what the problem was until her screenplay partner, SuJenna, a unit publicist, came back from location shooting in New Mexico. I was at Melissa's when she got a call from SuJenna and after putting down the phone suddenly got flirtatious and evasive with me. Click. I used to be like that with Rose O'Malley when she found out I had another girl somewhere.

No, not Melissa.

"Why not me?" She placed a cool hand on mine in Molly Malone's, in the late afternoon, with hardly anyone but Sean around. "I don't know why you can't deal with an Irish Republican failed actress ex-cop would-be screenwriter dyke. What else did you expect to find in West Hollywood?"

Fag. Pansy. Fruit. Cocksucker. And now Melissa Shannon. Yeah, I remember now, Jane Greer had been pretty hostile to Bob Mitchum in *Out of the Past*.

Melissa pointed out, "You could live anywhere in California, Gus. Yet it's West Hollywood, Queer City, every time. What does that tell you?"

"So I'm a latent homo."

"Or not so latent," she responded. "I've known lots of guys who were great in the sack and weren't straight."

"Stop trying to recruit me," I said.

Melissa smiled sadly. "You'd make a lousy open gay. Given your history, you'd probably become one of those dreadful old queens who shout the loudest on marches while their fingers go creepy crawly up some young dude's tush. Spare us all."

I exhaled with exaggerated relief.

"But that," she insisted, "doesn't let you off any hook. You're of my dad's generation and probably never had the gay option. Maybe that's why you're so cunt-crazy. Overcompensation. No, let me finish. I read your novel, the one about splitting from the States. No wonder your gay friends want to castrate you. You're really stupid about us."

That "us" again.

I sat back to look, really look, at Melissa. In a pale gray silk jacket and a tight black skirt four inches above the knee, she was a knockout, cool and exciting. Producers must have been crazy to turn her down for parts. Why had she let me make moves on her?

"Fear," she said bluntly. "Loneliness. SuJenna was away. Maybe I wanted to prove something. Most guys are too scared to approach me. Maybe because I let them twist in the wind a little before kissing them off. I learned in junior high I had a kind of power over guys. I liked it. It kept the distance I needed to work out my sexuality."

"I hate that word," I said. "As soon as people say sexuality instead of sex, fucking becomes a political issue."

"That's funny coming from you."

Were those women she first came into Molly's with, er, um?

"Yes, if you want to know. But we don't fuck each other. I only do that with SuJenna."

"And me," I added. "Sean," I said, turning to the eavesdropping bartender, "I'll give you a complete report later." He backed off unapologetically; Molly's was filling up. I looked around. You couldn't trust anybody anymore. Was that guy over there ...?

"You really *are* like my dad," Melissa said, licking salt off her margarita. "Once a year I invite him down to the Gay Pride parade, the one on Santa Monica Boulevard. So he drives his Cadillac Seville in from Irwindale, where they think you're off the wall if you drink Michelob instead of Bud. Yes, he knows about me, and it's probably what gave him his first bad prostate. I get SuJenna to stay at her own place, and I take Dad out to breakfast at Hugo's, and afterwards we sit in the bleachers and watch the floats, and Dad looks so sad. He loves parades. He was Marine First Division in the Pacific in your war. And you can see he really digs all that energy from the marchers. He stands and salutes when the Gay Vietnam Vets come past. But then a guy will kiss a guy, or a woman will give her lover a crotch feel, and he sets his jaw ... just like you right now. Personally I don't care too much for all that public making out either, it's the wrong sort of statement. Probably comes from our insecurity—okay, exhibitionism. And Dad positively cringes when that 'Mothers and Fathers of Gays—We Love You' float comes by, led by all those parents trying not to look as if their worlds had collapsed. Dad and I haven't worked it out yet, not really. He just has to live with it, like I do. We've got this neat little deal: back home in Irwindale or when his IRA buddies are around, I'm male meat; otherwise, I'm who I am. The important thing is, we haven't totally stopped talking. It isn't perfect. I lost part of Dad when I told him, and he sure lost his baby girl. But we've, oh, I don't know ..."

I leaned across and kissed Melissa. She kissed back. "I couldn't tempt you, could I?"

"Sure you could. You did. But if I kept being unfaithful to SuJenna, sooner or later I'd do the same to you. Is that what you want?"

I thought about the old Jack Benny tag, "Don't rush me I'm thinking it over." An Irish folk group walked in. Melissa loved them. Her second-greatest character flaw was a passion for Van Morrison and the Chieftains.

"Well"—I echoed Joe E. Brown's line in *Some Like It Hot*— "nobody's perfect."

Except Mom.

Pauline "Polly" Schneider Schwartz Black wasn't a "Jewish mother," a lie even Jewish moms buy. We sons don't fear their ravening lust for us so much as the terrifying possibility they may not sexually desire us. Polly Black, as the Movement knew her, was a heroine by any standard. She suffered stinging abuse and ostracism from her family and even her comrades because she had run off with the married man she loved, stuck loyally to him and her child through strikes, jail, long years in garment factories, and jobs as waitress, maid, and cook. As cook's boy in a South Haven resort, where she worked summers to give me an unwanted break from Chicago's steamy alleys, I hated the guests, from our old neighborhood yet, who only had a few dollars more and pretended they were Rockefellers and drove Polly like an ice-cart horse. And I hated her for my inability to protect her from the exploitation she gladly accepted to keep "the family" (her and me) together.

The myth of the Jewish mama is the joke of the Jewish son living down to the failure of a father whom he cannot bear to see fail. If he identifies, as I did, with the man instead of the woman, and the man "fails," then who is to blame?

Mrs. Portnoy, naturally.

Mom, Dad, and I were like a royal theatrical family, the Barrymores or Foys or maybe even the Redgraves of labor organizing. Give us a stage—a shop with substandard wages, a foreman who hassled his women, a long-distance emergency call from a besieged union— and we shuffled off to Buffalo, Erie, Akron, Flint, Chattanooga. Jake Schwartz's technique was simple but effective. Called "the little Jew" by the other American Federation of Labor organizers, in his bowler hat, three-piece suit with silver cigar cutter on a chain across his vest, and high-button shoes with spotless spats, he'd walk into the saloon nearest the unorganized plant, pick on the biggest guy there, and knock him down. "Get their attention first—their dues will follow," he told me one of the times he let me come along. "But why'd you hit him, Pop?" I asked. "Tomorrow when I show up at the gate, they'll remember me. How I stood up for myself when he called me a dirty Yid." "But Pop, he never did," I said. Jake Schwartz smiled through his cigar-rotted, anxiety-ground stumps of teeth. "He was thinking it."

Mom had her own slow-burning style, Ethel Barrymore to Jake's more explosive John. Her rules were simple. Never walk a picket line looking less than beauty-parlor perfect, never whack a scab when the cops are around, never take a promotion as forelady or straw boss. Poise is all. If you lose it, you lose the strike, the shop, the campaign. Even in handcuffs, she kept as cool as her idols, Kay Francis and Myrna Loy. "Don't push me, officer, I've just been manicured," she warned the deputy who rode us out of Cairo, Illinois.

Hit 'em before they hit you, Dad advised. Be an example, Mom insisted.

So I compromised by hitting 'em as an example.

"My father thinks Reds should be shot. He would have hated your folks—bleeding hearts who couldn't even pay the rent," Melissa said.

But many of her secular IRA saints had been socialists, hadn't they?

She shrugged. "Dad says all politics is religious at root. Anyway, you know us Irish. Others make progress, we make history."

"Stop pretending to be Cathleen ni Houlihan," I snapped.

"I will when you stop pretending to be a sixty-year-old greaser who never grew up," she hit back.

Here it comes.

"And you're a—"

"Don't say it. Don't you dare."

We glared at each other. I shook my head. "Looks. Brains. How can you—"

"You mean," she cut in, "do this to you?"

"To yourself."

"When it comes right down to it, Gus, you're just like those Johnny Cash clones I grew up with."

"I like Johnny Cash."

"I thought so."

Stalemate.

Then, "I miss you, Gus. Really do. I don't even know if I prefer women to men. It's just this particular woman. Do you understand?"

She saw my expression and kissed me gently on the lips. Sadly: "Welcome to America, friend."

Welcome also to the Losers' Club, men who'd lost their women to other women. Up at Kelly Klein's house the Mouse Packers were puzzled at why I was so upset over Melissa. They had all taken, and given, such sexual battery, why balk at gay? When your kid's lesbo (Danny), your wife's left you for Lisa (Mort), your shrink hints at your latency (Gabe, Baxter), and your ex-wife says she suspected all along (all of us), why fight it? Sometimes, I said, a man has to stand up for himself.

Kelly, Danny, Baxter, Mort, Bull, and Gabe chorused, "Why?"

Bull called us "a bunch of statistically insignificant flakoes, dis-placed masochists guilty for bein' alive after the Nazis cleaned out your Polish cousins, Mama's boys cryin' in your beer 'cause the old lady's into liposuction and hasn't made an honest-to-God knish since Papa's hernia. Self-hatred as an art form, wimpishness raised to style and points on a picture deal, what a bunch of sorry-ass self-satisfied navel pickers you guys are."

Kelly said, "Does that mean you love us?"

Bull studied his Mexican Baseball nines-and-threes-wild-low-hole-matches-the-pot-open-face-card-must-double hand, and mut-tered, "Shee-it, you think I'd be spendin' time with you Gold Card Jewboys if I could relate with my woman? I'm here for the same reason y'all are, to keep from killin' her or myself."

Having found my Rockets A.C. again, all I needed was a doctor to keep me alive.

Up to now, Gabe aside, I'd been insulated from California medical reality because I was in the habit of saving up my aches and pains for Britain's National Health system to deal with. American doctors, even the ones who'd helped save my life, scared me because unlike British medics, they made a profit from my illness. I have known two entire generations of English doctors who do not know what it is to receive payment from a patient and therefore prescribe accord-ing to need, not to sustain their own lifestyles.

To this day, I cannot tell whether any of my L.A. doctors is skilled because health-care delivery is so mixed up with avalanches of legal-urgent pay-now-this-instant-or-go-to-jail demands that I often can't hear the diagnosis in the fiscal blizzard, and also because I have learned that in privately funded hospitals diagnosis too often follows a money trail.

"Big news! Hold the presses!" Dr. Gabe Levitt, my medical Deep Throat and sometime cardiologist, slurped his fourth or fifth coffee at breakfast, crumbs from his total-lard-content Danish smearing his white jacket. Once a week, often the morning after our Friday night card games, when Gabe, a born poker loser, required consol-ing, we met for breakfast around the corner from his hospital, Bev-erly Hills Memorial. B.H.M., as it was known, was a sort of medical Pentagon, so big that staff rode around on thick-tired scooters in the sprawling corridors, sometimes bumping into prominent movie stars or producers who swore by this huge private clinic because of its snob value. B.H.M. had a world reputation for its glittering charity balls.

Gabe frowned at my trashing his hospital. "That's my job. Anyway, you won't let us do open heart or angioplasty or laser, or any of the stuff we're good at. Isn't your life worth fifty grand? I've seen your angiogram, baby, and you're a second heart attack waiting to happen."

I glanced at his unhealthy Danish spattered on a paunch that stood out like a pregnancy.

"I burn up calories fast," Gabe muttered, gobbling.

"If you're so keen on 'procedures,'" I asked him, "how come you're never a patient in your own hospital? You've got diabetes, shingles, and gallstones, I'm told."

"Are you crazy?" Gabe stopped in mid-bite. "I wouldn't let any of my colleagues touch me. If I get seriously sick, know where I slip off to? Canada. They have a rational health scheme like you Brits. Not as good doctors as us, but I want to know my guy is looking at me, not his wife's *schrei* to spend a month in Fiji or his anxiety about putting the kids into Chadwick or some other cockamamie private school. American doctors scare even me."

Gabe rode several hobby horses. American medicine was too hi-tech, too invasive, too inhumanly detached, and above all, too money-obsessed. Yet he made a comfortable (two hundred and eighty thousand dollars annual) living, enough for a Bel Air house and the accursed private school for his own children. Cleft in his chosen stick, hating the profession he loved, he'd sometimes refer me to colleague-specialists who were "smart" or "terrific" or "well qualified" or "respected" but whose financial and even medical habits he criticized. Wasn't he putting me into a double bind?

"Gus, be realistic." Gabe ordered his sixth full-strength coffee of the morning, and it wasn't yet eight. "I am the best there is. Or, put another way, the best you're likely to find. I never lie to you. My function in your life is not to appreciably lengthen it but to bypass— excuse the expression—my colleagues when they try to shorten it by crushing your breastbone with unnecessary open-heart or stabbing you in the neck to clear up what everybody else walks around with all their lives or anything else we strive to do to improve your 'quality of life' on our platinum-plated operating tables."

But Gabe, how is a guy to know which way to turn?

"That's your problem," he said. Instead of giving me a straight answer about whether to have a bypass, he kept changing tack. "All

I do is alert you to medical feeding frenzies or hospital politics when some schmucky top-scoring MCAT whiz kid wants to open you up as part of his royal road to hospital preferment, or tell you when the second opinion you've appealed to is related by marriage once removed to the doctor you already mistrust. Don't tell me I don't earn my fee."

"So your job is to turn me off medicine altogether?"

"No," Gabe said. "I would gladly pay to practice what I do. It's my calling, where and how I get my kicks."

What was going on at Gabe's house? His wife, a social heavy hitter, was often mentioned in the *L.A. Times* society page. Better I shouldn't know.

I examined this advertisement for American medicine: overweight, harassed, sallow, tormented, happily trapped in a system he did not wish to escape but could not help trying to warn me off, dedicated, keeping doubt at bay with the lousiest diet I had ever seen in a grown man. Then his beeper sounded and he headed for the wall telephone next to the cashier. Gabe had ten, count 'em, ten phone numbers, including his car phone. He was harder to get than Michael Ovitz.

"Except," Gabe leered at me as he came back, "with luck I get not just ten percent but the whole of your income. Ha ha ha, see you next week. Try to stay alive or at least away from doctors." His expression darkened, and he leaned over to pat me down. "Whew," he said, "just checking to see if you're wired."

Peculiar doctor, Gabe. He was faintly disappointed I was still alive. In this he was a little like Luther Luck, who also (I felt) thought Old Gus had let down Young Gus, and vaguely disapproved. "I know very few people who can retain their youthful idealism," Maybe I should tell Gabe and Luther beacons were for birds. Still, you couldn't dine out forever on radical burnout.

Problem was, my younger self, too, demanded a loyalty oath of me now. He was a socialist, I a survivor. Against everything I knew to be so, back and heart notwithstanding, he insisted that I hang in. It was ridiculous. The show was over, tents folding, animals asleep or dispersed. Yet I, in his name, kept knocking at the ticket window demanding admission to a circus that had left town.

"Throw away the goddamn crutch," the Mouse Pack's Bull Buell advised. "Why import your fuckups to a movement already on its last legs," said ex-activist Kelly Klein. "Good riddance," opined Baxter

224 / CLANCY SIGAL

Johns, "because the left has always been your excuse for not making a decent income." And at SAS Frances Dellinger pretended to wipe away crocodile tears. "Stand on your own two feet for a change. Be a man—whatever that is these days, if anything." Even Melissa had little sympathy. "Maybe being a socialist," she said, sponging herself in the bath, "is a decoy. It lets people see what you want them to see while you're concealing the other stuff." She lifted her head for me to shampoo. "Know what? Ordinary reality spooks you."

Even my ex-comrades patronized me. Ruth Silverman, my oldest friend in the world, a Rockets A.C. ladies' auxiliary from Chicago, I'd known her forever, said, "You're so out of touch, my darling comrade. We ex-es no longer need a party or fancy ideology to disguise our social concerns. The FBI did us a big favor by destroying the organization. It freed us. Why not enjoy your freedom? Fly, my little eagle, even if your left wing is broken."

How tempting.

Skee said, "You remind me of a guy I knew once. A Red like you. He thought the more money he lost at cards the more saintly he was becoming. Then, the only time he won a huge pot, his pals waited around for him to give it all to charity. 'Well, fellas,' he finally said, 'it's a good idea in practice but will it work in theory?'" Skee waited for the laugh, and then the others arrived for the meeting.

It was called Workers Resistance–U.S.A. (L.A. branch), and no way was it like the Rockets A.C.

Of course we met in the standard storefront office with toilet in back, the usual radical slogans on the wall (VIVA LA HUELGA), and a floor that hadn't been swept since the McNamara boys bombed the *L.A. Times* in 1911, if not before.

"Hey, we'd love to meet at the Polo Lounge or Ma Maison. Can you arrange it?" Skee said. At my age, he was still on the assembly line at GM Van Nuys.

They called themselves Workers Resistance–U.S.A. because they were about workers' control, workers' rebellion (wildcats, sitdowns, "rolling stoppages"), workers' defiance of Japanese-style "team concept" and other speedup methods. Irreverently, I thought of them as my "Mao's Pack," another small group of certified losers, except that these guys were (a) not Maoists, whom they loathed as pseudoradicals doing the boss's job, and (b) strangely cheerful and relaxed, in a totally Los Angeles style, about the task of creating an alternative work culture.

Each member came to the group from personal experience: a longshorewoman who'd fought hard to get into the union, a telephone operator fired by PacBell for union agitation, a local union official permanently angry with his exec board, a studio prop man who couldn't stand the union-busting going on all over Hollywood but (like most of the group) also on the outs with his union leadership, an Iranian labor organizer almost executed by the Shah then chased out by Khomeini, a one-armed World War II vet and carpenter who had met the Russians at Torgau while serving with the Sixty-ninth Division and could not have cared less about de-Stalinization, a retired plumber who liked to hang around younger union guys, and a couple of elementary teachers trying to start a union of schoolkids. Two labor generations passing history back and forth like chips in a poker game, and I sat there—or rather, kept jumping up and down to ease my back for the allotted ninety minutes (then I was gone)—wondering why I always ended up in small groups that never had a chance of "winning" anything except their own personal autonomy.

"I'll tell you why," said Skee, who looked and moved remarkably like the movie song-and-dance man Dan Dailey. "Like the rest of us, you're a collective-action addict. And as a professor you're now part of lower management for the first time in your life and scared to death of it. Next question."

Skee's group let me exercise the Marxshire-made half of my brain at serious risk of rotting from underuse. In the tiny Workers Resistance cell, London subway drivers, Marseilles dockers, and Bombay textile workers seemed brothers and sisters, pertinent, whereas most of the time if I tried telling my L.A. friends about British or overseas events their eyelids fluttered within seconds. It used to be called international working-class solidarity, words used by Jake and Polly without embarrassment, but not by me, not anymore.

After my first meeting, when Skee drove me home, he said, "You sure ain't an active union man anymore, and you keep misquoting Marx to prove your credentials, but who knows, you could be our own Adam Michnik. Between us, kiddo, the Polacks and the Jews can still change the world, you with me?" Michnik, a professor jailed by Polish Communist authorities, had been a vital intellectual link to Lech Walesa's shipyard workers in Gdansk.

Skee was serious. At my next meeting I arrived in the middle of a debate that was to bedevil us for months: how to help create an American "working-class consciousness" in the context of, among

other things, a widening gap between an underclass and more tech-
nologically sophisticated workers, the growing feminization of
poverty, the increase in non-English-speaking workers and decline
in paid union membership, etc. Betty, the longshorewoman, had an
idea where to start. Back east, Harvard U., after a long and bitter
battle, had just agreed to sign a contract with its clerical staff. Soon
Yale might follow. Why not here in L.A.?

Charlotte, the laid-off phone operator, turned to me. "Say, Gus,
you're on the job over at SAS. How about writing a leaflet targeted
at the office workers there. Bet they're ripe."

Oh gawd.

I wrote my first U.S. union leaflet in over thirty years, or rather,
rewrote it until it was just right. "This is so beeyootiful," gasped Doris
Brown, a computer clerk in SAS's payroll department. "Isn't it lovely?" She handed my leaflet to Pete Mendoza, a campus janitor ("Cus-
todial technician, if you don't mind"). Doris and Pete, union sympa-
thizers but quiet about it, I'd found through Workers Resistance.

Pete Mendoza examined my creation at length. "Er, Professor
Black," he said with a hint of apology, "it's great as a piece of writing. But I don't understand it. Do you understand it, Doris?"

Black and buxom, Doris said, "No, but it is very elegant."

My leaflet had failed its first test.

"Maybe," Doris said tactfully, "we could work on it together?"

So it wasn't hopeless. Out there, over the mountains into the
flatlands of the Republic, where the consuming shadows made us
real, the same classes contended for power and advantage. Much
had changed. I'd have to learn Spanish—more than a third of
Southern California came from below the Rio Grande—and watch
my mouth around coworkers like Doris and Pete whose heads
ached with my Archie Bunker jokes long after I forgot them. I, son
of immigrants, having fought to make a place in the dominant culture, was now part of an increasingly besieged white subculture
that held the power but not the strength.

Control was the word. The poorer nations had imported themselves bodily into California, providing a vast pool of underwage,
uninsured, vulnerable hungry labor without which the region—sixteenth in world GNP—would collapse overnight. My San Andreas
State, sited loftily between Beverly Hills and Pacific Palisades–Malibu, seemed a private oasis of white suburban money until you
looked closer and saw the connection—Marx called it nexus—
between the college and L.A.'s peculiar, now increasingly typical,

dual-tier economy: the intermingling of the professional careers our students were headed for and a growing sweatshop understructure. It was even more complicated because for the first time in anyone's memory even favored students could no longer look absolutely forward to living better than their parents. This anxiety of competing for fewer places created in them a fierce demand that I come up with a magic formula that would guarantee them the right grades; my rambling asides and built-in wanderings they barely tolerated as an assault on their futures. Get on with it, Professor Black, it's our lives you're fucking with.

How would Workers Resistance–U.S.A. deal with that?

Reaganomics put an end to my Flying Dutchman act.

Until now a Boeing 747 made my decisions by periodically lifting me from Primrose Hill to West Hollywood and back again, a soothing, lulling anaesthesia. After being "committed" to everybody and everything for so long, it was a blissful release not to have to think about it.

Then Luther Luck dropped an ultimatum on my head.

"I have to fire you or make you permanent. How would you like to be full-time tenure track?"

"You are kidding?"

"For your sake, I wish I were."

I laughed. "Holden wouldn't like it." J. D. Salinger's teenage rebel Holden Caulfield in *Catcher in the Rye* was a quasi-real person the author sometimes invoked to prevent him making immoral decisions, such as selling his novel to Hollywood.

"Holden," Luther drily replied, "probably had a private income."

The catch was, I'd have to live in California year-round.

"Forget it," I said.

" All right," Luther said.

"I'm a Londoner," I said.

"Of course you are," he said.

"London is my home," I said.

"Yes," he said, "you have friends there, fame if not fortune, the satisfaction of having conquered a difficult country—why go into exile a second time?"

The most intelligent thing that popped into my head was, "Fuck you, Luther."

"As the Germans asked the besieged Americans at the Battle of Bastogne," said Luther, "is that a positive or negative 'fuck you'?"

Luther was putting a gun to my head, and he knew it. He explained that because the Reagan administration was turning off the spigot of federal funds for student loans, schools like SAS were trimming their budgets of allegedly excess fat. Of course, the first to suffer were the cafeteria workers, making four to six dollars an hour, whose request for a raise was refused. Although SAS's top bureaucrats were safe, indeed had voted themselves a cost-of-living increase, they were determined to get rid of older teachers and part-timers like me rather than cut their own bloated salaries. "Blame it on Reagan or anybody you want," Luther said. "Stay or go. But choose."

My first thought was not about the job but about safety valves and escape hatches. In England, I always had boltholes to hide in and let off steam. Commitment to San Andreas State would mean what? Aside from U.S. military deserters, what was out there, east of the 101–165 Interchange? In Britain, at least, I had Cwybran and Ashton under Lyne and Bishop Auckland and Moss Side and Cumbernauld and Liverpool 8, where I could lose myself among friendly strangers. But what was here?

Maybe, to buy time, I should jump into my newly bought (on the SAS credit union) classic white '65 Mustang convertible with red upholstery to see for myself what Luther's package looked like unwrapped.

"Forget it," Luther snapped. "I'm tired of giving going-away parties for you. Decide."

Watching the guests slowly dwindle to their cars in the cool Marina Del Rey night after my farewell party at Luther's beachfront condo, I had one of those large thoughts of which Luther so disapproved. Here is home but never home, there is never home, but that makes it the home I make of it. America is promise and disappointment, England is risks Americans can't even imagine. In Marina Del Rey they don't even know where the Seven Sisters Road is. But curiously, Luther did. As a platoon leader in Vietnam, he had gone out on patrol with Don McCullin, a north London–born combat photographer, Seven Sisters bred, who had taken the pictures on my first nationally bylined story in a British newspaper, a dance hall riot by teddy boys he had introduced me to. Though we did not know this till later, the riot was staged for our benefit, and a boy was killed. The story kicked off my career, and McCullin's too. Odd coincidence Luther should know Don.

I had gathered together a lot of old friends at Luther's, which vaguely resembled Joan Crawford's house in *Mildred Pierce*. Random selection of old CP comrades, WR militants,Committee of Correspondence survivors, Mouse Packers looking a little uncertain, Melissa (who alas had brought her SuJenna, a stout, motherly, aerobic Gertrude Stein), the sightless SDS militant turned Ferrari owner Ted Gollan, who brought along his friend Tom Hayden to show me an economic democrat in the flesh (but where was Jane?), Frances Dellinger with a toy boy on her arm half her age ("But truthfully he's too old for me, calls me 'dear,' can you beat that?")—indeed, everybody but the losers.

Funny, that. I'd tried hard to locate several pals who had disappeared into the social mist, about whom nothing was known but rumors: Mack was screaming in a locked mental hospital ward, Chuck drowned himself at Zuma, and Jay was in Folsom for multiple child molestation. Yet three phone calls revealed that Mack was a handyman who couldn't pay his rent ("Need any jobs done?"), Chuck a K Mart undermanager with a terminally sick wife, and Jay a hospital orderly at Camerillo State. They were alive but poor. No, they wouldn't be at my party. Jay and Mack hemmed and hawed, but Chuck said, "Why should I travel all the way to L.A. to get put down when I can get it done here in Sacramento?"

My childhood friend Ruth Silverman cleared up the mystery. "Okay, so we got a few facts wrong, but in spirit we got them right. Can't you see how we think? If Mack and Jay and Chuck can't afford a good restaurant or season tickets to the Chandler Pavilion or a cabin in the Santa Cruz mountains, they're dead. Or worse." But all they were was broke, I said. "All they are," Ruth said emphatically, "is failure. Poor we give to at the office."

Ruth, my Chicago sister who never was, was on the city council. She was one of several local Communist women—including a college dean and a bank first VP—who resurfaced after the purges to take on what we used to call leadership positions. Southern California sometimes seemed to be run, in its "caring professions"—social work, probation, even criminal justice—by a female network of former comrades, many of them appointed, or condoned by, "Governor Moonbeam," Jerry Brown. The Party, for all its blundering, had been an excellent springboard for later careers, a training academy in self-confidence.

Ruth didn't like me harping on the past. "You Party guys alway looked good at six a.m. leafleting some foundry in Bell or Vernon.

But I was overweight and the wrong shape: a typical Yetta Samovar
wanting to do the right thing for her male authority figures, including you. It was not my happiest period." But she was ace at demys-
tifying mythologies for me.

As we leaned against the wood-slat halfwall of Luther's indoor
jacuzzi, surveying the motley crowd, I asked Ruth if she would
answer a really intimate question.

"I'm still faithful to my husband, you bastard," she said.

No, not that. Something even more private. Why did so many
younger women in today's movement look so bad?

Ruth grimaced. "The world in flames and look what's still on
your mind. Okay, little boy, try this on. Blame it on the women's
movement. Looking lousy is an act of liberation. It shows you don't
care about pleasing men, which women my age were conditioned to
do without even thinking about it. If you'll notice, the ex–Party
women of our epoch still look fairly good, for our age. We're like
your mom that way. Remember how she never went on strike without a perm? Today, inconceivable. Progressive women, oh, say, up
to their forties, at least of our tendency, sincerely believe it's radical,
committed, to look grungy. I only," she concluded wistfully, "wish I
had their guts."

Poor Ruth, a Jewish Sophia Loren, tall, olive-skinned, and
heartbreakingly beautiful, was the sexiest grandmother I knew.

"Anyway," she inspected me, "look who's talking. Who's buying
your schmatte these days?"

*Webster Wallach and his Further Thoughts cohorts accuse American
Reds of hypocrisy if they are affluent as well as left. Foreigners, too,
often remark that the world's last Marxists appear to be American leftists who have not yet got the news.*

*Webster & Co. miss the point. As proof take the crowd at my going-
away bash. Only in America has Marxism, or socialism, worked.*

*Let me explain. Historically, American leftists, of all stripes, have
been bruised and battered by different storms of persecution. Thus,
over time, a "beloved community" (the phrase belongs to SNCC) has
been forged out of shared hopes and a common enemy and a sense of
besiegement that goes way back. We built a fortress of love, in times of
great danger, against the lures and temptations of a system we
opposed. At the same time, certain radicals, by nature enterprising
and well organized, slowly acquired comforts on approximately the*

same scale, and for the same reasons, as the rest of the American lower middle class. The result is a left-wing culture, now into (at least) a fourth generation, that is mildly secure—two cars, a small house, health insurance—and rooted in a "sort of" Marxism that is both impermeable to outside influences (we are no less provincial than other Americans) and, in human terms, has established community, solidarity, all that. We have had a good life in America without giving up our ideals, even the ones that have turned other countries into revolutionary prisons.

So the actual experience of many American leftists is that regardless what happens elsewhere, "socialism" is viable. For us, it works because the community survives in America. Ironically, we have built socialism in one country, the U.S.A. Which is one reason why indeed we may be the last True Believers.

Out on the beach, Luther and I stood side by side, gazing at the dark Pacific as we telepathically examined each other's thoughts. Finally Luther turned to me and raised his glass. "Give my regards to Piccadilly. But I still need a quick answer."

Luther's wife came in to bring him to bed, and as we helped him upstairs he said, "Go where you'll be happiest. Or does that make it impossibly complicated?"

BOOK 6

SPEAK
FOR
ENGLAND

Y ou've been in England thirty years and I'm your first Jewess?"

I didn't tell her about Anthea.

Dark, small, and impossibly large-eyed, she bared her teeth in a wide smile. "Don't you just love that word? Jewess. Would you believe grown Englishmen still call me that? Must excite them. Sexy and anti-Semitic at the same time. Reminds them of when we ritually murdered goyim and drank their blood, or haven't you read your Chaucer? Wonder if it's why Mrs. Thatcher loves us so. By her, we're probably the only real English left. She has this thing about the Chosen People, you know. Appoints whole carloads of us to her cabinet so we can take the blame. Shrewd woman. She must be Jewish." And lifted her head back to shriek with laughter.

Sarah Montefiore buttered a brioche and popped it into her heavily lipsticked mouth, almost negroid in its fullness. I couldn't take my eyes off her. How did she keep that trim, lithe figure?

"It's me metabolism, oy vey, what a curse." She mimicked an old Jewish lady. "Lets me eat anything. Be a dear and ask for a trifle more jam."

We were in the Polish patisserie at the foot of Primrose Hill opposite my flat, just a few doors down from a house on Regents Park Road that bore a blue plaque noting that Karl Marx's collaborator, Friedrich Engels, had lived and worked locally; almost within sight of our sidewalk table, the Old Man himself was buried in Highgate Cemetery. Sarah and I met here almost every morning for breakfast. Sometimes we spent whole days together. But not the nights.

235

"It's not on, it's really not," she said. "So don't be a bore about it. It would ruin a perfectly delicious relationship. That jam, please?"

You can find a Primrose Hill in New Delhi or Los Angeles, anywhere the educated classes buy. After years of searching I had found my perfect small village, smack in the middle of urban mess. Primrose Hill, NW 1., where stately stagnant Regents Canal idles past low banks on which girls in their Hermès scarves and Harris tweeds walk their oversize must-cost-a-bunch-to-feed-the-monster Afghans and Borzois, and full of plaqueless houses where precedents were established. No wonder Freddie Engels liked it hereabouts. This would be my Shangri-La, I thought when I first found the flat after Helen and I split up.

But the Volvolvians are moving in.

An undercurrent of social unease electrifies much of Primrose Hill now. Here reside Thatcher's Children, who like to sneer at her but reap her benefits nonetheless. Demi-liberalism, discreet and inactive anguish, is mandatory in Volvolvia, where guilts, nourished in "really excellent" private academies or "magnet" state schools that the arts-conscious middle classes monopolize for themselves, ignore Liverpool and Sheffield for Managua or Soweto, anywhere far away and musical. Volvolvia's 2.8 children, dubbed Simon and Samantha, not Santa Monica's or the Upper West Side's Max and Molly, their nannies not from Oaxaca but from adjacent jobless Camden Town, have all the right (left) ideas, but in the image of their fathers, flourishing ad agency and TV production company executives, they're nascent, closet Tories without Conservative honesty about their naked greed as the main motor of human behavior. These fretfully handsome fathers, absent all day in offices and studios, come home, gaunt and overworked, to youngish, slightly pinched wives who saunter around Primrose Hill, self-consciously tired, with slung babies à la Ghana Mama, "dressing down" in an aggressively ugly way no working-class mum would dream of parading in Hackney or Chigwell. At weekend parties the palefaced Ghana Mamas become cocktail mothers blazing with pretty resentment, unvoiced except in breakdown, about their lost careers. Who's to blame? Why, Phillip, of course, little Simon, Arabella, and Dylan's father, poor Chardonnay-sipping sucker.

The point of Primrose Hill is that there's so little sexuality, which demands risk, and Volvolvians are people who try to minimize personal danger to themselves while riding the riskiest current of all, the Laffer Curve. Having it both ways, money and a superior attitude to it, comes naturally to the not yet quite well bred.

The legacy that adult Volvolvians pass on to their kids, the next generation of the New Dispensation, is an unerring sense of how to fill in a Filofax and feed off a culture while not contributing to it, except to seek their "authentic selves" in bad art. Nice kids, slightly less snotty than Hampstead, also less serious, can't be bothered to slog through the *Guardian*, the "heavy" typo-strewn bleeding-heart newspaper, so over morning cappuccino they consult instead the *Independent*, a near-perfect mirror of anxiety resolved. What makes these young men so astonishingly, poetically unattractive while the young women, always in elaborately torn jeans, are so nicely, safely, serenely sexual without sweat?

"Easy, mate," advised Sarah, "or you'll choke on those sour grapes."

Sarah had been my first female victim on arriving back in Primrose Hill.

Even at a misty distance through my Zeiss binoculars, she had cut an ambiguous figure, in a 1930s cloche hat, Barber raincoat, and soft suede boots absurd for walking in the wet: an English eccentric inviting you into, rather than excluding you from, her walled private garden.

Of course I made all the old moves, which she shook off like a pitcher rejecting a catcher's sign. The sign she took had to do with our shared history.

Sarah Montefiore was my own past as a female: a fortyish ex–women's liberation activist who had actually been at the first Oxford conference where I'd met Helen. "No, don't even think about what might have happened if you'd spotted me first. You and Helen were fated. So it didn't work out, you had a lot of years together. None of my marriages came even close."

Sarah was a self-confessed villain addict. "I marry the ones who treat me worst. You'd have thought the women's movement would have taught me something, but I'm still doing it. Probably why you don't turn me on. Show me a man who's beastly to a woman, especially if he's tolerably educated, say Balliol or Magdalen, and can be taken out in public, important that, and my pain sensors simply vanish. What do you think old Siggie would have said about that?" She nodded in the general direction of nearby Swiss Cottage, site of Freud's last consulting room.

Hard to believe this dark, compact, utterly organized woman could also be self-destructive. "This"—she gestured at today's outfit, the outrageous earrings and black velvet jacket open to the bosom Restoration-style, sheath-tight blood-red hip-hugging leather skirt, impractical white open-toed shoes, and oversize sharkskin bag—"is my disguise. But you know who I am, don't you?"

I sure did.

Sarah and I were a good team partly because we knew where the bodies were buried and didn't shirk personal responsibility for the killing of England. The left, our left, which had supplied the "vision" even of Conservative governments, had somewhere along the line forgotten that politics was not about programs or policy documents or even (heresy!) which party held power, but in the small print. Who said the phones had to be so inefficient? Who thought up the unworkable single-operator buses that displaced the old Big Reds that maneuvered so nimbly through London's narrow streets? What architect kept designing, what town clerk nodded at, what laborers installed Corbusier-style balconies that sheared off at the sixth floor? Why was it nearly impossible to get through to your local council with a complaint about a cracked sidewalk? Who picked up the trash how often? Why should Mussolini have a monopoly on trains running on time? Didn't all the -isms come down to our own personal experience, which we denied at the risk of becoming counterrevolutionary in terms of our own sense of how things actually worked?

"In my job," Sarah said—she was an advice columnist—"all that cant about 'improving the quality of life' usually translates as infidelity, bad sex, menopause and menstrual cramps, mugging, rape, dead-end jobs. Details, man, details—I want the plumbing to work in my New Jerusalem, don't you?"

By different roads at different times Sarah and I had emerged from the soup by our own efforts. No looking back. We could not afford any more major blunders. And needing to take ourselves as we were, not as we would be, we needed each other's help.

"What's a busted flush?" Sarah asked after breakfast as her Yorkshire terrier, Chloe, romped neurotically around the bench we often repaired to atop Primrose Hill to watch the London skyline change shape.

I told her.

"Hah," Sarah said, "so it's always a losing hand?"

"Not," I said, "if you keep your nerve."

"That's all right, then," she smiled, snuggling happily up to me in the perfect pleasure of the company of someone you don't have to be in love with.

Sarah, who believed ferociously in her own history, gave me the courage to believe in mine too. But now we had to be practical, she insisted. No more detours. "Write your own third act this time, Gus, or it's a cast-iron certainty another Rose O'Malley or Willie Last will come along to write it for you. Even secret defectors have to come in from the cold."

"What's a secret defector?" I asked.

"Oh, I just made it up. It's basically knowing that things have changed, regretting it, accepting it, but only admitting to 'trusted' people, like members of a good club or MI5, that your views have changed. To the outside world, you appear to stand by your former positions, e.g., feminism, socialism. In a way, it's quite a snobbish thing. But then, we come from a race of snobs—it just might save us."

I told Sarah I'd come back to England to figure out my third act, but I didn't know where to begin. Always in the past I'd hit the road, whirling like a dervish, to find the answers.

Sarah advised, "Relax. Just sit on a bench and it will come to you, I promise."

It did, too.

It wasn't my England anymore, but it wasn't the Brits' either.

Elsewhere, the Berlin Wall had fallen, and Prague was free. The USSR had a constituent assembly for the first time since 1917. East Germans stormed the Communist Gestapo building and danced in the corridors flinging around their own dossiers. Hungarians, Poles, Croats, and Serbs were at each other's throats again, a sign of liberty. A cleansing wind swept in from the Russian steppes. Except for Rumania, it was done bloodlessly.

But the Britain I've come back to belongs to a new breed of Thatcherite iron men, direct descendants of the Blue Woad People who used spiked clubs and tossed sick infants over jagged cliffs. Their ebullient primitivism, replacing the discredited, muddled compromises of social democracy, has released new, occasionally creative energies. Not since the eighteenth century has naked money been so respectable. Property developers, marginally restrained under Labour, now fall upon ancient, lovely neighborhoods like Chelsea–World's End and Kings Cross–Somers Town, raping and "renovating" almost at will. The Thames, hemmed in by public urinals disguised as award-winning office blocks (one frankly shaped like a computer), has become a mere sewage gate for commuters into the City financial center.

Why balk at triumphant Thatcherism? Some of it appeals to me. Her messianic, dogmatic fervor reminds me of Marxshire's fat years. There is a new excitement in the air that permeates even the left, forced to think for the first time since the 1940s—Maggie's version of the "Russian spring." Still, the bloody tackiness offends me. If I will be oppressed, I wanted it done in style, not by used-car salesmen with Brilliantine in their hair. Life in a semisocialist country had confirmed my elitism more than my socialism.

A cool, pleasant Marxshire autumn in Anne Boleyn Crescent, a tiny pedestrian precinct protected by anti-auto bollards in back of Primrose Hill. It's a bright late September morning, sun slanting through the planes in front of stately Victorian houses exuding London's new odor, fresh water-based paint. When I can't stand the traffic jams up by Regents Park Road, I often come here for the Pissarro view of London, a broad sweep straight down almost to the canal. That is, if Pissarro had put Volvos and BMWs into his pictures.

The image makes me laugh.

"I'm glad," growls a gruff voice, "somebody sees something funny about this do. Care to share the joke, mate?"

Slowly I turned to size up the latest sample in my Mass Observation poll, conducted from a single bench, on Where Does Gus Black Belong?

Old but athletically built, gnarled yet handsome, Alf Holdsworth, seventy-four, is a retired carpenter who lives in a council flat round the corner from the bench we're sharing in the Crescent. His hands, lying in his lap, are almost double size from use.

"What's so bloody funny, then?" Alf repeats in an angry, friendly way.

"Oh, all this," I say, meaning the excellent view and ridiculously pleasant weather.

"See what you mean—some joke," Alf responds, and his tone makes me take a sharper look at the unswept streets, phalanxes of For Sale or Sold signs, and A-registration Volvo-Peugeot-Renaults practically stacked on top of one another. Alf's voice thickens with disgust. "And they call this affluence. No wonder the lad went bonkers."

Who?

Yesterday, Alf reports, a twenty-two-year-old meat porter from down the road fatally stabbed his mother and set fire to their council flat, then sat down on the floor in his boxer shorts to wait for death or police, "whichever arrived first."

Why did he do it?

"Who knows? Maybe he figured it all out and it drove him potty," Alf says. "It," or as Alf prefers to call it, "the right fuse in the wrong plug," is the link between the boy's otherwise unexplainable crime and "this." Alf gestures almost violently around him. "Can't you see?" he demands. "His sort, my sort. Don't have it anymore. They took our history. Now they're bloody even taking our homes. Wouldn't that drive you to murder?"

"No," I say primly, "it wouldn't, even if I knew what you were talking about."

"All you bloody Marxist intellectuals are the same," Alf declares as if he'd known me for years.

"You know nothing about me," I protest.

"Faces," he says mysteriously. "Faces are like that Raskolnikov in what's-'is-name's novel. Faces can't help confessing."

Nor could Alf.

Loss is Alf's obsession. "My heritage," he says as if stating a stone-cold fact, "was stolen." He is sure what this means: not so much that the owners of England oppressed or exploited his class of workers but that historians and writers like myself acquiesced by "always getting it so bloody wrong, don't you?" We, the intellectuals, are so clueless, so out of contact, that, we champion the side of those who keep Alf penned up in "my own bloody awful ignorance." He blames himself, and his kind, for being "slaves of books we haven't even got the skill or patience to read that lie to us about ourselves. We're taken captive by a culture we're not even part of."

He resents as a personal insult, not an abstract wrong, that his life as a working man is held in lesser balance than the Masterpiece Theatre pageant of armored kings and barons on caparisoned horses that is usually presented as "the" British history; perversely, he is equally suspicious of attempts by the left to make an alternative, working people's history. "We're Humpty Dumpties, aren't we, and not all your E. P. Thompsons"—a Marxshire historian of the

English working class, Alf reads like a man possessed—"can put us together again. The past haunts the future, but we've no past anymore. If this is our future, bloody hell!"

I've never had much patience with garrulous old men like Alf, who lost his way somewhere back there. All he is now is bilious, cantankerous, and embarrassingly syrupy about a thing he calls "Merrie Olde Englande," which he invokes without irony and which is, to him, a real place in a tangible history he has reinvented for the common people of which he is an uncommon part.

Trying to talk to Alf can be a pain. He won't let go. And he asks such an awful lot from writers and has too much respect for us as a trade; what would BenGy make of him and his uncomfortable demand that we be held accountable, indeed culpable, for what we write? Alf has a point to make that has taken him years of slow late-night reading and hard thinking to figure out: that once, as recently as Cobbett's and Mayhew's time, in a cruder but better England, there lived a coherent, unified race of "South Saxons"—"my people"—whose rediscovery by the intellectuals he despises might yet help heal, even redeem, the country. Almost overnight, he insists, in the mere decade it took for the Industrial Revolution to bite, a thousand years of a whole, holistic South Saxon culture was destroyed by industrial capitalists, and its memory erased by their educated minions, scribblers like me. Perhaps, he concedes, a trace of a similar such "culture" survives in Wales and Scotland, but for England, a devastated site of disinheritance, it's too late. "Look around you, mate," says Alf, "I rest my case."

"I am," he asserts, "the last of seven generations of the Industrial Age. There won't be any more like me and what went before me." Then he invites me round to his flat, filled with self-made furniture, including exquisite Chinese lacquer cabinets hand-carved out of discarded wood from building sites he still occasionally works on when the foremen are desperate for ancient skills.

His body may be retired but not his hotly overactive mind and hands, constantly at work on new carvings. He's one of those old men I'll probably grow into who write rafts of unpublished Letters to the Editor; his hobby is to catch out famous literary names in historical or practical error in the newspaper. From behind the couch, while his wife looks on bemusedly, he retrieves a thick scrapbook containing a few old photos and many handwritten "Dear Editor" screeds, with some replies he has received from the famous. Literary England—some of these names really are well known—

does not come off well; few of the writers have responded with even minimum grace or politeness. It says something that the only two who troubled to take on Alf and his daft, dense argument were Rose O'Malley and my friend Leo Rossiter. Score one for Marxshire.

But Alf does not make a distinction between left and right—all writers are usually wrong most of the time because they fail to acknowledge his truths. And his truths grew out of shocks he is perfectly open about since (after all, he is English) they are social rather than personal, or rather such a mixture that intimacy is not offended. First—how often have I heard this?—Labour's failure to follow up the massive 1945 "vote for socialism" with anything like a full-blooded radical program; second, the cold, curt rejection by left-wing intellectuals who would not hear him out more than twenty years ago, when he warned from his own work experience that "unmanned production" was imminent (fewer people to make more goods) and would permanently alter how we lived and behaved. "It's my face they wouldn't listen to, you see," he explains. "This mug of mine isn't very acceptable, is it?" He has a blunt, rather beautiful worker's face but is convinced his class-stamped look puts the local intelligentsia off.

The third shock is something we share: a fear and dislike of the present. What shaped us both was a traditional "authority of skills," a work discipline, now all but obsolete. Back on the bench outside, Alf dismisses in a single word the whole new gentrified culture of Primrose Hill: "Shit."

"But you can't ignore what's happening, it's a reality," I say.

He grimaces at a passing group of younger people, yuppie scions wearing their cash insignia, jeans with carefully torn knees, some of whom I recognize as the children of the publishers and mediacrats who have taken over the Hill district from its previous tattily bohemian tenants. "Them," Alf observes, "they're caught in a maelstrom of change they haven't a clue about—or want to. They're the 'urban decay.' No real families, no known history, breeding a culture of social workers and therapists and keg lager that's pure piss." Angrily, he blames the expanding middle class for inaugurating a culture of irresponsibility that would have no place in a decently run society. It follows that Alf idealizes his own south London (Peckham) childhood, where neighbors kept keys on a string that anybody could pull through the latch and a petty thief got serious jail time at Bow Street; today, as we both know, even violent rapists get probation. Once upon his time the streets were swept daily "by men who had to for their wage, but also because it was good to have a clean street. Look at this mountain of dead leaves and dog turd."

And so on. We all know people his age. His day done, friends mainly dead, too little to occupy skilled hands, reads too much in the nearby public library (hours cut in half by Thatcher), not enough people to talk to, and snubbed by the younger Labour socialists hereabouts. Maybe it's because my comrades hear the music under the notes, a Wagnerian horn blast of National Socialism, of Otto and Gregor Strasser, the populist Nazis, *Volk und Blut*, the fury, rage, and frustration of a real man who talks in the haltingly large abstractions used by the self-taught, pursues a thought to its logical or otherwise conclusion with a mind-blinding tenacity, has a roaring impatience with points of order and therefore our form of democracy, and frankly is an embarrassment to us busy-busies. His complaints against the dying of his light he should either keep to himself or stop blaming other people for, right?

His past haunts my future.

All the days Alf and I sat on the bench sunning ourselves I was also faithfully attending my local Labour ward meetings in the basement of St. Botolph's, which Alf Holdsworth wouldn't be seen dead in. We Labourites who speak of our movement as a "broad church" are not kidding.

My pal Leo Rossiter has been drudging away in these airless basements most of his life. He doesn't have to; he's your ultimate volunteer. His socialism is a continuation of old commitments. Thrice wounded in military massacres (Narvik, Dieppe, Arnheim), antifascist to his knobby knuckles, Leo is too smart to think Thatcher is a fascist. But for him, "Thatcherism," a denial of fairness to the least privileged, is a modern reenactment of his generation's core trauma, the thirties Depression and its political consequence, the betrayal of Czechoslovakia to Hitler by the Western democracies at Munich. Leo came of age ashamed of England because the "men of Munich"—whose spiritual grandsons still sit in Whitehall like ivory gods—sold out the best to the worst. In a sense, all of his novels and books and pamphlets are evocations of a war worth fighting, and which he has not the slightest doubt will always have to be fought, on beaches if necessary, or in stuffy church basements during the armistices. Anyway, attacking Tory scum is fun. But Leo is impatient when I tell him about Alf Holdsworth's suspicion of socialists knitting away in dank church cellars.

"Your friend Alf," retorts Leo as I hasten to catch up with him on the morning walk I alternate with Sarah and coffee, "is all well and good, but who's to do the actual work of the Party then? I'm sorry he won't join us but no point losing sleep over the walking wounded, not in this war. We have to keep a cadre going in the dry time. Anyway, passing resolutions in nearly empty halls is an innocent hobby for the powerless, eh?"

When St. Botolph's strikes eight a.m. we separate as usual to our work, Leo to his writing desk and his fifteenth—yes, fifteenth—novel, me back to the round of pickups and stray encounters Leo calls my "watch on the Thames," a reference to an old Lillian Hellman play, *Watch on the Rhine*, about German antifascists. A chilling joke because it evokes memories of another democracy that chose prosperity over liberty.

Heinz Hoffman knew all about that.

I did not have to go fishing for "Hintzie" Hoffman, he found me.

"Gus Black!" he shrieked over the phone, "the crap artist and saver of souls! Would you like to save mine? Listen to me, Shit Pen, and I'll make you famous and rich. That other *merde* maker, Thomas Keneally, he too found a vulnerable Jew—is there any other kind?—selling leather goods in Los Angeles and made a fortune peddling his story to those Jews in Hollywood. Elie Wiesel gets rich pretending he was a Holocaust victim. And that charlatan Simon Wiesenthal fools the gentiles into believing he's chasing Nazis too old and feeble to go to the toilet on their own. What lying excrement they are! Are you still listening, Shit of Shits? Only Hintzie Hoffman is alive to tell the tale. I will give you fifty percent of the millions—you hear me, *millions*—you will make off my blood. No, you can't come to me, where do you live? Ah so. Primrose Hill. Of course, where else? The shit capital of Europe."

He was an hour late, then waddled into view, refusing to look at me, circling my bench in Anne Boleyn Crescent until I called out, "Mr. Hoffman, is that you?" He looked over his shoulder, then up into the sky, scratched his enormous bald head, blew his puffy red nose, did a little jig, and rasped, "I used to meet my Gestapo lover like this. He was much better looking than you, of course. You are uglier than your photographs or how the makeup whores do you on

BBC. Such lies you tell! I'm sure you are the man for me." He came over, bowed stiffly, a pockmarked Michelin Man pretending to be a Prussian lancer, clicked his heels, and offered to shake hands, once, vigorously, Continental-style. When I reached out I saw that there was no hand below his right wrist. "Ha ha ha ha ha ha ha!" he said. "Now, business. First you must sign this contract"—and pulled out a completely blank sheet of paper. This guy was totally nuts.

I brushed him off that day. But refusing to stay brushed, Hintzie mounted a campaign of phone calls and abusive notes—later I found out he did this to other journalists too—that wore me down. Once again we met at the foot of Primrose Hill, and because I didn't know what else to do, I flipped open my notebook. After all, talking to the mad was my job. "Commence firing," I said. He leaned his dwarfish bulk toward me threateningly. "That is no joke. When I get through with you you'll wish I'd shot you with a Luger instead of the bullets from my mouth, you stinking heap of turds."

Meeting intermittently over several weeks, we soon abandoned the pretense that I was going to make us both rich by selling his story. "But you must listen," he demanded. "Why should I go to my grave and leave nothing behind but good consciences in the rotting skulls of these shit-steaming connivers, the collaborators and kapos who crawl over Britain like maggots?" Was it revenge? I asked. "Pah," he shrugged, "I'm too impotent for that. Too cowardly to kill my tormentors. All I can do is crawl under your skin and make you itch the way I itch." Here he began scratching himself wildly until I put a restraining hand on him. So ...

Heinz Amos Hoffman is somebody's bad joke on the Holocaust, the survivor Jew come back to haunt your banquets, funerals, state occasions, even Royal weddings. "*Scheisse!* Shit! Listen to me! There are murderers among you. Your dearest chums, your lovers, your fucking husbands and fathers! Me you try to starve. But *them* you can't give enough! I have lists, exact dates, bills of lading, receipts with every single name. I am a dead Jew who owes his life to a Gestapo pervert! Only I speak the truth. *Scheisse* ... shits!" Try that on at Fergie and Andrew's wedding at Westminster Abbey (which he did).

His tale, if it was to be taken straight, was that an SS captain spared his life for ... Hintzie, who has obsessive recall about the grisliest details of camp life, becomes vague at this point. Except: "I made him love me, he loves me, the day of liberation I strangle him. Next question, you filth?"

For forty years, successive British governments have felt the lash of his tongue and his sudden, embarrassing intrusions into their inner sanctums, where he wangles past guards and secretaries to scream his agony. He has a single stark indictment: that since 1946 Nazi mass killers have, with official collusion, found comfort and refuge in the United Kingdom. For a long time, nobody listened, or else they had him arrested as a public nuisance; once he pushed Britain's chief rabbi into a grave he was praying over. Establishment Jews, whom Hintzie accuses of complicity with the Foreign Office in easing the passage of Nazi murderers into Britain in order not to make waves, deserve to be interrupted at their most private moment. "My dream is to surprise the Prime Minister, any PM, shitting in the toilet."

Conveniently, doctors have labeled Hintzie a "self-hating psychotic, acting out aggressive excremental fantasies" linked to intolerable guilt caused by his admitted collaboration with his camp guards. One small problem: a team of independent journalists and a House of Commons select committee recently confirmed much of Hintzie's story, down to the fine print, and there is heated parliamentary debate about whether to bring these elderly Jew-killers to trial. Thus, Hintzie, ridden with uncontrollable lusts of hatred and self-loathing, has been proven right in many of his crazy fumings, but that is just another lash on his nearly hump back. Today, now, he is dying in a piss-smelling men's hostel, still crazily unsatisfied and despite the facts unvindicated, a fat Peter Lorre who absolutely refuses to let anybody off the hook he occasionally dons in place of his missing hand. "You want my story, Gustavus, you schvanz? You thief. What will you give me in return? Half your fee? You don't deserve even that, you kapo, you collaborating swine!"

Hintzie is a lunatic, of course: he confuses the Nazi sadists with the most respected, honorable men in Parliament, the Cabinet, the media, the police and armed forces. Mad, utterly round the twist. What murderers? What us?

In the furor over the just-uncovered Nazis hiding in Britain, nobody mentions Hintzie. Some of the investigative journalists he sparked dropped him because of his extreme demands that we share his life and pain. Who can blame them? All Hintzie wants of us is that we devote our lives to his guilt and join with him in pillorying British Jews at the highest level. Actually, I was tempted, and for help went to the reference librarian of Britain's main antifascist archive just behind Broadcasting House. Of course she knew of Hintzie.

"Who doesn't—including the chief rabbi and the Prime Minister? For some reason Hoffman hates Mrs. Thatcher most of all because she makes such a point of admiring and promoting Jews." She smiled bleakly. "Do I believe him? Of course not, and how dare I not? He reminds us how much unfinished business there is. I don't mean only the few Mengeles still left. Atonement is very unfashionable. Life has to go on. Mr Hoffman cannot bear to think that God somehow was occupied elsewhere when all this happened. He's like a little child tugging at our sleeve, but even today we won't listen. So he shouts. Attends memorial services and jumps into the grave. Strips naked in front of the West German embassy. Even goes on television with vague threats, rambling accusations. He is a total embarrassment, even to me. He ridicules my work and reduces its credibility. What can I tell you? Now he's blaming all of us, including you and me. I ask you, is this rational?"

Of course Hintzie is an aberration, a diversion. How can one mad, boil-infested, pus-dripping Jew tell us anything about contemporary Britain?

Sarah was unhelpful about Hintzie. "You're soppy about him," she warned. "He says anything he wants because nobody listens. It's different with you and me because we have public platforms. We can't afford to think the way he does, because people *do* pay attention to us."

She was referring to my BBC microphone and her newspaper. After nosediving from a great success as a sixties feminist filmmaker and then years of wandering in an occupational wilderness because grainy Tri-X documentaries about office cleaners on strike were out of style, Sarah forced herself to retool as a print journalist and hit lucky with a Dear Abby column in a mass-circulation daily. What made her different from the other Agony Aunts was that instead of waiting for letters, Sarah went out to meet women in prisons, battered wives' hostels, dope clinics, and their homes: essentially the same technique she had used with a camera. "But it was a near-run thing," she told me. "The week they picked up my column I couldn't pay the rent or even feed Chloe. Left-wing broads were definitely not in that year."

She stubbornly would not draw a connection between Hintzie, Alf, herself, and me. "I'll tell you exactly," Sarah said, "what a loused-up Jew and a bitter old carpenter have in common with us—nothing. But I see from your eyes you don't believe it. Once a Marxist always a mug, I say. So come with me to the armpit of England and see where *that* fits on your dotted line."

You don't have to go to Peru or Ethiopia to tour the Third World; it's in Brent, only twenty minutes' drive from Primrose Hill across one or two London postal codes including Mrs. Thatcher's favored Finchley. Brent is one of those mixed-race London boroughs run by a "loonie left" council, a favorite butt of tabloid newspapers who use the district's free-spending utopian schemes to attack the whole idea of coalition politics led by blacks. Brent, a dumping ground for "urban problems" (poor people of different races with a disproportionate call on social services), would be up against it even if the council was competent.

Hummingbird Farm "estate," technically a public housing project but a prison compound in all but name, last year had been implicated in a flaming riot against the police in which a young constable was speared in the stomach and nearly beheaded. From the moment it was built, Hummingbird was one of those model schemes that won architectural awards but nobody wanted to live in, and now Sarah—protected by her three-hundred-pound "minder," a bodyguard paid for by her newspaper—was probing why by talking to the women caged up there. I just tagged along, eavesdropping on her interviews, then a couple of days later went back on my own.

Since they didn't like white or strange faces on Hummingbird, I lied that I was an American movie producer scouting locations for a horror film. A white guy fixing his motor said, "You've come to the right place, mate," as we both ducked some garbage thrown from an upper balcony. The guy didn't even look up, just sidestepped as if he'd known it was coming.

And there it was, the whole corpse of British welfarism laid out in front of me: surveillance cameras, lifts that didn't work in towering infernos that no one bothered to set on fire, graffiti coating the walls like a whore's pancake makeup, smudged concrete buildings with tiny rectangular panes more slit than windows, approach roads littered with broken glass, dumped furniture, rubbish strewn everywhere. Hummingbird's main square had a stretch of something that must have been grass, low dusty bushes (just tall enough to hide a mugger), some spindly trees seemingly propped up by heaped piles of black plastic bags bursting with trash, and a few boarded-up but warily open shops. The white news agent's and Asian grocer's windows were enclosed by wire mesh, and the scrubby, filth-ridden square swarmed with large dogs running free in a happy pack. Not a "community policeman" in sight, but inside plenty of urine pools at the foot of the lift shaft. Along the corridors heavy locks, electronic eyes, thick security doors ...

I was used to bad housing developments—including Chicago's Cabrini Green and the Robert Taylor projects—but Hummingbird was something else. Apathetic, raging people. Naked hate, even terror. I tried telling myself it was just as bad in Conservative-run boroughs, and that Labour/socialist councils like Sheffield and Norwich, which didn't pretend to be liberators of the world's oppressed, ran efficient, humane towns. Anyway, the English were a dirty race at the best of times.

Face it. Hummingbird Farm was trail's end for municipal socialism as practiced by race politicians—black "community spokespersons" allied with guilt-transfixed whites who could not balance a ledger or tell the difference between an award-winning blueprint and screaming misery. Why do architects always give themselves bouquets for "model housing" they would never dream of inhabiting themselves? And we blamed all this on Mrs. Thatcher! Never. The Iron Lady's social service cuts only meant we had to look after our own with more reasoned care, not less; to be wise instead of correct; to resist by making people, as well as vile Tory regimes, accountable. Conservative policy was turning increasing numbers of London's working class, those who couldn't afford to buy their own homes, into "housing niggers." But we acquiesced in dirt, as if our squalor proved the villainy of the opposition. Who cared when people lived like this?

Eventually I found residents willing to talk, but not one, including poor blacks, had a good thing to say about Brent council. They hated it in the knowledge that it was their own doing it to them. "There's only one thing to do with this place," a dreadlocked young black man told me. "Like in your Saint Louee, U.S.A. Blow the muthafucka up."

We Marxshiremen always claimed to represent the lowest, the oppressed, the trapped, that the test of a civilized society was how it treated its prisoners—and Hummingbird's residents certainly were that. Yet in all the "radical rethinking" provoked by Mrs. T's decade-long reign, hardly anybody paid attention to the piss at the bottom of the lift shafts. Goddammit, either blow the muthafucka up or force the residents to clean up their own shit or ... I was fed up with excuses for bad living, including my own.

I needed to get out of London.

* * *

Britain's dirty secret is that it is no longer the United Kingdom but a hollow hub surrounded by a periphery in revolt. Gorbachev isn't the only one with an ethnic problem. The "provinces," or regions, are in effect another country, or rather, several unruly subnations dominated by London and speaking their own dialects, even languages. Gaelic, Welsh, Scoh-ish, Geordie, Scouse, etc. Great Britain is a fiction ruled by creative minds with an imperial memory.

For me, life beyond the poisoned orchid of Greater London makes the metropolis bearable. It's where the muscle work and raw materials used to be. Now, industrial strength almost gone, the work-molded people are left behind to shift for themselves in England's version of Youngstown and the Ohio River steel valleys. There's dereliction, but also strength, a different humor, leaner pleasures. Once it was north, north to freedom, now it's west, beyond the marches, to where Britain's spritual Jews prevail, still, in South Wales.

Hywel David Lloyd George Morgan, best man at my wedding, is a coal miner/intellectual from valleys where brains and brawn go together naturally. Miners' lodge libraries traditionally were the best stocked in the nation—Shaw, Marx, Rousseau, Bellamy, Jack London, Gorky. Carousing is the finer South Wales art, but oratory and writing come a close second. Brainless macho is not regarded as a manly virtue in the valleys.

But family is what counts in the Rhondda and Merthyr. Hywel's da and grandda and great-grandda all were workers in pits named Deep Navigation, Cwmrai, Blaenant, Lady Windsor, Taff Merthyr, Glenneath, Ynysgerwyn, pits now closed to all but old men's memories, Morlais, Brynlliw, Treforgan, Blaengwrach and Garw. Hywel's mother's mother ran a General Strike soup kitchen for miners in 1926, his mum did the same for striking Aberdare miners sixty years later. The social extension of family is the union, which isn't a valley religion, it's more important than that. South Wales is where *not* being a Communist is unconventional. In Maerdy's pub all you can see at shift's end is a small sea of *Daily Workers* interspersed with *Racing Forms*.

Thus, Hywel Morgan has done all the things expected of a valley boy: played pro rugby, married a local girl, smashed up the local police station with his brother for the hell of it, been a Communist. But he is also a sixties-shaped man, a product of art school sit-ins and Arts Lab be-ins, a Jimi Hendrix fanatic now scrambling up the Labour Party ladder with the heedless passion he rock-climbs Snowdonia. Currently he's out of the pit and Labour Member of Parliament for a mid-Glamorgan constituency, soon to be shadow Energy Minister, and maybe, if the cards fall his way, deputy Opposition leader. It's not pure fantasy that our Hywel is a future British Prime Minister—Lloyd George with Eric Clapton in the tape deck.

"Oh, I could do the job"—Hywel brims with blind confidence— "everything but put on knee britches for that bloody German bitch in Buckingham Palace." Welsh miners are not Royalists.

But they're not crazies either. Romantic realism drenches their lives. The conflict between opportunism and a religiously rooted idealism molds the souls of most valley boys however much, like Hywel, they despise Chapel and choir as middle-class cons. Denied and jeered at, hellfire evangelicism still runs in their veins. Men like Hywel, beset by strong women and a demanding tradition of union militance, naturally cynical yet hopelessly literate in the dream of working-class revolution leading to universal liberation, turn to drink, to sex ... or to politics.

"In my case all three," he laughs with a disarming mixture of guilt and boastfulness.

It has to do with family, region, the physical look of soft rains on low mountains sometimes indisguishable from the slag heaps of discarded coal mines. Yorkshiremen say, "Aye, there's money in that muck." Valley people hold Yorkshire in mild contempt as a lower form of humanity alert more to money than poetry. This slightly sentimental self-view sometimes seduces them into acting the stage Welshman, not much different from the wholly incredible characters in one of their favorite films, *How Green Was My Valley*.

Then came The Strike, the great work stoppage of '84 that broke the National Union of Mineworkers, a magnificent self-mutilation.

Hywel said bitterly, "I'm getting tired of losing, aren't you?"

He must be kidding. Losing is also a valley tradition. Martyrdom comes easy to a region that sent whole families to fight on the losing side in the Spanish Civil War. But there's a limit even to Hywel's appetite for more catastrophes. Margam is where he stops.

Follow this. Margam is a computerized "superpit" just built by the National Coal Board in South Wales, where jobs are scarce as pearls. The Coal Board tells the union there's a deal at Margam if the men will agree to work a longer week, one day more than the normal five. Not extra hours, same number spread out over six days. Eight hundred badly needed jobs are the prize. But there's a snag. Historically, for health and family reasons, the union has insisted on no more than five straight days underground. The five-day week is enshrined on U.K. union banners the same way the eight-hour day used to be in America. Torn between loving loyalty to past militance and breaking with tradition to save their jobs, the South Wales section of the union argues, debates, mulls, chews over, then votes overwhelmingly ... against the six-day week, against their own jobs. Regimental battle honors win over pragmatism.

What does Hywel do when confronted by a collective union decision that's like playing Russian roulette with bullets in all chambers? Hywel roars with laughter and slaps my back till it hurts. "He gets drunk. He gets laid. He goes into Parliament."

Talent has been fleeing the depressed valleys for ages. Its best people stay, its best people leave. Hywel, raised on Keir Hardie, Aneurin Bevan, Mick Jagger, and Janis Joplin, straddles cultures, generations, even regions. There is a fire in his belly that sets him aflame with creative lust: to write, paint, screw, and win one for his people. "I'm a valley boy. Just like Richard Burton. And what happened to him? He let all those corrupt, depraved, decadent leeches out there in London and your Hollywood exploit him." He pauses dramatically. "God, just let them at me!"

It was our habit, on the last day of my visits, to walk together, alone. Today, because I couldn't manage high ground anymore, Hywel led me out to a low plateau on the outskirts of the village facing the mountains he loved to climb. The air was damp and bracing. From here we could see smoke curling from fifty chimneys (free NCB fuel was burned even on warm days), one of which was Hywel's; he didn't seem to have a problem being a property owner.

"It's different for us Welsh," he said. "We're not rootless cosmopolites like you Chicago Jews. We *own* this bloody principality, so why not the houses in it."

We went on a bit, into lower ground, down a cool ravine that suddenly shut out all sounds.

"Not so long ago, before the strike"—Hywel sat on a rock and pulled from his knapsack a surplus army canteen filled with wine, which he dangled in a little stream to chill—"I would have said we belong with 'the left,' which explained who and what I was forever and ever amen. But nobody I know knows anymore what it's supposed to mean, do they? It's worse than a loss of faith: it's the not knowing. I tell you, boyo, it's a terrible thing when an atheist loses his religion."

He leaned down to inspect the canteen. "But we'll survive, you know, us Welsh. Have done against even worse than the fearsome Her." He laughed. "She's a real beast, isn't she? If she could, she'd destroy every last one of us."

Us who?

He spat an obscenity, then laughed again and offered me the canteen. "To tell you the truth, I'm not sure anymore. Except none of us wants to be one of them."

He looked up at me. "But what about you and America, then?"

When I started to waffle, Hywel cut in. "Oh, shove all that crap. All great cosmic issues come down to, Who's the woman in your life and how do you pay the rent?"

From South Wales I took the long way home, a train up to Liverpool across to Manchester, Bradford to Hull down to Doncaster and Rotherham back to Kings X London. The wounds were all too visible.

The regions were like a great dying beast. They had been bled for so long that whole city centers hardly existed anymore. Liverpool was always in season to scorn for its feckless violence—"the arsehole of England" I'd heard City bankers (who could help revive it) call Scouseland, the Beatles' home. It was too cunning, quick and dangerous, like Paul, John, George, and Ringo before they got all cuddly. The great port that gave Liverpool its life expired naturally from a loss of transatlantic ship traffic, and the Liverbird screeched in the Turneresque sun to no effect in the workless desert. People were dying up there, listen.

Something had happened. Maybe in the sixties, I'm not sure. I felt it first during the Moors Murders—a sort of Lancashire Loeb and Leopold atrocity but without Clarence Darrow to explain why Myra Hindley and Ian Brady, local teenage lovers, stabbed and tortured children just to tape their dying screams. Their trial in Chester, which I covered, was like a north country Nuremberg, pasty faces of evil not much different from those of people I knew and liked. That's when I noticed the change in the north. A vicious streak, always there, spreading and staining, bonds straining, protest swallowed in delicious porno knife thrusts. Provincialism denied outlet, disappointed, caged up in housing estates rats refused to live in, hey tha' shoot oop's guid enuf for tha', *fleurs du mal* of late-twentieth-century capitalism without the capital without the charity without without. Moors, valleys, second homes, desecrated archeological sites once venues for my wanderlust, monumental steel mills now gypsy encampments, the old Admiral Nelson stands starkly alone on a leveled wasteland miles in each direction that once housed gigantic, gorgeous, muscle-happy factories. Where did we go wrong? Jack the Ripper knew. A Bradford, Yorks, lorry driver, he tore the guts out of a dozen, maybe more, "prostitutes," leaving his complaisant wife to sue for libel anyone who suggested ... well, you know ... behind torn shades drawn blind telly on loud what shit-screaming dreams of *Übermensch* at last triumphant over somethingsomebodysomefuckinsoul. Hull docks empty too.

Solidarity is a great labor tune and an obsolete idea that has outlived its time—except in the north of England. As our world goes free market, it's almost impossible to tell new people arriving from the Martian planet of Upward Mobility what solidarity is. Like jazz, it has to be felt. Otherwise, it can seem threatening, or at best irrelevant. At its simplest, solidarity is an expression of love within a group. U.S. Marines know it as well as members of the Transport and General Workers Union. Semper fi. Always faithful, help your buddy in trouble. Bolton, Blackburn, Macclesfield, Wigan, Stockport, Merseyside, Accrington, and South Shields rest on a shrinking shale bed of solidarity, the only civilized response a new working class could make to the savage violence of their modern birth.

I am in solidarity with people who no longer feel solid. Secret defectors have a duty to keep their hands dirty.

On the London-bound train some men get on at Macclesfield, Leicester, Northampton—the Liverpool syndrome. They are laborers heading south for a day's work. Some carry tools with them. These Midlands Okies travel cheap day-return, back with their families maybe by midnight, up at four a.m. six or more days a week. And Mrs. T prates about "family values." Amazing God does not strike her down. He's probably afraid to strike in Her domain.

The men in my compartment remind me of Nigel, my last intimate contact with the grrreat Bri'ish wukkin' class.

* * *

Nigel, my nemesis, was a little Scouse bastard of a Liverpool "brick-ie" who wore a gold ring in his ear and squatted in a derelict house one street over from 23 Vicarage Terrace. One day, begging for work ("Missus, I'll do anything"), he knocked on our newly painted black varnish door with its antique knocker. A common sight hereabouts. All sorts of Scouses, Geordies, Scots, and whatnot rummaged through our upscaling streets hungry for jobs they couldn't find at home; they made me feel like a feudal baron dispensing gold coins to the starving populace. Helen invited Nigel in for tea, then hired him to build a high wall separating us from the world's worst sculptor, our neighbor, whose mammoth phallic abstracts stared balefully down on us from his backyard.

Did I say Nigel was a lazy sod, a world-class skiver? Helen hadn't expected him to be anything else, but I felt that he should be a shining embodiment of all the virtues of an English working class I'd come to know, starting with hard work. At first amused, then slightly disturbed at my growing preoccupation with our resident worker, Helen counseled me to let Nigel be, the wall would get done, he was our contribution to the unemployment crisis. Instead, he became my obsession.

Teeth grinding, I got into the habit of hiding behind the second-floor-rear net curtains, spying on him as he lounged about drinking cheap wine and smoking, not honest English Woodbines, mind you, but pricey Gauloises in their distinctive blue package. Hey, Nigel! I'd call out, there's a good fella, how're we doing? He'd look up, yawn in my face, and wave insolently at his boss-oppressor, s.o.b. took me for some poncy guilty liberal. So I'd stroll down to the garden with little jokes, stuff likely to endear me to this classic son of Liverpool, where goldbricking is an art form. Naturally the more stick I gave Nigel the more he slowed down, if that was possible without him actually toppling over a corpse. Soon I was spending hours at my window forward-obs post, working up a fury against this ungrateful prick who was doing exactly what I myself had done years ago on building sites. Finally a fuse blew, and I stormed downstairs, grabbed the little rat with one hand, and threatened to brain him with one of his bricks in the other. "Ye're fookin' loony, you are." He looked up into my blazing red eyes and cried out with more energy than he'd ever used on the job, "Missus! Yer man's gone mental!"

I shoved ten quid into his denim jacket pocket and kicked him out the front door. Instead of slouching away, he leaned on our gate. "You want to watch it, mister," he advised. "With all Maggie Thatcher's hospital cuts, you'd be shit out of luck tryin' to get admitted to an asylum." Then he sauntered down the road whistling the Liverpool football club's theme, "You'll Never Walk Alone." Most of the rest of the day I sat alone in my upstairs rocking chair, trembling with rage, and that night Helen and I had our first violent fight.

Sarah's only comment on my Nigel story was that I'd been foolish to let him go before he finished the wall. "That's how the middle class does it. It's a simple enough trick to learn, but somehow you don't seem to have the knack."

She had no patience for my Helen miseries either. After all my wanderings, I'd begun to miss my wife horribly, the possibilities and even what The House represented. Sarah finally snapped, "Self-indulgent bilge. You and Helen were practically predetermined by our feminist critique. Your fate," she concluded firmly, "was always in Rose O'Malley's hands."

But I had to see for myself.

Across the great river from the Tate Gallery and Vauxhall Bridge, into the unmapped country of South London, where after we closed escrow I had joked that even the air smelled fresher. "I'm not sure the people do," Helen had replied realistically.

Only the dead know Brooklyn, but who knew Bermondsey, Battersea, Balham, or Brixton? I would, I vowed. Stanley plunging once more into terra incognita to find a culture foreign even to itself and to settle, finally, his own dark heart.

What ambitions to place on a title deed to a House that still had auxiliary outdoor plumbing.

There it was. Perfectly nice and respectable on a tidy little double-fronted road with sandblasted yellow brick facades, well-tended front gardens, Crime Watch window posters, Vote Labour stickers. But where was my Mrs. Miniver?

Slumped in the back seat of an idling black taxi, I stared at the three-hundred-thousand-dollar crypt of our love on the sunny side of Vicarage Terrace. It still rankled that the Masons Arms locals had snubbed us. By what right?

Squatters' rights. They owned England. We only had a mortgage on it.

Was Sarah right that Helen and I were acting out Rose's feminist critique? In the end, Rose had evaded the logic of her own writing because, once done, it did not belong to her anymore, she could (and did) disown it. The singer sang songs that lured others over the chalk cliffs. Helen had been perhaps too strictly consistent, too seriously committed to passions and perspectives that finally overwhelmed her with their "internal contradictions." I knew there was a plainer explanation but—

"Say, guv, the meter's still tickin'. I can make more money on the move, if you don't mind." The taxi driver snapped me awake. I nodded him on, but slowly, thinking, I could have had all this, and Marxshire too, a second life. Sadly, I told the cabbie to turn around. Just as he started his tight circle, I ducked below the window as if shot.

There she was, my Helen. Of all times. What's that? By God, she did not look unhappy, had not at all degenerated from Mrs. Miniver to Mrs. Rochester. I'd been so sure of her, of her loyalty to our devastation, she *had* to be hiding behind thick curtains in a dark room on the top floor of The House. But now, here, in the flesh, how *dare* she look so good? She was dressed ravishingly well, in a stunning gold sable (!) half-coat, an elegant slim-line skirt, and a pair of those fabulously expensive Italian boots she used to wear before we got married. Where did she think she was, the Ritz?

And the bloke with her. No! She was actually holding hands with the local bimbo, the TV star, the pale-eyed BBC man of the hour, savior of the poor and confessor to the grief-laden in his Sunday night program *Keeping In Touch*. What a jerk. Helen and I used to giggle at his witless, bumbling parody of compassion. ("Tonight we have with us the blind and deaf parents of a Downs syndrome baby who, even if they cannot directly hear your applause, I am told will feel the vibrations, so let's salute ...") If Jeremy Irons had even less blood, he'd be this guy. Okay, popular; sure, a natty dresser; money dribbling out of his tiny pink ears. But above the eyebrows, *nada*. What's that? He's kissing *my* Helen, on *my* street! *Un*believable. Had Mrs. Rochester gone stark raving?

Arm snugly in arm, they slipped into my, goddammit, *my* House, then the drapes were discreetly drawn on the ground floor we'd never really finished. Stunned, I sat up in the back of the taxi.

"That th' missus, then?" called the cabbie over his shoulder. "Real stuff, that. Nunna my business, of cose—"

"That woman"—I shook my head in disbelief—"could have had me instead of *that*."

"If you ass me, mate, she's awready had you," and he laughed, revving his Austin diesel.

We drove north to singlehood again.

"Where to, guv?"

How the hell should I know? Helen's infidelity, her poor taste!, her refusal to go crashing in flames, the idea of what she and Mr. Bimbo were up to at this very moment, drove me nuts. Blindly, I ordered the cabbie to Victoria station. Only one place to go. Paris, the boat train. Paris was where you fled when you couldn't stand the English one more moment but didn't have the money for Greece or Italy.

"He's one of *us*, you know. Absolutely no question. Changed his name, of course. They all do. Good man, though. Our sector in '45. Opportunistic more than brave. Still, in those days, that was more than enough. Military Medal from the King himself. Mind, you can't tell much from medals, can you? My really dangerous stunts never even got mentioned in dispatches. Yet look what they gave me the V.C. for. Bloody chairborne fools. That's still what's bonkers about England, you know. It's all done from behind a desk, nobody does any real work anymore, do they?"

I had been scanning the airmail London *Times* obituary of a recently deceased World War II hero when the drawl cut in: "One of *us*, I can always tell." And I'd turned in my wicker chair at the Dôme on the Boulevard Montparnasse to an extraordinarily lanky Englishman of the sort lazy journalists call "distinguished." Since he assumed a relationship with me in minutes, clearly he had not lived in the home country for a long time—almost forty years, he admitted. "Miss it? Are you mad, boy? Do you miss the dentist's drill or the termagant's shriek?" I'd never actually heard anyone say "termagant."

Cecil Sebag-Sassoon. "Sephardic, of course, very pukka, not like those comeuppity Yids Lawson and Montagu, well, what can you expect?" he sighs, lounging at, rather than on, a seat at his "club," the terrace of the Dôme. He is still incredibly handsome: tall, rangy, every inch Stewart Granger as a behind-the-lines operative, which Cecil was.

War tales interest him less than "who is" and "who isn't" a Jew ... of a certain sort. Most improbably, Cecil is. Not your ordinary sort but implacably upper-class—"like the literary chappie, Sassoon, fox huntin' and all that, except despite my old pacifist uncle I rather fancied war."

Cecil is my last pickup in Paris, the nearest game preserve for animals wounded by London's jungle. "Are you American or English or what?" he'd demanded from his adjacent table, his "or what?" with only one meaning. "Christopher Columbus, Marat, Galileo, Orde Wingate, Olivetti, even General Franco—all *juif*, y'know." His strange fixation is to locate other Jews of the "best sort," including his own younger self.

"It takes one to know one," he says, tapping his long aristocratic nose with his finger. As usual with Cecil, there is a double meaning: Jew and exile.

The old man, mid-seventies I reckoned, has all the self-absorption of the elderly. He shoots me this line about his war record, then the next day brings to the Dôme faded photocopies and even more tattered original documents to verify that Captain Cecil Sebag-Sassoon, V.C., D.S.O., was the goods.

Except that Cecil is still there, like George C. Scott's General Patton "remembering" he'd once been to Carthage.

Normally, if Britons of that vintage reminisce about the war, it's minor key, downplayed, not done to make large claims for personal valor. But Cecil still speaks, in present tense, of what happened. "Doesn't embarrass me in the slightest to talk about it. Russkies got it right, calling it the 'Great Antifascist Patriotic Struggle' or some-such, they're not as afraid of emotions as we are. 'World War Two'— now, I ask you. That doesn't describe where I was."

A polo-playing scion of colonial wealth (father owned bauxite mines in Jamaica), Cecil enlisted as commando on 4 September '39. Later, landings in North Africa, Sicily, storming Monte Cassino with the Poles, etc. Wounded eight times, still carries five bullets in his solid, elongated frame. "We called 'em M-and-B's—for May and Baker, the company that made this devilishly clever sulfa powder. My batman just stuffed this shite in the bloody hole—mixed with the blood it was a bit like a mudpack, probably got the idea from the ancients, like all the good stuff."

Cecil is possessed by a single fragment of memory he can't seem to pick out of his tough-bird skin. The few months he spent behind German lines working with local partisans permanently marked him. "Bloody Reds to a man, don't you know. But brave. Tried to recruit me and wouldn't that have been a wheeze? Jewish Old Harrovian gone Commie. Well, why not, old Kim Philby did it to a turn. Funny thing is, I never knew that Kim was. Traitor, that is. Or at least that's my story and I'm sticking to it. Fag, y'know. Tried making me at Cambridge. Maybe if he hadn't done that I would have signed on with him, though I don't much care for double agents, to tell the truth. Straightforward trickin' 'em's my sort of thing." Which, according to his papers, he had done with lethal competence by blowing up bridges and roads and troop concentrations in northern Italy in late '44.

As the twenty-two-year old head of his Special Forces mission, and in the name of all Allied troops, he had accepted the surrender of a major German battle group. "Funny thing, that. An American officer came along as part of the do. Brought with him those Nisei troops of his—Four Forty-second Regimental Combat Team, was it? You should have seen those Italians' faces when these slant-eyed heads began popping out of tanks. Gave me a start, too, I can tell you.

"But Jerry wasn't much into surrendering. Can't blame him. Not after all those bloody reprisals against the Italian resistance. Know what the Nazis liked to do? Rip out their hearts and stuff them with bread rolls. Don't ask me why."

The war, by exhilarating and inspiring Cecil, had also exhausted him. "Much like Blighty itself," he says. "We like war, we English. Always have done. Good sport, if played by certain rules. But this do played us out. I know it did me. For a long time pretended not. Went into business, married, had a family, all that. But it was the war, you see? Couldn't forget. Gradually, funny this, my memory of it got sharper as the others forgot. Natural for them, I suppose. No wonder you Yanks have so much energy, your wars hardly ever touch you." He says it as fact, not criticism.

GAS—Great Antifascist Struggle, as Cecil mockingly calls it— has kept him oddly young, even schoolboyish. "You see," he tries to explain, "once you've been touched by the comradeship of battle and know why you're fighting—that's the thing, to know why—the stench of combat is like a perfume. It fevers the brain and you think you can see the future, a perfect postwar arrangement—oh yes, we used to sit around the chilly ravines of Vaglia and Chiavazza, too risky to light campfires, and chew on frozen potatoes and argue about the shape of the peace. Amazing, isn't it? Because we took our lives seriously, we didn't want to throw away our deaths. Not like wars today. All that colonial bullshite. You in Vietnam, us everywhere we can still manage an armed erection." He taps my knee vigorously. "You can't divorce a man from what he's fighting for, can you?"

He interrupts himself. "But then, we haven't had lunch, you poor boy. D'you have a car, I can't afford one anymore, I know this quite pleasant little bistro under the trees by the Marne. *Le patron* is one of 'us,' you know ..."

Afterwards, at my hotel, I reread Cecil's dispatches, which he has turned over to me in an ancient brown envelope. "Captain Sebag-Sassoon's unit made some unsuccessful attempts on a snow-covered plateau. ... major drop on newly cleared ground ... 165 Bren guns, 80 Piat grenade launchers, 5727 hand grenades ... With no warning at all, a *Zug* of Waffen-SS swept into their village.... Captain Sebag-Sassoon endured a month of interrogations at the Sicherheitsdienst HQ in Verona.... The partisans suffered 600 fatal casualties and were awarded five 'Medaglie d'Oro all valor militare.'... sabotage operations ... dropping ground ..."

It also has to do with an aristocracy of memory.

I go back to the Dôme for a last talk with Cecil, but he isn't there, not for breakfast, lunch, or aperitifs at dusk. I stay an extra day, but no show. So what if I don't see him again? The *patron* says it is unusual for Cecil to miss a morning at the Dôme but *oui, bien sûr*, assures me he will return the envelope to its owner.

Cecil is a real expatriate. As asides, he hates the working class, unions, the Labour Party, low-rent Jews, desk-bound anybody. Arrogant old bastard. Trying to live by a defining memory whose only reality is in a brown envelope he doesn't even care enough about to retrieve.

Curious thing about Cecil, there's a reunion of his old Special Forces group on the Isle of Wight, he'd showed me the item in the London *Times*, but he had no interest in going. "A bunch of old farts, if you ask me. All that marching in bowler hats with rolled-up umbrellas past the Cenotaph on Remembrance Sunday. Rather misses the point, doesn't it? Anyway"—he'd leaned over to me at a splendid riverside lunch—"they really aren't one of us, are they?"

I always come back to my addiction, the Smoke. We've been through so much together. Lately, a second Blitz by screaming Stukas of redevelopment. Clockwork lemon. It isn't going to get better either, not in my lifetime, not with an EEC parliament in Brussels even more unresponsive than Whitehall if that is possible, or an EEC-induced firetrap Chunnel between Dover and Calais whose high-speed trains are set to devour immense tracts of our prettiest counties. Already Kent is disappearing into British Transport's gorgon maw, soon Hampshire, Sussex, Essex, and Suffolk will be mere rail sidings for a planned gigantic terminus. The Victorian railway-building boom wounded but did not demolish London. But can you duplicate the whole of America in a country the size of Oregon? Come to London while you have the chance.

> "O! Grub Street, how do I bemoan thee
> When Graceless children scorn to own thee ...
> Yet thou has greater cause to be
> Ashamed of them, than they of thee."
> —JONATHAN SWIFT

From my bench atop the unmurderous grassy knoll of Primrose Hill, London's spires were partly blotted out by the *2001*-type office blocks of the New Dispensation. Fleet Street, beyond the Law Courts in front of St. Paul's, was invisible in a thicket of urinal-looking architecture. Anyway, the Street was gone, most of its news-papers having fled behind suburban hi-sec walls miles from anywhere. If news proprietors wished to deliver a death blow to drunken journalistic militance, they'd found a way even more per-fect than breaking the unions: make employees live at work as they did at home (only creches were lacking, and they'd be coming soon).

Leftists who mourn the passing of a Street of Shame that stood for unreconstructed male chauvinism at its coziest deserve what they get: Rupert Murdoch and Robert Maxwell.

For thirty years a grubby, crowded, traffic-jammed lane between Ludgate Circus and Aldwych anchored by the great cathe-dral at one end and Lincolns Inn at the other had kept me alive. The "nationals," mass-circulation papers, were printed in these ramshackle, badly lit, warren-filled buildings on either side of an eighteenth-century narrow passage that ran, fittingly, above the Fleet sewer—British journalism's Broadway and Forty-second Street, its Tin Pan Alley, where hicks like me came to break in. Hus-tling for jobs, you could cover the important dailies and weeklies in a single short morning, take a liquid noon break with Lunchtime O'Boozer, then spend the rest of the afternoon pleasantly inventing chance encounters, "accidental" drop-ins, gathering or dispensing vicious but useful gossip, the stuff of fee-for-hire assignments.

I'd never met a British newsperson who had taken a journalism class; few had been to university, and it showed in their libel-driven inbred prose, so maddeningly difficult to find the Five W's in the lazy oblique spaces between words so utterly lacking in U.S. pyramid-high, fact-dominated reporting. It's no boast that I learned to write in and on Fleet Street, where editors did not praise, they bought.

"Have you lost your mind entirely, Black?" demanded BenGy Tyler over vermouth cassis at the best table in the ship-turned-into-a-three-star-restaurant moored next to the influential newspaper, formerly of Fleet Street, of which he was now, astonishingly, editor in chief. My former *Vogue* superior waxed scathing. "I can't believe you still pine for five hundred yards of Dickensian cobblestones that reeked of the horse-drawn shit nobody had bothered to clean in two centuries—a haven for witless nonentities without a shred of literary excellence. Scam artists. Smut peddlers. Criminal alcoholics. Scribblers posing as professionals purveying filth pretending to be news. M'boy, your average British journo is an ill-educated, incompetent lout without even the courage of his Yankee counterpart, who at his best keeps an unfinished bad novel in his bottom drawer along with a bottle of whiskey so cheap not even the night cleaners will touch it." He exhaled with immense self-satisfaction. "All that, thank Christ, is over now." He waved a surprisingly plump arm at the riverside Docklands development of which his paper, a Tory mouthpiece, had a large chunk.

"There's the future, m'boy"—where did he get this "boy" stuff, he was ten years my junior—"and it bloody well works. Starting with number one, yours truly. I'm on a hundred thou—pounds, that is, not your cheap Yankee dollah—with shares and bonuses and my own private motor launch to commute me to work from Pond Street, Chelsea, no less, where need I remind you half the Cabinet resides. Don't moan to me about Thatcherism's New Men, they are my next-door neighbors. I am"—he fixed me with a fiendish gaze—"abominably pleased with myself."

BenGy prosperous, fat, sleek, with perks—fine. But a convert to vulgar Thatcherism?

"Ah, snobbery, the *old* way of sustaining class relationships." He ordered for the both of us without consulting a menu. "We"—who was "we" now?—"have no need of quaint linguistic supports like accents. It's all over, Black. Not only your ancient class struggle, which began to fade even before the ink dried on the Communist Manifesto, but elitism as we used to know it." He leaned forward and made a pudgy fist, suddenly reminding me of Sidney Greenstreet in *The Maltese Falcon.* "Power, m'boy—naked, brutal, unhypo-critical, clearsighted—has replaced the old Platonic order. Educa-tion used to matter almost as much as property, but all that's changed now too. The Athenians have romanized themselves, and I am a Socrates turned into a Caesar." Then he surprised me. "We used to be a good team. Care to sign up?"

But, story of my life, BenGy didn't even give me a chance to sell myself before he turned down his own offer. "No, you're fired. If you took a job on my paper, you'd be a mediocrity like most of my underlings, and I vaguely recall being more committed to your liter-ary growth than you were. Bad idea. You'd become my house radi-cal, and Lord knows I've too many of them as it is. Thus"—he made an imperial gesture like Peter Ustinov's Nero in *Quo Vadis*—"I here-by release you to scrape a living from what may remain of your meager talent."

I could have taken everything, even the motor launch, but not his attire. Instead of the usual impeccably white suit and shiny gold-knobbed cane, red silk cravat and Panama hat, he had on, or it had him on, a sober, plain, expensive stockbroker's suit—no Tom Gilbey this time, it looked suspiciously like Savile Row—with a broadstriped-in-purple shirt and ... my BenGy with a detachable collar? In vain I searched for a trace of self-conscious irony.

"Don't give me that superior look." He slumped in what I sup-posed was a Roman sprawl. "You romantic losers give me a pain." He pointed a fat finger at me and delivered the ultimate putdown. "There is a romance to success, too."

Mornings on Primrose Hill were growing misty and cold. A milk-white wintry haze hung over the still-green grass leading down to the zoo, where the lonesome Siberian wolves howled my song. Ha-woo ha-woo ... I answered back across London's cityscape. Ha-roo ha-roo ...

There it was, the Splodge, the Wen, at my feet a sweeping view all the way to the Channel on rare transparent days, putting me back in the picture from which I had a habit of dropping when it changed from Canaletto to Francis Bacon.

Ha-woo ha-roo.

Top of the world, Ma. Down there, at the bottom of the hill, Helen, Sarah, Hywel, BenGy, the Hon. Billie Stoutheart, Alf and Hintzie and Rose lived and worked normally, and out beyond, on the waters feeding the beaches that Hitler funked, men still hauled in nets of mussels for tomorrow's frozen dinner. It went on, despite. So would I.

Communism was gone. So was socialism as I'd known it, a mulligan stew of Jack London, Henry George, Gene Debs, Emma Goldman, Upton Sinclair, Polly and Jake Black. The belief system that had formed me was swiftly evaporating in the liberating gusts from the East. I had not the slightest intention of abandoning socialism-as-intended, yet I'd have to spend the rest of my life scanning this personal religion for seeds of its own betrayal, much as the Communists now warily looked at the toppling statues of Lenin and thought, Did we go wrong on the first day?

We had prided ourselves on being practical, not utopian. It worked, too, here and there. Not romantically and boldly, as it seemed to in the Soviet Union at first, with unfurled banners and lightning flashes, but more modestly, how many days of sick leave, social services, all that. In the rush to cancel the gulags and the "command economy" (a thousand clowns masquerading as economists), we forgot social democracy: Britain at its best. With its strong, firm roots, British socialism was an untranslatable mélange of Methodism, Marxism, pacifism, imperialism, and jumble saleism. Yet we too were suffering our dark night of the soul, though we denied it. An idea had come to its end, and it was time to think again, create afresh, dream new.

Was it possible to dream without always, always keeping your hand on the holster?

Because those were real people down there. My vision of what I wanted for others would have to be, in the strictest fidelity, what I wanted for myself. No fudging that. God help us all, whatever good I saw in the future looked strangely like what I had just lived through in my own past. The experience of one's life became a possible guide through the chaos of the coming night. The sun always comes up. Maybe that was the first sentence of the new socialist manifesto.

Regrets? Sure. I failed to meet the poet Philip Larkin when I had the chance; I fell into the river at Glyndebourne and never did hear Peter Pears in person; and I spent too little time in the countryside. Or with the suburban yeomanry Out There, the Evensong faithful, rural constables, *Times*-crossword-devouring vicars, bird watchers and train spotters and jumble sale organizers and district nurses and seaside rep players and choristers and bespectacled banner-waving kids who showed up at the last nights of the Proms.

My heart wasn't in Thaxted or Something-by-the-Sea. It preferred the grungy, faction-ridden cities or industrial villages, a marauded England. I'd never been part of a real English revolution. But I'd helped along something now disowned even by its makers. We tried.

So had Marx and Freud, two Jewish men who dominated my life. You could see them from here, glowering in Highgate, frowning in Swiss Cottage. A couple of patriarchs who slept with their house-keepers—we should have factored that in. Currently it was fashionable to put down intellectuals like us who led messy lives and tried to change things. I wished our Marxshiremen had been more willing to ease my graceless falls, more like Mrs. T, who forgave, even loved, her colleagues who traduced her movement's women. Confusing, this. Conservative politicians who tout family values fuck each other's wives or chuck their pregnant girlfriends while cutting child benefits for the poor, yet socialists judgmental about people like me fight hard for the rights of single parents. Who the Christians, who the infidels?

It would be fun to stay and fight the Great Her. Thatcherism held no terrors for me. All around I could see how She energized not only the entrepreneurial working classes but also my own Labour Party, which hadn't had such a fine enemy in decades. The really poor, crippled, and helpless She stepped on with such amazing lack of ambiguity it was almost bracing—for everyone but them. She meant to erase not only socialism for the next thousand years but also if not poverty certainly the poverty-stricken.

Stay and fight. Dig deeper in the trenches. That was the ticket—

"Bollocks!" cried a voice from the other, hidden side of Primrose Hill. Unseen, unheard by anyone but me, mocking. "Double bollocks!" "Have you ever heard such undiluted crapaceous nonsense in all your life, now I ask you!" "He's had it up the arse and doesn't even know it now don't you regard that as a little abnormal bit rich practically hermaphroditic and certainly shall we say not done just not done not this bloody annum it isn't?" "Man, ye've overstayed yir welcome by at least the time ye've been hir just bugger off we'll get along perfectly waill wi'out ye!"

Auditory hallucinations had been part of my life since the schizophrenic sixties. Weren't they of everyone's? My third acid-and-madness-sensitized ear was used to hearing symphonies of the great poet-prophets—Blake, Shelley, Bunyan. But who were these new guys? Ah, those other unacknowledged legislators of the human race—John Cleese, Dudley Moore, Billy Conolly. Comedians. Not even *Jerusalem* or *Pilgrim's Progress*. Clever, shrewd, limitless obscenity, pinpoint accuracy, coont care a fu fuh nuthin ya fuckin cun eye seh Algie djuh heah what happened to owld squatter in Bahrein? In the absence of true north, the comedians now spoke for England. Plus my personal loonies, the carpenter Jew commando, etc. There could be worse. At least they dug deep into the insane shit. Sooner or later, you had to deal with the madness because it was around every corner now, glaring and stupefied. And—

"Talking to ourselves again, are we? I've been looking all over for you." Sarah broke into my hyperreality. She looked around expectantly. "I was sure there was someone else up here with you."

We sat together on the bench atop the hill, watching the cold sun burn away the fog and sipping coffee from a thermos Sarah had in her Vuitton bag. While Chloe romped around us, I thought, Maybe Sarah could be The Woman to help me sort myself out?

She leaned her dark, kerchiefed head on my shoulder. "If only, comrade. If only ..."

We looked at each other. She tapped my head. "You look so serious. What's happening in there?"

"Nothing," I said. "Just the secret of the world."

"Oh, that," Sarah said.

The secret of the world eluded me. Another day, another minute, a second more and I'd have it, right here, palm of my hand. What had I learned so far? How to lay words on a strip of paper for money. How to muck along for long periods of low expectations. How to make love in a drizzly climate. And how in a nation of rotten plumbing to fix my own ballcocks. That's not much in thirty years.

"What did you expect, socialism in our time?" barked Leo Rossiter, ex-commando, novelist, old friend. I'd come to say goodbye, still wishing Leo or somebody would utter the magic word that would keep me in Marxshire. We were having gin and tonics in his front room overlooking the Albany Street army barracks blown up only yesterday by the IRA; terrorists had sneaked past civilian guards hired when Mrs. T privatized military security, planted their Semtex, and probably sat rocking with laughter on nearby Primrose Hill when the place went up. Leo, an old soldier, gazed across at workmen clearing away debris and commented, "Blew out our windows too, had the glaziers in all this morning. You can always tell when the economy's bad, they come when called. I suppose it's one answer to unemployment."

He turned to me. "So you're going, then? Had a long innings, you did. Good timing. End of Reagan, start of—well, who knows? Maybe the long night's over for you, chum."

Leo was one of the few Marxshiremen I knew who wasn't anti-American. "It's like anti-Semitism, isn't it? Proceeds from inaccurate assumptions to untenable conclusions. Your country's a convenient handle for our dilemmas. Maybe we envy your admirable capitalist efficiency. On second thought, our national character couldn't take too much of it. You Yanks always were the niggers— can't use that nowadays, can we?—acting out our primal sexual fantasies. My friends and I practically nursed at the breasts of Billie Holiday and Bessie Smith. Benny Goodman, Marlon Brando, we love you at a distance. Up close I reckon it's your half-deranged optimism—'pursuit of happiness,' who else would stick that in their Constitution, certainly not us—so off-putting. Offends our instinct for borders, hedges, limits. A trifle goes wrong your side of the Atlantic and you lot go berserk; sack your gardener and he comes back at you with a handgun. Here we expect a lot less and that's what we usually get.

"No, I couldn't leave England now. Too curious or too old. We nearly made it, you know. Yes. A mass labor party created in the crucible of democratic struggle, not just words, you know, they describe a reality, a century of literacy and more of artisan rebellion: now, there's a recipe for how it should be done. None of that Russian or Chinese Mongol butchery, we got rid of that with the Tudors. We almost made it in our time. World economics did us in, I reckon. Or maybe the Royal thing. Marx was right, only he got the wrong opiate, it's the bloody throne that lames their minds. My poor father knew that. Can you imagine an anti-Royalist vicar in Tunbridge Wells? No wonder Mother went mad."

Leo's father, whom I'd met, was a one-armed C. of E. clergyman wounded and gassed at Ypres in the Great War. Leo himself had been through the whole 1939–45 "show" from Narvik to Arnhem. A prolific novelist and muckraking journalist, he was an embarrassment to the English literary establishment because of his bullheaded naturalism and rocklike commitment to old-fashioned Marxshire values. The critics didn't dislike Leo, just ignored his work (including fifteen novels). We'd known each other since the night I pulled a pack of policemen off his back as he held fast to the iron railings in front of No. 10 Downing Street in the aftermath of the first anti-A-bomb rally. Arrested, he served jail time for refusing to post a peace bond, while I slipped away into the noisy night of a Whitehall melee. "If you'd only let things be," he liked to say, "the rozzers wouldn't have done me. But then, you never did learn the rules of our game, did you? You always wanted affection. Real character flaw, that. Our sort hate beggars for love. You learned the hard way. You'll be going back a wiser man, I daresay. I'll miss you. Like the devil. The others won't. The comrades. Never forgave you Rose. Or how you came along and without a by-your-leave, asking nobody's permission but your own, just started in on us, always trying for an argument, but all you got was snubbed, right? Jews. Americans. Oh well, you did my heart good if not your own."

And, as brothers, we kissed. Blushing, he pushed himself away. "The French do this sort of thing so much better, don't you agree?" Leo, Military Cross (twice), Mentioned in Dispatches, could take anything but emotion. Maybe that's why I was getting out for a while. I was almost like them. Too English. That would give them a laugh.

Leo took me down to the street. The military, now hastily replacing private guards, patrolled the road with rifles cocked in the crooks of their arms, kneeling in doorways with the "Belfast swivel." "Wonder," mused Leo, examining the street scene with a professional eye, "if we could chat with those lads about the crimes of British imperialism in Ireland, all that. A little subversive propaganda, just for old times' sake, hmmm?" Already I could see him mentally composing a leaflet to the troops, just as in the 1943 North African desert he'd been part of a widespread movement in the military known as the soldiers' parliament, in which men elected their own delegates to put forward political demands about the shape of a postwar world. A little sadly, he said, "I haven't been to jail in years. My children don't even believe I ever was."

At Camden Gate, with Primrose Hill in sight, Leo left me. Goddamn if his eyes weren't wet, cocky little bantamweight had a soft heart after all. I said so. "There"—he scratched his beard furiously—"that's the sort of thing I mean. You're always trying to tell us who we are. We *know* that, old son. Now go and irritate your own people. Anyway, take care. God bless. Write. And come back anytime. We'll always be here. Our main virtue, wouldn't you say?"

* * *

Now a last dig at my English roots.

Rye is a lovely, dull seaside town in southern England. Rose, a country girl at heart, had a large garden there, with house attached, which she liked working in. The wildest thing about her self-described "retirement home," where she continued to pound out novels about human monsters and visions of the present dressed up as futuristic prophecy, was the flourishingly unkempt grounds of her beautifully disordered garden. Just like Rose herself, I decided, getting out of my rented Escort.

Rose lived alone now. Alastair, my Aly, was somewhere off in central Africa as a trained agronomist; we hadn't been in touch for years, though once, in the sixties, I had offered him refuge from the torments (as I remembered them with Polly) of growing up a late adolescent with a single, sexy mum. "No," he had replied soberly, "you can't be my dad now. It's too late for that. Anyway, from the look of you, it would be the old story all over again, and I'd have to take care of you. Ma and I'll fight it out okay." Apparently, they had, too.

I opened the creaking gate and went into the house, whose door was open. Once again Rose was seated in her old wicker chair by a lattice window, smoking like a chimney, brooding over—astonishing workmanship!—that same old Royal portable typewriter. I almost expected to see a sheet of paper in it, "THE CASE OF G.B ..." Rose looked up and caught my eye. Suddenly she laughed, knowing exactly what was in my mind. I had to laugh too. I'd once seen Tony Zale and Rocky Graziano with their arms wrapped around each other after one of their bloody, brutal bouts, smiling idiotically at each other as the final bell sounded. Rose and I, too, had probably set a record for scar tisue per round fought.

We were not exactly friends, more alley cats with a respect for each other's claws. But we weren't enemies. Among other things, she had used my body to break her block. And she had been my best friend in a bad time. Those were solid accomplishments, I felt.

"So, my friend." She did not try to rise. For the first time, I noiced a cane propped against the wicker table. "Oh, that," she shrugged, "just my knee acting up again. This damp air isn't much good for it. It's just that I love it so down here. Don't you?"

What sort of kiss should I give her? As usual she offered her cheek, but I drew her out of the chair and planted a corker right on her lips. "You're always wanting to make a gentleman out of me, aren't you, Rose?" I said.

She kissed back. "Just tried to civilize you a little." She reached for the cane, and I helped her out back to an enormous kitchen looking out onto a lush truck garden. I willed myself not to ask what was for dinner.

We had a perfectly reasonable tea—but with store-bought scones. I couldn't believe it.

"Yes, I have to apologize for those," she said unapologetically as she saw me examining one, "but I'm so busy these days."

I thought, You were never too busy to bake your own for me once. The scones, more than anything else she might have said or done, told me where I stood. As she herself might have said, Oh well ...

Zale and Graziano had had three major fights and were spoiling for another even at the end, with blood flowing, noses broken, eyes blackened, and ribs cracked. As Rose poured me more tea, I understood both fighters for the first time.

My ship, the S.S. *Vandalia*, a cargo of hooked-down containers plus a few passengers, plowed through an Atlantic as stormy as the ocean I'd crossed to England the first time. Then Budapest was falling, Suez aflame, America seemingly congealed in a gray flannel ice age. I'd deserted my country without regrets and was coming back the same way.

Home is where the fight is. Now I had two homes.

I was going home, the other one.

There was a woman aboard the *Vandalia*. Only a dozen of us tramp-steamer slowpokes on a container ship that was a seagoing lesson in how technology had permanently changed all the old jobs I took for granted as the basis of my life and politics. Marie, alone, late thirties, had one of those strangely beautiful American faces at once fresh-scrubbed and wearily knowing. Passengers ate at the same large table midships, so it didn't take long for us to exchange life stories. She was the widow of a U.S. Air Force F-14 pilot who crashed in West Germany. No kids, no job, a little insurance and his pension, a lot of memories, and a shaky future. On long strolls around the S.S. *Vandalia*, we didn't talk all that much. What I heard I liked. Great voice, like Kay Starr mixed with Anita O'Day. No wonder, she'd been a band singer with a USO troupe when she met her husband.

Over meals, I kept slipping off my hornrims, a sure sign I'm interested. But how would a patriot like Marie take the two of us— me and my past? One night west of the Panama Canal I broached the subject when we were alone in what passed for the ship's bar, an alcove off the small mess room.

"I'd like to talk to you about something," I said uneasily.

She gazed at me. I coughed and cleared my throat. She leaned forward and gently put her manicured hand on my arm.

"It's all right if you're gay," she said.

Had life in England changed me that much? "No," I said, "absolutely not. That's not it."

"You're married?"

Not exactly.

"Then ..."

I told her about my being an anarcho-Commie.

Marie thought for a moment, then said, "Well, there goes your security clearance. You won't be an astronaut now."

"I'm serious," I said.

"I know you are." She could not resist a smile.

"But," I persisted, "you don't know what it's like being a Red. I come from a totally alien culture from yours. It's like high-risk sex."

"That good?" She laughed. "You think you know about danger. I was a Viking pom-pom girl in the sixties."

I drew a blank.

She explained that the Vikings were the football team of James Monroe High School in San Fernando Valley. "Like, when everybody else was doping and screwing their tiny little heads off, or protesting Vietnam and going to Grateful Dead concerts, I was into baton twirling and Ritchie Valens. And you talk about ridicule and abuse?"

Was she putting me on? Of course, gently. Didn't they indoctrinate her as an Air Force wife?

"Didn't they indoctrinate you as a whatever-you-are?" she replied.

"It's different," I said.

"You want to argue about it?" she asked.

I took her hand. No.

We docked in San Pedro–Wilmington one early January morning. Marie lived in Echo Park: "On my street we have a lesbian commune, a one-parent-family church, a bookstore for animal rights activists, a storefront legal office for poor people, bunches of Latinos who hate gays and gays who love Latinos, and a Scientology health food shop. Talk about alien cultures. Welcome to America, buddy." We exchanged addresses without once having kissed. I watched her go down the gangplank, turn and wave, then disappear into a taxi. I was staying on board to talk to some of the crew who were arguing as they hunched over a radio in the galley crackling dispatches about a war in the Persian Gulf. While we'd been at sea, once again an American president had ordered combat troops into action. Idly, my mind elsewhere, I searched my pockets for some loose American change to make a few phone calls from the dock to friends who might be harboring deserters, this time from a line in the sand instead of an Asian jungle. I listened to the radio with half an ear, thinking of Marie, then was gradually drawn into the argument among the crew. Anyway, I didn't feel like chasing her. Either would or would not happen.

Later, up on deck, I looked over the harbor, past Terminal Island and the great arching Vincent Thomas bridge, to the hills above San Pedro. Small houses dotted the terraces. It almost didn't look like America, more like Portsmouth or Southampton, England, except for the pastel oil pumps in the channel. I felt great. There was a new country out there waiting for me to write my name on. And, maybe, if my luck held, a friend who was also a woman.